Tuesday
2:30 - 4:30

MECHANICAL
POWER
TRANSMISSION

WILLIAM J. PATTON

Red River Community College
Manitoba, Canada

PRENTICE-HALL, INC., *Englewood Cliffs, New Jersey 07632*

Library of Congress Cataloging in Publication Data

Patton, W. J.
  Mechanical power transmission.

  Includes index.
  1. Power transmission.   I.   Title.
TJ1045.P34   621.8   79-15705
ISBN 0-13-569905-3

Editorial production supervision
and interior design by: James M. Chege

Cover design by: Edsal Enterprises

Manufacturing buyer: Gordon Osbourne

Printed in the United States of America

10   9   8   7   6   5   4   3   2   1

PRENTICE-HALL INTERNATIONAL, INC., *London*
PRENTICE-HALL OF AUSTRALIA PTY. LIMITED, *Sydney*
PRENTICE-HALL OF CANADA, LTD., *Toronto*
PRENTICE-HALL OF INDIA PRIVATE LIMITED, *New Delhi*
PRENTICE-HALL OF JAPAN, INC., *Tokyo*
PRENTICE-HALL OF SOUTHEAST ASIA PTE. LTD., *Singapore*
WHITEHALL BOOKS LIMITED, *Wellington, New Zealand*

CONTENTS

iii

5   TORQUE CONNECTIONS, COUPLINGS, AND CLUTCHES   *135*

PREFACE

Most machines are an integrated collection of power transmission components. A tractor for example uses an internal combustion engine as a
power source. Power from the engine is taken to the drive wheels or power
take-off through a geared transmission, a drive shaft, clutch, brake, and
other components. Alternatively a hydrostatic transmission may connect
the engine to the drive wheels and a fluid power system may operate a front
end loader or backhoe attachment to the tractor. Power transmission
systems then are mechanical or fluid power. Both types of system of course
use mechanical concepts such as force and torque, as opposed to electrical
power transmission, which follows entirely different principles and concepts, such as voltage, current, and reactance.

Recent years have seen increased acceptance of fluid power systems, and
hydrostatic transmissions have made inroads into applications previously
served by electric motors. To keep abreast of modern trends this book
describes both types of mechanical power transmission.

WILLIAM J. PATTON

Manitoba, Canada

1

ENERGY AND POWER

Mechanical power transmission refers to the business of moving energy or power from the place where it is generated to the place where it is used by mechanical devices. The cheapest power transmission device is electrical wiring, which moves electric energy from one location to another. Mechanical power transmission transfers energy through belts, gears, sprockets, shafts, power takeoffs, hydraulic valves, pneumatic hoses, and other mechanical devices, many of which may be seen in the equipment of Figs. 1-1, 1-2, and 1-3. In the automobile, power is generated in the engine and transmitted to the drive wheels through such power transmission devices as a transmission, a driveshaft, a differential, and universal joints.

In ordinary conversation we hear the word "power" used in figurative ways, as in the phrases "athletic power," "staying power," or the "drawing power" of an entertainer. Whoever uses such phrases means not "power" but "ability." In the physical world, power is not ability or capacity, and so it is important to be clear in our understanding of what power and energy are exactly.

1-1 ENERGY

Energy is the capacity to do work. Such energy is available in many forms. The heat energy in a gallon of gasoline does work by moving a truck along a highway. Nuclear energy is used to generate electricity for electric motors to drive fans and other machinery. The chemical energy in a car battery operates the starter motor of the car. The energy of a waterfall can drive

FIGURE 1-1 *An air-operated rock drill on crawler tracks. By means of pneumatic positioning cylinders, the drill column can be positioned at any angle from vertical to horizontal.*

FIGURE 1-2 *A rear view of the drill of Figure 1-1, showing the air motors and two-strand drive chain that drives the tracks.*

a waterwheel which in turn drives an electric generator to create electric energy.

Energy, the most fundamental principle of the universe, must first be generated, then transmitted to the point of use, then put to use by energy-consuming devices. This basic energy circuit is a universal thing. Consider only a few typical cases.

2

FIGURE 1-3 *Another example of mobile equipment requiring power transmission components: a tractor with a front-end loader and tree-mover, both attachments hydraulically operated.*

1. The sun generates energy, which is radiated through space, then consumed by plants for growth.

2. Energy is generated in the digestive tract of animals and man by digesting food, transported by the blood to the muscles, and consumed in the muscles as work.

3. Energy is generated by the engine of a tractor, then transmitted through a power takeoff to a device hooked to the tractor.

4. Energy is produced by an electric motor, transported to the headstock of a lathe by belts and gears, and consumed by the cutting tool.

While electric power transmission is an alternative to mechanical power transmission, electric power is not the subject of this book. Nevertheless it is a very common practice to drive machines with electric motors. The electric motor may be considered both as an electrical and a mechanical machine. Its input is electrical, but its output is mechanical work. The cheapest and most efficient method of transmitting energy, especially over long distances, is as electrical energy through electric wiring. Electrical energy therefore is important because it is cheap, efficient, easily controlled, and clean. Sixty years ago the cheapest way to make coffee was by a mechanical method: boiling water on a wood-burning stove. Now the electric stove is cheaper. But note that if the electric utility supplying the energy for the electric stove generates electric energy in a coal-burning electric generating plant, the coffee is still produced by a fire. The only difference is a superficial one: the fire has been removed from the kitchen to the generating site. Sometimes the more things change, the more they remain the same.

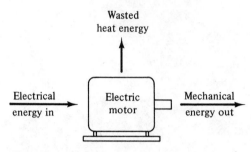

Energy in = Useful energy out + Wasted energy

FIGURE 1-4 *Energy conversion in an electric motor.*

1-2 FORCES

The units by which we measure energy and power in the English system used in North America are perhaps a little confusing because there are so many of them. To understand them, we must begin with the idea of *force.*

A *force* measures the action of any body on another body, such as a boot on a football, or the force of a tire against a pavement. The unit of force is the *pound,* or in the new S.I. metric system, the *newton.* For example, an automobile may weigh 3000 lb. This is the vertical force exerted by the automobile through its tires to the pavement against which it rests. Similarly the pavement exerts an upward force of 3000 lb against the automobile. A horizontal force of 100 lb may be required to tow or move the car. This towing force or drawbar pull is the force required to move the car on horizontal ground against all the friction forces in the automobile, including friction between tires and pavement.

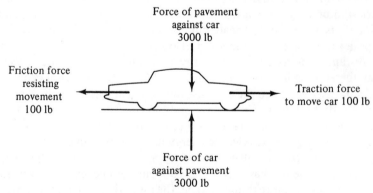

FIGURE 1-5 *Forces on an automobile.*

A static force is a steady force that acts on a motionless body, and the analysis of static forces is therefore called statics. A force that causes movement of a body is called a dynamic force, and so the study of dynamic forces is called dynamics.

The basic principles that apply universally to all types of forces are the three laws of Newton (Isaac Newton, 1642–1727):

1. Any body at rest tends to remain at rest, while any body in motion tends to remain in motion in a straight line, unless an external force causes a change in motion.
2. If a force acts on a body, the body will be accelerated. The rate of acceleration will be proportional to the magnitude of the force and inversely proportional to the mass of the body.
3. For every force there is an equal and opposite force.

An example of the third law is the case of the 3000-lb automobile mentioned above. The other laws are equally familiar from experience. If a vehicle is in motion in a straight line, a sideways force is required to make the vehicle turn a corner (first law). If the vehicle is very heavy, a strong sideways force is required to turn it, because the vehicle tends to continue in a straight line.

It is often necessary to analyze the forces acting in a machine or vehicle. This can be done for the grain box of Fig. 1-6. Suppose it is required to find the loads (that is, forces) on the front and rear axles. The wheelbase is 10 ft and the box is 14 ft long. The box weights 2000 lb empty and carries 7000 lb of grain. The known forces are shown in the figure. The total weight of the loaded grain box is applied at its center of gravity. The forces at the

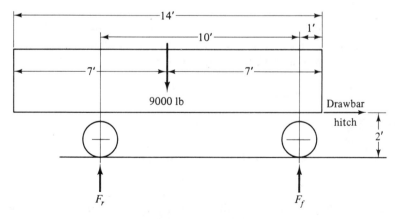

FIGURE 1-6 *Box trailer.*

front and rear axles are shown as F_f and F_r. If the grain box is not accelerating or turning, then all forces are static forces, and all forces are in equilibrium; that is, they cancel out according to the following conditions:

1. The sum of all vertical forces must equal zero.
2. The sum of all horizontal forces must equal zero.
3. The sum of clockwise moments must equal the sum of counterclockwise moments.

For the sum of all vertical forces to equal zero, the upward forces F_f and F_r must equal the downward force of 9000 lb:

$$F_f + F_r = 9000 \text{ lb}$$

The second condition does not apply to this particular case because there are no horizontal forces.

To explain the third condition, we use the word "moment" in statics to mean torque or leverage. This may be explained by supposing that the front wheels are blocked and cannot roll. Then if the downward weight of 9000 lb was removed, the force at the rear axle, F_r, would rotate the box about the front axle in a clockwise direction. Its rotating moment is F_r times its lever length of 10 ft, or $10 \times F_r$ ft-lb. Similarly the 9000-lb deadweight has a moment in the reverse direction of 9000 lb $\times$ 6 ft or 54,000 ft-lb. But the third condition says that these two moments must be equal, so that

$$9000 \text{ lb} \times 6 \text{ ft} = F_r \times 10 \text{ ft}$$
$$F_r = 5400 \text{ lb} \quad \text{and} \quad F_f = 9000 - 5400 = 3600 \text{ lb}$$

Any point on the body may be used to determine moments. Suppose that we take the center of gravity of the box instead of the front axle. Then the force at the rear axle exerts a clockwise moment about this point, and the force at the front axle a counterclockwise moment.

$$\text{Hence } 4 \text{ ft} \times F_r - 6 \text{ ft} \times F_f = 0$$

Substituting the values already found for F_r and F_f gives

$$5400 \times 4 = 3600 \times 6$$
$$21{,}600 = 21{,}600$$

Next consider a different condition. The grain box is being towed by a tractor. The tractor pull is 400 lb, applied to a drawbar 2 ft above ground level (Fig. 1-6). Determine the loads on the two axles for this case. Taking the vertical forces first

$$F_r + F_f = 9000 \text{ lb}$$

Take moments about point O where the front wheels touch the ground.

$$\text{Clockwise moments} = \text{counterclockwise moments}$$
$$10\,F_r + 400 \times 2 = 9000 \times 6$$
$$F_r = 5320 \text{ lb}$$

Then $$F_f = 3680 \text{ lb}$$

As a result of the drawbar pull, there has been a slight shift of weight from the rear to front axle.

Since there is a horizontal force of 400 lb to the right, there must be an opposing friction force of 400 lb to the left, acting where the wheels touch the ground. Friction is proportional to the weight on the wheel, so that there will be a greater friction force at the rear wheels than at the front wheels.

Pressure measures force in units of pounds per square inch (psi) of surface area, or in the S.I. system, newtons per square meter (N/m²). Thus if the weight of a 3000-lb automobile rests on 60 sq. in. of tire in contact with the ground, the ground pressure is $^{3000}\!/_{60}$ or 50 psi.

1-3 WORK

Work is performed when a force moves through a distance in the direction of the force. For example, suppose a 100-lb force is required to push or pull an automobile. If that automobile is pushed 10 ft, then 100 lb × 10 ft or 1000 ft-lb of work is done. Work is one form of energy, and mechanical energy is usually measured in foot-pounds.

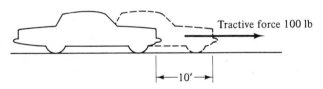

Tractive force 100 lb

Work done = 100 lb x 10 ft. = 1000 ft–lb

FIGURE 1-7 *Work in moving a vehicle.*

EXAMPLE: 1-1: A force of 100 lb is required at a cutter bit on a lathe in order to remove the chip from the workpiece. If a round bar 4 inches in diameter is being turned on the lathe, what work is done in 1 revolution of the workpiece?

SOLUTION: In 1 revolution the cutter bit must move completely around the 4-inch bar. This is a distance of 12.4 in. The work done is 100 lb × 12.4 in. = 1240 inch-pounds = 103.3 ft-lb.

It is important to note that work and also power, discussed next, may be negative as well as positive. A power transmission system, such as a gear box or a chain drive, has an input and an output, and can be driven from either end. If driven from the input, then the work is taken to be positive, as when the engine of an automobile moves the vehicle along a road. But if the automobile moves down a steep slope, the wheels may drive the engine, that is, the work is received from the output end of the transmission. In this second case we have an example of negative work or negative power, the expenditure of energy backward from load to prime mover.

1-4 POWER

Power measures the rate at which work is done or energy is expended.

$$\text{Power} = \frac{\text{work}}{\text{time}}$$

It requires more power to do work in less time.

Consider the above example of moving a car 10 feet with a 100-pound push or pull. Suppose the car is moved the 10 feet in 1 second. Then, for this case,

$$\text{Power} = \frac{\text{work}}{\text{time}} = \frac{100\,\text{lb} \times 10\,\text{ft}}{1\,\text{s}} = 1000\,\text{ft-lb per s}$$

If the time required is 1 minute, then the power is 1000 ft-lb per min, or $\frac{1}{60}$ of the former case.

In the complex English system of units, power may be measured in a number of ways. The first unit of power adopted, the horsepower (HP), was developed by James Watt, who needed a suitable unit of power by which to rate his steam engines. He rated these engines in terms of the number of horses that the engine could replace. Watt made measurements on the power output of draft horses, and found that the average horse could produce 22,000 ft-lb per min. He added a 50% safety factor for his steam engines by defining a horsepower as a power output of 33,000 ft-lb/min, or 550 ft-lb/s.

Heat is another form of energy, and power can be measured by the heat output in a period of time. In the English system heat is measured in Btu's (British thermal units), the amount of heat required to raise the temperature of a pound of water 1 °F. The usual power unit for heat is the Btu's per hour (Btuh).

The electrical unit of power is the S.I. unit, the watt or kilowatt (KW = 1000 watts) per hour.

To convert from one unit of power to another, the following conversions are needed:

$$778 \text{ ft-lb} = 1 \text{ Btu}$$
$$1 \text{ HP} = 33,000 \text{ ft-lb/min}$$
$$= 550 \text{ ft-lb/sec}$$
$$= 746 \text{ watts}$$
$$= 0.746 \text{ KW} \left(= \frac{3}{4} \text{ KW}\right)$$
$$1 \text{ HP-hour} = 2544 \text{ Btu}$$
$$1 \text{ HP-min} = 42.4 \text{ Btu}$$
$$1 \text{ KW-hour} = 3412 \text{ Btu}$$
$$1 \text{ KW-min} = 56.8 \text{ Btu}$$

EXAMPLE 1-2:   A fractional horsepower alternating-current motor is rated at ¼ HP output. In an hour of continuous operation the motor develops 636 Btu of wasted heat. What is its electric power input in kilowatts and its efficiency? See Fig. 1-4.

$$636 \text{ Btuh} = {}^{636}\!/_{2544} \text{ HP-hour} = \frac{1}{4} \text{ HP-hour}$$

SOLUTION: The power input of the motor must be equal to the total power taken out of the motor, which is

$$\text{Power input} = \text{useful output} + \text{wasted power}$$
$$= \frac{1}{4} \text{ HP} \quad + \quad \frac{1}{4} \text{ HP}$$
$$= \frac{1}{2} \text{ HP}$$
$$= \frac{3}{8} \text{ KW closely, since 1 HP} = \frac{3}{4} \text{ KW}$$

The motor efficiency is 50%.

EXAMPLE 1-3:   Suppose that an automobile has a fuel rate of 18 miles per gallon of gasoline, and that a horizontal force of 100 lb is required to propel the vehicle along the pavement, such that there is no wind resistance. Making these assumptions, and taking a gallon of gasoline to have 150,000 Btu of heat energy, what is the apparent efficiency of the automobile?

SOLUTION: It requires 100 ft-lb of work to move the vehicle 1 ft. But 1 Btu = 778 ft-lb, so that 1 Btu will move the car 7.78 ft along a road.

Now 1 gallon of gasoline contains 150,000 Btu. Therefore 1 gallon has the capacity to move the car 150,000 × 7.78 ft, which is 220 mi. The efficiency of the car, based on these assumptions is

$$\frac{18 \text{ mpg}}{220 \text{ mpg}} = 8.2\%$$

If only 8.2% of the input energy to the motor appears as useful work in moving the vehicle (at slow speed, since wind resistance is being ignored here), then 91.8% of the energy in the fuel is wasted. Only a relatively small amount of the lost energy is wasted in friction. Most of it represents heat lost to the water in the radiator (at least 30%) and lost also in heating nitrogen and other gases drawn into the cylinder and discharged from the exhaust. *Inefficiencies in power transmission, friction included, always result in waste heat.* Therefore very inefficient power transmissions will generate large amounts of heat, and may require cooling arrangements such as an automobile needs. Even bearings, brakes, and clutches may require cooling arrangements to remove energy lost as heat.

1-5 FRICTION

Friction is both a necessity and a nuisance. We could not walk without friction between our shoes and the ground. We could not drive automobiles without tire friction or brake an automobile without tire and brake friction. But often friction is a costly nuisance. Frictionless bearings and gears would be invaluable for power transmission if only they were possible, and zero air friction would make the cost of jet aircraft travel very economical in terms of fuel. Without friction, power chain drives would never need replacement, but belt drives would not operate.

But all moving objects lose energy and power because of friction. Friction is a force parallel to the sliding faces of two bodies in contact, and arises because of the resistance to movement caused by interlocking small surface irregularities on the two contacting surfaces (Fig. 1-8).

The friction force between two surfaces is proportional to the pressure between the two surfaces. No relative movement of the two contacting bodies is possible until the force of friction is overcome. When movement is about to occur, the friction force is some fraction of the normal force between the two surfaces. This fraction is called the *coefficient of friction,* and the symbol designating this coefficient is the Greek letter μ (mu).

As an example, suppose a vehicle weighs 3000 lb and the coefficient of friction between its wheels and the road is 0.03. We are supposing for simplicity that there is no friction in the bearings or other parts of the vehicle.

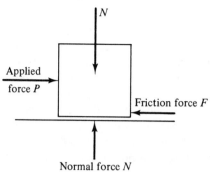

FIGURE 1-8 *Friction force.*

In order to move the vehicle, a pushing or pulling force must be used which slightly exceeds the friction force. This friction force is

$$F = \mu N$$

where N is the normal force between wheels and ground.

$$F = 0.03 \times 3000 = 90 \, \text{lb}$$

The forces on the vehicle are shown in Fig. 1-5. Note that if the vehicle is pushed backward then the friction force reverses; a friction force always opposes motion. If the force applied to push or pull the vehicle is less than that calculated from the coefficient of friction, say 80 lb or 25 lb for the vehicle discussed, then the resisting friction force is also 80 or 25 lb. The opposing friction force may take any value up to the maximum given by μN.

Suppose the force applied to move the vehicle exceeds the friction force, say 100 lb. Of this 100-lb force, 90 lb is required to overcome friction and thus to initiate movement. The 10-lb force remaining will, in accordance with Newton's second law of motion, accelerate the vehicle up to a speed at which air friction or other friction effects will reach 10 lb of opposite force. In this final condition all forces are in balance—100 lb of moving force opposed by 100 lb of resisting force—and the vehicle will move at a constant speed.

Actually the coefficient of friction may have more than one value. The *static* coefficient of friction that opposes the start of motion is always larger than the *dynamic* coefficient of friction that applies after the body is in motion. It is always more difficult to start a vehicle moving than to keep it moving.

1-6, TORQUE

Torque is defined as a turning effect. A crescent wrench is a torque instrument, since it will rotate a nut against resistance to rotation. Torque involves two quantities, a *force* at a *distance* from the axis of rotation. The distance from the axis of rotation at which the force is applied is the leverage. Torque may therefore be increased either by increasing the force or the distance at which the force is applied or both. The units of torque are pound-inches or pound-feet. Since work is measured in foot-pounds, it is preferable to measure torque in pound-feet so that the two concepts are not confused.

Force

FIGURE 1-9 *Torque.*

Torque with rotation results in work, as in the following example.

EXAMPLE 1-4:   A force of 15 lb is exerted at the end of a 12-inch crescent wrench in turning a nut on a bolt.

(a)   What torque is exerted?

(b)   What work is done in turning the nut one revolution?

(c)   What force is exerted at the threads of the nut, if the bolt is ½ inch in diameter?

SOLUTION:

(a)   The force is 15 lb and the length of the lever arm is assumed to be 12 in. The torque is 15 lb × 12 in. = 180 lb-in.

(b)   The force of 15 lb is exerted through one revolution of the crescent wrench around a circle 12 in. in diameter. The distance around this circle is 37.7 in. The work done is

15 lb × 37.7 in. = 565.5 lb-in.

(c)   The torque exerted at the threads is the same torque that is applied at the wrench, that is, 180 lb-in. However, the torque arm of a ½ in. thread is the radius of the threads, which is ¼ in.

$$\text{Torque} = 180 \text{ lb-in.} = \text{¼ in.} \times \text{force at threads}$$

The force exerted at the threads = 720 lb.

Torque and Power

To see the relationship between torque and power, suppose the above crescent wrench to be driven by some kind of motor arrangement to rotate it. Rotate the wrench 1 revolution per minute. In each revolution 565.5 in.-lb of work is done, as calculated in the example above. This work is done in 1 minute, so that the horsepower output is

$$\frac{565 \cdot \frac{5}{12} \text{ ft-lb/min}}{33,000} = 0.00143 \text{ HP}$$

If the wrench is driven at 2 rpm, then the horsepower is doubled. Horsepower and torque are related by the following equation:

$$\text{HP} = \frac{2 \pi \ TN}{33,000} = \frac{TN}{5250}$$

where T = torque in lb-ft
         N = rpm

For torque in lb-in., use HP $= \dfrac{TN}{63,000}$

Torque Conversion

Suppose an electric motor delivers 2 HP at 1720 rpm to a 3-in. V-pulley on the motor shaft. The V-pulley drives a 6-in. V-pulley on another shaft by means of a V-belt. The driven shaft rotates half as fast as the motor shaft, but receives 2 HP, neglecting any inefficiency in the drive. But for either shaft

$$2 \text{ HP} = \frac{TN}{5250}$$

If one shaft rotates at half speed, then the same horsepower can be maintained only if the torque in that shaft is doubled. Thus the drive acts as a torque converter by means of a speed change. Gear trains, belt drives, chain drives, and many other types of power transmission act as torque converters by altering speeds.

1-7 BRAKE HORSEPOWER

The useful power taken from a machine or engine is called the power output or brake power, and is measured as brake horsepower. This power is measured by using a brake to absorb the useful power output. While brake horsepower is nowadays measured usually by dynamometers, the simpler Prony brake is still in use. A Prony brake dynamometer is illustrated in Fig. 1-10. This type of dynamometer absorbs the power output of the engine or machine in the friction of a number of wood blocks forced against the rim of a wheel fixed to the output shaft. The belt holding the blocks against the wheel is attached to the arm *L,* and the end of the arm rests on the platform of a weigh scale. The weight scale indicates the force exerted by the arm *L.*

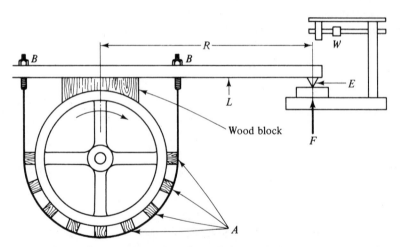

FIGURE 1-10 *Prony brake for measuring brake horsepower.*

To make a brake horsepower test (BHP), the wood blocks are loosened from the wheel so that the dead weight of the lever arm can be weighed. This dead weight will be called W_0. The engine is then run up to the speed at which the brake horsepower is to be determined, and the brake blocks are closed against the wheel. Brake friction causes the lever arm to increase its force against the platform scale; this force is measured. Designate it W_f. Then net force against the scale produced by the Prony brake is

$$F = W_f - W_0$$

The length of the lever arm in the figure is given as R. This is the distance from the center of the output shaft to the point of application of the force F against the scale.

Power must be measured by the Prony brake as foot-pounds per unit time. To find the distance through which the force F acts in 1 revolution of the output shaft, consider that in 1 revolution the force may be considered to travel the circumference of a circle of radius R. This distance is $2 \pi R$. Alternately, the same torque applied to the ouput wheel is applied all around the periphery of the wheel; the result in foot-pounds of work is the same. In 1 minute the wheel rotates N revolutions. Therefore the work done in 1 minute is $2 \pi RN$. Hence

$$2\pi RNF$$

$$\text{BHP} = \frac{\text{Distance per minute} \times F}{33,000}$$

$$= \frac{(2 \pi RN) F}{33,000}$$

$$= \frac{FRN}{5250}$$

EXAMPLE 1-5: Determine the BHP developed in an engine operated at 1200 rpm. The scale reading on the Prony brake is 182 lb, less the dead weight of 22 lb, and the effective length of the brake arm is 48 in.

SOLUTION:

$$\text{Net force} = 182 - 22 = 160 \text{ lb}$$

$$R = 48 \text{ in.} = 4 \text{ ft}$$

$$\text{BHP} = \frac{FRN}{5250} = \frac{160 \times 4 \times 1200}{5250}$$

$$= 146 \text{ HP}$$

1-8   VELOCITY AND ACCELERATION

Velocity and *speed* mean the same thing numerically. Velocity is the distance traversed by a moving object in a unit of time, and is calculated by dividing distance by time:

$$\text{Speed or velocity} = \frac{\text{distance}}{\text{time}}$$

If an automobile travels 30 miles in 1 hour, then its speed is 30 miles per hour. Since the automobile will travel at a varying speed over the time interval of one hour, this will be an average velocity. Velocities may be uniform or variable.

The change in velocity of a moving body in a unit of time is called *acceleration*. Acceleration is calculated by dividing the change in velocity by the time during which this change occurs:

$$\text{Acceleration} = \frac{\text{change in velocity}}{\text{time}}$$

EXAMPLE 1-6: Suppose an automobile starts from rest and reaches a velocity of 60 mph in 1 minute. What is its acceleration?

SOLUTION: The time unit commonly used for acceleration is the second.

$$60 \text{ mph} = 88 \text{ fps}$$

$$\text{Average acceleration} = \frac{88 \text{ fps} - 0 \text{ fps}}{60 \text{ s}} = 1.47 \text{ ft/s}^2$$

Acceleration is in units of feet per second per second, or feet per second squared. Acceleration is positive if the velocity increases, and negative when velocity is decreasing (deceleration).

The most important case of acceleration for us is the acceleration due to the earth's gravitational attraction. This acceleration is 32.2 ft/s² at sea level (9.8 meters/s²). This value is given the symbol *g*. An acceleration of 2*g* is 64.4 ft/s². for a case of 1*g*, the velocity of a body will increase by 32.2 fps, assuming no air resistance.

1-9 KINETIC ENERGY

A moving body has energy due to its motion. This energy of motion is called *kinetic energy.* Kinetic energy is calculated from the formula

$$\text{Kinetic energy} = \frac{1}{2} \frac{W}{g} V^2 \text{ ft-lb}$$

where
W = the weight of the moving body (lb)
V = the velocity of the body in (ft per s)
g = acceleration due to gravity (ft/s²)

EXAMPLE 1-7: A 4000-pound vehicle is traveling at 60 mph. What energy is required to stop it?

SOLUTION: The vehicle can be stopped by applying an opposing energy equal to its kinetic energy. The opposing energy may be supplied by the vehicle's brakes, or by an obstruction.

$$\text{K.E.} = \frac{1}{2} \left(\frac{4000}{32.2}\right)\left(88\right)^2 \quad \text{where} \quad 60 \text{ mph} = 88 \text{ fps}$$
$$= 480{,}480 \text{ ft-lb}$$

To brake this vehicle to a stop, all this kinetic energy must be converted into heat. 1 Btu of heat = 778 ft-lb. The heat generated by the tires and brakes is

$$H = \frac{480,480}{778} = 617 \text{ Btu}$$

1-10 POWER REQUIREMENTS IN A VEHICLE

The basic power concepts discussed in this first chapter are perhaps best illustrated by considering their application to a vehicle. We will assume a vehicle weighing 4000 lb, with 1500 lb of this total weight carried on the rear wheels, which are the driven wheels. The tires will be taken as 16 inches in radius, which is the size of a 7.00 × 17 or 7.50 × 17 tire.

In the design of a vehicle such as a car, a truck, a tractor, or a railroad locomotive, the designer must take account of all the loads against which the tractive effort of the vehicle must operate. A tractor may have to drag farm implements, or a car may have to pull a camping trailer. The resistance of road friction must be overcome. So must wind resistance. Grades must be climbed; these grades are only 5 to 8% on highways, but may be much greater for off-highway vehicles.

The designer of the vehicle works from the friction formula

$$F = \mu N$$

where F = the friction force providing traction
          μ = coefficient of friction between driving wheels and ground
          N = weight on the driving wheels

All the forces to be overcome are added together, and F, the driving force or friction force at the wheels, must be large enough to overcome these resisting forces. If the friction coefficient is not high enough to produce the required traction, then the weight on the driving wheels must be increased.

Friction coefficients for vehicles.

Rubber tire on a hard, smooth road	0.6–0.8
Lugged tire or lugged track on dry earth	1.4
Steel wheel on steel rail	0.3

The usual resistances that a vehicle must overcome are these:

1. Road resistance (low for pavement, high for earth or sand)
2. Starting force. It requires extra force to start a vehicle.

3.   Grade resistance. Extra force is needed to lift a vehicle and its load up a hill.

4.   Accelerating force. Acceleration requires additional force. Very heavy equipment requires a heavy acceleration force.

5.   Air resistance. Air resistance is not significant except at speeds above 20 mph. It is larger for larger frontal areas; at 60 mph a large trailer truck uses as much horsepower to overcome air resistance as to move its load along the highway.

6.   Trailer traction, trailer acceleration, and trailer air resistance.

EXAMPLE 1-8:   The traction requirements of an automobile are to be determined, and it is desirable not to require more than 100 HP to provide this traction. The following data apply:

SOLUTION:

1.   Weight of vehicle is 4000 lb.
2.   Weight on rear drive wheels is 1500 lb.
3.   Tire radius 13.6 in.
4.   Road friction is taken as 0.7.
5.   Road resistance plus starting force is 60 lb per 1000 lb of vehicle deadweight.
6.   Grade resistance is 250 lb.
7.   Accelerating force is 300 lb.
8.   Air resistance is 150 lb.

To determine whether the vehicle can handle these loads, first apply the basic friction equation to the tires.

$$F = \mu N$$
$$= 0.7 \times 1500 = 1050 \text{ lb.}$$

This is the maximum tractive force obtainable.

Consider next the case of starting the vehicle on a grade. The accelerating force is not involved until after the vehicle moves, nor is air resistance.

$$\text{Starting force} + \text{grade resistance} = 60 \times \frac{4000}{1000} + 250 = 490 \text{ lb}$$

This total is less than the available tractive force, so that the vehicle can be started.

When the vehicle is moving at speed, it must overcome road resistance, air resistance, and sometimes grade resistance and acceleration force. To consider the worst condition, add all four together:

Road resistance	240 lb
Grade resistance	250
Acceleration force	300
Air resistance	150
Total	940 lb

There is enough traction to overcome this combination.

Finally check the horsepower requirement for the above total traction requirement at, say, 50 mph.

To obtain a speed of 50 mph, using a 13.6-in. wheel radius, the wheels must revolve at 618 rpm. The torque is 940 lb × 13.6 in. = 12,780 lb-in.

$$HP = \frac{TN}{63,000} = 12,780 \times \frac{618}{6300} = 125 \, HP$$

The expected 100 HP is insufficient.

In addition to traction requirements, the engine of the vehicle must also provide power for such auxiliaries as the oil pump, radiator fan, etc.

1-11 VEHICLE TIRES

Rubber is molded into articles that provide the frictional traction that makes land transportation possible: soles and heels of footwear, conveyor belting, and tires.

In a vehicle, the train of power transmission devices between the driving motor and the driven wheels brings power, torque, and speed to the final elements of the power train, the tires. The tires consume power and develop torque by virtue of the torque developed by friction with the ground surface.

Natural rubber is stronger than most of the synthetic rubbers and generates less heat when flexed. It finds its chief applications in the tires of aircraft and large off-the-road excavation machines. Tires for automobiles, lift trucks, farm equipment, and trailers are made of synthetic rubber, usually SBR or styrene-butadiene rubber, with substantial amounts of carbon black. Carbon black, like synthetic rubber, is a product of petroleum and natural gas. It gives the rubber tire improved abrasion resistance, hardness, and strength, and also protects against ultraviolet radiation from the sun.

Polyurethane rubber is an unusual type of rubber that provides remarkable performance in lift trucks and other industrial trucks. This tire rubber does not require carbon black. Polyurethane rubber has the notable advantages of high tensile strength and remarkable abrasion resistance to broken glass and machining chips. However, it is a more expensive rubber and develops more heat when flexed. Its coefficient of friction is unusually low for a rubber but this does not affect its performance as a lift truck or industrial truck tire. It is not used in inflated tires because of its high heat buildup (hysteresis).

The hardness of rubber is measured on a scale of arbitrary numbers known as the Shore A durometer scale. The hardness measuring device is a small instrument held in the hand, with a pointed indentor that penetrates the rubber. The amount of penetration is indicated on a scale graduated in durometer units. Automobile and lift truck tires have a durometer hardness of A70, which is a suitable hardness for traction purposes. A higher durometer will increase the life and load-carrying capacity of the tire but will reduce traction. A lower hardness would improve traction but tire life would be reduced.

Vehicle tires are made in traction and free-rolling types. Traction tires have tread patterns designed primarily to grip the ground surface. Free-rolling tires are not designed for traction; they are used on all types of trailer equipment. The tire design may be pneumatic, semi-pneumatic, or cushion.

FIGURE 1-11 *Large pneumatic traction tire in a lift truck tire-handling attachment.*

The pneumatic tire must be used in outdoor work, especially over rough terrain or soft ground, and for vehicle speeds exceeding 10 mph. This tire absorbs shock better than the other types. The semi-pneumatic tire has a hollow center but no air valve. The solid tire or cushion tire is restricted to industrial trucks working inside buildings.

The cushion tire is made in two types: the pressed-on and the molded-on tire. The pressed-on tire is cured onto a steel band which is itself pressed onto the wheel of the truck. Being easily replaced, the pressed-on tire is used for drive or steer wheels of industrial trucks. The molded-on tire is cured directly to the wheel.

FIGURE 1-12 *Cushion tires on a life truck.*

For the same load capacity the cushion tire is smaller than the pneumatic tire and thus reduces vehicle size and clearance in industrial trucks such as lift trucks.

Ply Rating and Tire Sizes

The term "ply rating" identifies a given type of tire with its maximum recommended load. It is an index of tire strength and does not necessarily represent the number of cord plies in the tire. A very small tractor might require only two-ply tires, while a very large farm tractor might require ten-ply tires.

Tire sizes are designated by the tire cross-sectional width and the rim diameter. A tractor tire size of 4.00-15 means that the approximate width of the tire is 4 inches when mounted on the widest permissible rim. The nominal diameter of the rim is 15 inches.

1-12 THE S.I. SYSTEM

There have been several metric systems of units. One of these was known as the CGS system, and was based on the centimeter, the gram, and the second. Later the MKS metric system was introduced, based on the meter, the kilogram, and the second as fundamental units of measurement. The

FIGURE 1-13 *Free-rolling tires on a radioactive container.*

metric system currently being introduced is known as the S.I. system, an abbreviation of the French Systeme Internationale. The current British system uses the foot, the pound, and the second as fundamental units.

The S.I. system has six basic units of measurement; all other units—for power, heat, energy, torque, etc.—can be derived from these six:

The unit of length   –   the meter (m)
The unit of mass   –   the kilogram (kg)
The unit of time   –   the second (s)

plus the ampere for electrical engineering, the candela for illumination, and the kelvin for thermodynamics. Only the first three are significant for power transmission.

To convert from the existing British system to S.I. units:

1 inch   = 25.4 millimeters (mm)
1 yard   = 0.9144 m
1 pound = 0.4536 kg

Multiples or decimal fractions of the basic S.I. units are used where convenient, for example, the millimeter or one-thousandth of a meter, or the gram, one-thousandth of a kilogram. The standard multipliers for multiples or decimal fractions are given in the table below.

Standard multiples of the S.I. system.

Multiplier	Number	Prefix	Abbreviation
1 million million	10^{12}	tera	T
1 billion	10^9	giga	G
1 million	10^6	mega	M
1 thousand	10^3	kilo	k
1 hundredth	10^{-2}	centi	c
1 thousandth	10^{-3}	milli	m
1 millionth	10^{-6}	micro	μ
1 billionth	10^{-9}	nano	n

Thus, for example, a thousandth of a millimeter is a micrometer or a meter.

Areas are given in mm² or m², volume in mm³ or m³. Speed is preferably given in meters per second, m/s. Density is expressed as g/mm³ or kg/m³. Note that 5 square kilometers is abbreviated 5 km². This abbreviation means 5 (km)², not 5k × m². Similarly 5 square millimeters is abbreviated 5 mm², which does not mean 5m³.

Unlike previous metric systems, the unit of temperature is the degree Celsius, not centigrade. The temperature scale is still the same (centigrade) scale; only the name is changed.

Combined units, such as kilogram-meters, must be abbreviated with care. Consider a torque of 5 kg × 3 m. This product is expressed as 15 kg-m, with a hyphen between kg and m. It must not be written 15 kgm. If a length must be multiplied by time, consider that 10 m × 10 s = 100 meter-seconds or 100 m-s. If written as 100 ms, this would mean 100 milliseconds.

As an example of conversion to S.I. units, suppose we convert 100 miles per hour to kilometers per hour. To convert 1 mile/hour to km/hour, we must multiply by km/mile, thus

$$
\begin{aligned}
\text{1 mile/hour} \times \text{km/mile} &= \text{km/hour} \\
\text{1 mile} &= \text{1760 yards} \\
\text{1 yard} &= \text{0.9144 m} \\
\text{1 mile} &= 1760 \times 0.9144 \text{ m} \\
&= \text{1609.34 m} \\
&= \text{1.609 km} \\
\text{100 miles/hour} \times \text{1.609 km/mile} &= \text{160.9 km/hour}
\end{aligned}
$$

The Newton

The S.I. unit of force is the newton (N). The newton is defined as the force which will accelerate a mass of 1 kg at a rate of 1 meter per second. That is,

$$1 \text{ N} \qquad = 1 \text{ kg m/s}^2$$
$$1 \text{ pound force} = 4.448 \text{ N}$$

Load or force per unit area is expressed in newtons per square meter (N/m^2). Gravitational acceleration at sea level in the S.I. system is 9.81 m/s^2.

EXAMPLE 1-9: Convert 1 ton per square inch to newtons per square millimeter.

SOLUTION:

$$1 \text{ ton} = 2000 \text{ lb}$$
$$1 \text{ lb force} = 4.448 \text{ N}$$
$$2000 \text{ lb} = 8896 \text{ N}$$
$$1 \text{ in.} = 25.4 \text{ mm}$$
$$1 \text{ in.}^2 = (25.4)^2 \text{ mm}^2 = 645 \text{ mm}^2$$
$$\text{Therefore } 2000 \text{ psi} = 8896 \text{ N}/645 \text{ mm}^2$$
$$= 13.8 \text{ N/mm}^2$$

EXAMPLE 1-10: Convert 100 lb-in. torque to newton-meters.

SOLUTION:

$$1 \text{ meter} = 39.37 \text{ in.}$$
$$1 \text{ newton} = 0.225 \text{ lb}$$
$$1 \text{ N-m} = 8.87 \text{ lb-in.}$$
$$\text{Therefore } 100 \text{ lb-in.} = 100/8.87 \text{ N-m} = 11.28 \text{ N-m}$$

Energy and Power

Work is the product of force times the distance through which the force acts. In the S.I. system, 1 unit of work is

$$1 \text{ newton} \times 1 \text{ meter} = 1 \text{ newton-meter} = 1 \text{ N-m}$$

This unit might be stated as 1 meter-newton, similar to 1 foot-pound, but this could lead to misinterpretation as 1 millinewton (mN).

The S.I. system gives the newton-meter a specific name, the joule (J):

$$1 \text{ joule} = 1 \text{ N-m}$$

The S.I. unit of power is the newton-meter per second, which is 1 watt (W):

$$1 \text{ watt} = 1 \text{ newton-meter/second} = 1 \text{ joule/second}$$
$$1 \text{ horsepower} = 746 \text{ watts} = 0.746 \text{ kilowatts}$$

EXAMPLE 1-11: A constant force of 45 N is applied to a body to move the body 1200 mm. What is the work done?

SOLUTION:

$$\text{Work} = 45 \text{ N} \times 1.2 \text{ m} = 54 \text{ N-m}$$

EXAMPLE 1-12: A force of 250 N is exerted over a stroke of 225 mm in a machine tool in 9 seconds. What is the power requirement in the cutting tool?

SOLUTION:

$$\text{Power} = \frac{\text{work}}{\text{time}}$$
$$= \frac{2500 \text{ N} \times 0.225 \text{ m}}{9 \text{ s}}$$
$$= 62.5 \text{ watts}$$

QUESTIONS

1-1. How are thrust and hydraulic pressure related to each other in the case of a hydraulic cylinder?

1-2. A hydraulic cylinder has a piston diameter of 6 in. and a rod diameter of 3 in. Pressure in the cylinder is 1200 psi. How many pounds of force can be exerted against a load
   (a) when the piston rod is advancing?
   (b) when the piston rod is retracting?

1-3. Convert all units in Question 2 to S.I. units and solve the problem.

1-4. **(a)** If the rod in Question 2 advances 36 in. under a pressure of 1200 psi, calculate the work done in foot-pounds.
   (b) Give your answer in S.I. units.

1-5. What is the meaning of drawbar pull?

1-6. What is the travel speed in kilometers per hour for 40-cm diameter wheels rotating at 350 rpm?

1-7. A force of 60 lb is applied with a lever arm of 16 in. on a pipe wrench to rotate a pipe coupling 1.3 in. in outside diameter. What force is applied at the surface of the coupling?

1-8. A mine cage weighing 10 tons is raised at a steady speed of 500 ft per min. What work is done in 1 min?

1-9. For Question 8, what is the horsepower output of the hoist motor?

1-10. A small warship develops 70,000 HP at its propellers when moving at 40 miles per hour (take 40 mph to be 60 fps). What is the drag force of the seawater against the ship?

1-11. Total air resistance against an aircraft moving at 240 mph (352 fps) in level flight is 600 pounds. What horsepower is exerted by the propeller?

1-12. What is the output horsepower of a hydraulic cylinder with a thrust of 12,000 lb through a stroke of 12 in. in a time of 3s?

1-13. A diesel locomotive applying 2000 HP at its wheels moves a train of cars at 60 mph (88 fps). What is its drawbar pull?

1-14. An electric motor with an efficiency of 85% has an output of 15 HP.
(a) What is its horsepower input?
(b) What is its kilowatt input?
(c) What is its waste heat output in Btu per hour (Btuh)?

1-15. A tire with a radius of 16.0 in. spins on a smooth road with a coefficient of friction of 0.4. In spinning, the tire does not move the vehicle. If the tire rotates at 120 rpm, how much heat is generated in 1 min? Weight carried by the tire is 1000 lb.

1-16. A pair of mating gears transmits 50 HP from one shaft to another at an efficiency of 98%. What is the power input and how much heat in Btuh is produced?

1-17. A worm gear reducer connects a 40-HP 1200-rpm motor to a shaft at a speed reduction of 40:1. What is the torque of the motor shaft and of the driven shaft?

1-18. A winch drum has an effective diameter of 18 in. and provides a torque of 800 pound-feet.
(a) How much work is done by the drum in 12 revolutions?
(b) What weight is lifted?
(c) What is the horsepower output at 100 rpm?

1-19. A hoist accelerates a load from zero to 650 m/min in 5 s. What is the rate of acceleration?

1-20. A truck decelerates from 60 mph (88 fps) to a stop in 15 s. What is the rate of deceleration?

1-21. What is the kinetic energy of a 2000-ton river barge towed at 12 mph (17.5 fps)?

1-22. Why must the rubber in a vehicle tire
(a) not be too hard?
(b) not be too soft?

1-23. What is the weight in kilograms of a pickup truck weighing 4300 pounds?

1-24. Give the speed in kilometers per hour corresponding to 60 mph.

1-25. A force of 15 kilonewtons is exerted over a stroke of 2.5 m in 6 s. What is the power developed in watts?

1-26. Calculate the power required to pull a chain 300 ft long weighing 15 lb per ft along a concrete floor against a coefficient of friction of 0.07 at 3 mph.

1-27. In a hydrostatic transmission of a tractor, a hydraulic pump drives a hydraulic motor. If the pump has an output of 50 HP and an efficiency of 90%, and the motor has an efficiency of 85%, determine:

(a) the input HP of the pump

(b) the output HP of the motor

(c) the total heat produced by inefficiencies in one hour of operation at these rated horsepowers, expressed both as Btuh and as horsepower.

(d) the overall efficiency of this transmission.

2

POWER SOURCES

2-1 MOTORS

The spark-ignition engine, fuelled usually with gasoline or propane, is popular in mobile equipment or in locations where electric power is unavailable. This engine is reasonably light in weight for its delivered horsepower, but suffers from some serious disadvantages:

1. Its efficiency is very poor, of the order of 5%.
2. It is noisy.
3. It produces toxic fumes.
4. Its fuel is a fire hazard.
5. It cannot be started under load.
6. Its maintenance costs are high.
7. It requires a range of accessory equipment, such as a radiator, air filter, electric ignition system, etc.

In large horsepowers the diesel engine may be more efficient and cheaper to operate.

When primary power is easily obtained from an electric utility, the electric motor is usually selected as the best source of rotary motion. Most electric motors are three-phase alternating-current squirrel-cage induction motors. Such motors are of simple and economical construction, are almost maintenance-free, and have an efficiency of 80% or better, although fractional horsepower sizes are less efficient.

FIGURE 2-1 *Engine-driven lift truck.*

An alternative type of motor to supply rotary motion is the fluid motor, usually operated on hydraulic oil but sometimes using air. The fluid motor has become increasingly popular in the last decade. Hydraulic motors are incorporated into hydrostatic drives, particularly on mobile equipment such as tractors. In these hydrostatic systems the fuel-burning engine of the vehicle drives a hydraulic pump which is the source of oil flow and pressure for the hydraulic motor.

The hydraulic motor is more expensive than an electric motor of the same horsepower, but may be preferred for a variety of reasons. The alternating-current induction motor is basically a constant-speed motor. To vary the speed, a limited range of speeds can be supplied by gear changes or pulley changes between the motor and the load being driven. The a.c. motor also is not well suited to frequent stops and starts under load, nor frequent and rapid reversal of rotation. However, it has a higher starting torque than an equivalent hydraulic motor.

The hydraulic motor is very small in size and light in weight for its horsepower output. In smaller sizes an electric motor will weigh about 30 lb per horsepower and perhaps half as much in large sizes. Hydraulic motors may weigh as little as a half-pound per horsepower up to as much as 5 lb per horsepower, depending on size and type. In efficiency they can match that of an electric motor.

The small size of a hydraulic motor means small inertia. There is so little mass in the rotor of a hydraulic motor that it can be reversed instantly even at high speeds. Electric motors draw very high currents during reversal, and inertia effects are very high.

The two types of internal combustion engine differ in the method of ignition of the air-fuel mixture drawn into the cylinders. In the spark-ignition engine, fuel is atomized and mixed with combustion air before entering the cylinder. This air-fuel mixture is compressed by the piston,

29

FIGURE 2-2 *Battery-powered narrow-aisle lift truck.*

then ignited by an electric spark. In the compression-ignition or diesel engine, fuel is injected into the cylinder after the combustion air already in the cylinder has been first compressed. This fuel-air mixture is ignited by the heat resulting from high compression of the compressed air. The diesel engine can tolerate a wider range of fuels than the spark-ignition engine. Though the diesel engine is heavier, it is more efficient.

Internal combustion engines are rated in brake horsepower, which is the delivered horsepower at the flywheel after friction losses of the engine are deducted. Brake horsepower is the actual rated horsepower delivered to the load against which the engine works. Since brake horsepower is proportional to the rpm of the engine, when making engine comparisons the governed rpm of each engine should be the rpm used in the comparison. Engine horsepower decreases 3.5% for every 1000 ft elevation above sea level, and decreases also by 1% for every 10 °F temperature rise above 60 °F, because combustion air weighs less per cubic foot if air pressure decreases or temperature increases.

2-2 ENGINE FUELS

The usual engine fuels for internal combustion engines are gasolines, propane, or diesel fuel. All these fuels are derived from petroleum and natural gas.

At the wellhead, petroleum always contains some natural gas, and natural gas always contains some petroleum ingredients. Most crude oils have chemical analyses that fall within the following limits:

Carbon	83.9–86.8%
Hydrogen	11.4–14.0%
Sulfur	0.06– 2.0%
Nitrogen	0.11– 1.70(1.70%)

Since petroleum chemicals are made up essentially of carbon and hydrogen, these chemicals are referred to as hydrocarbons. Both carbon and hydrogen are excellent fuels. Nitrogen is inert and harmless, except as an air pollutant from engine exhausts. Sulfur in fuels is damaging to engines, since it forms highly corrosive acids when burned, and is removed from petroleum products by chemical treatment.

The fuel for a spark-ignition engine is a cracked gasoline, that is, a gasoline processed through a catalytic cracker at an oil refinery. For ease of starting in winter in a cold climate it is usual to add butane to the gasoline. Any gasoline requires a sufficiently high octane number to resist detonation (knocking) during combustion. Octane number is expressed as follows.

Iso-octane is a hydrocarbon with an octane number of 100; it is arbitrarily assigned this number because it has excellent combustion characteristics in a spark-ignition engine. N-heptane or normal heptane on the other hand is a poor fuel which will knock severely if used in such an engine. N-heptane is assigned an octane number of zero. A blend of 80% iso-octane with 20% n-heptane is for example assigned an octane number of 80, that is, an octane rating is the percent iso-octane in a mixture of iso-octane and n-heptane. The octane-heptane mixture that gives the same engine performance as a certain gasoline determines the octane number of that gasoline.

Diesel engines rotate at low speeds and therefore can tolerate a rather wide range of fuels, but the viscosity of the fuel must be suited to the fuel injection system. Knocking is possible in diesel engines also. The cetane number of the diesel fuel corresponds to the octane number of gasolines. The two hydrocarbons which are blended to give the cetane number are cetane, rated 100, and alpha-methyl-naphthalene (abbreviated AMN) rated zero. A fuel with a cetane number of 40 would have the same ignition quality as a mixture of 40% cetane and 60% AMN. Cetane numbers for good diesel fuels are not as high as the octane numbers of quality gasolines.

Propane and butane, liquified petroleum gases, or mixtures of the two, may be used as an alternate fuel to gasoline in spark-ignition engines. These liquified petroleum gases (LPG) have an octane rating of 100 or better, a higher rating than gasolines. The higher octane rating makes higher compression ratios possible; when converting from gasoline to propane, sometimes a thinner head gasket is used to improve the compression ratio slightly.

The exhaust fumes from burning LPG are not especially toxic since much less carbon monoxide is produced as compared to gasoline. Since LPG is odorless, a mercaptan (sulfur) compound is added to give the characteristic smell of LPG fuel. The burning of the mercaptan does not harm the engine.

After leaving the propane fuel tank, the propane is delivered to the engine as a dry vapor. This fuel therefore does not dilute the oil in the crankcase as gasoline does, nor deposit varnish or carbon in the engine. Longer life is obtained from propane engines, and spark plugs and oil changes are less frequent as compared to gasoline operation. However, the LPG exhaust is hotter, and stellite valves and valve seats must be used.

Refuelling with propane is a safer procedure than with gasoline since it is not possible to spill fuel. Even if a propane line is broken, the propane tank outlet closes immediately with the sudden increase in flow. The propane fuel system however is more complex and costly than the gasoline system.

Propane vs. gasoline engines.

	Propane	*Gasoline*
Normal state	Gas	Liquid
Heat energy per lb	21,600 Btu	19,500 Btu
Critical compression ratio	12:1	up to 11:1
Percent of fuel combustion	85–90%	up to 70%

2-3 THE INDUSTRIAL STORAGE BATTERY

The storage battery is an electrochemical device which converts electric energy into chemical energy through the medium of the battery charger, and stores this energy until it is released as electric energy. Virtually all storage batteries are of two types: the lead-acid battery and the nickel-iron battery. All batteries have three components basic to the production of electric energy: a solid material electrically positive, a solid material electrically negative, and an electrolyte connecting the two.

The positive material in a nickel-iron battery, also called an Edison cell, is nickel oxyhydrate, $NiOOH$, and the negative material is iron sponge. The electrolyte is alkaline potassium hydroxide, KOH, and water with the addition of lithium hydroxide. During discharge, oxygen is transferred from the positive to the negative electrode material, this chemical action converting the positive electrode to nickel hydroxide, $Ni(OH)_2$ and the negative electrode to iron hydroxide, $Fe(OH)_2$. The reverse chemical action occurs on charging. The open-circuit voltage of a nickel-iron cell is 1.2 volts, though this varies with the state of charge or discharge of the cell and may range from 1.0 at complete discharge to 1.75 volts at complete charge. Connecting 5 cells in series will result in a battery of 6 volts. When current is drawn from the battery, the effective voltage of the cell or battery is reduced by the voltage drop across the battery due to its internal electrical resistance, and this voltage drop will increase with the current drawn from the battery. The specific gravity of the electrolyte is 1.210 to 1.215 at 77 °F.

The internal resistance of the Edison cell is much greater than that of the lead-acid cell, but the Edison cell is lighter in weight, more rugged, and has a longer life. These advantages explain its selection for industrial trucks such as electric warehouse lift trucks.

In the lead-acid battery, the positive material is lead peroxide, PbO_2, the negative material sponge lead, and the electrolyte sulfuric acid. On discharge, the acid electrolyte separates into hydrogen and SO_4. The hydrogen combines with oxygen at the positive plate to produce water. This reduces the specific gravity of the electrolyte. The SO_4 combines with the lead of both plates to produce lead sulfate. Charging reverses these chemical reactions. The open-circuit voltage of the lead-acid cell is 2.0 volts, higher than that of the nickel-iron Edison cell, but may vary from 1.8 volts at discharge to 2.6 volts at full charge.

The lead-acid cell is composed of interleaved positive and negative plates kept from short-circuiting by separators of insulating material such as rubber, wood, or glass mat. Separators have vertical grooves on one side only. The grooved side is against the positive plate to allow circulation of the electrolyte around the positive plate, where the chemical action is greater. There is one more negative plate than the number of positive plates so that both sides of each positive plate will be acted upon chemically, the reason being that the active material on the positive plate expands and contracts as the battery charges and discharges, and both sides of the positive plate must expand and contract to prevent warping. The plates are made of a lead alloy grid or latticework which supports the active material of the plates. Batteries needed for long discharge times or low currents require heavier grids, while light grids are used where heavy discharges of short duration are required, as in automobile batteries. Both positive and negative grids are usually of the same design and alloy composition, but the negative grid can be lighter in weight because it is less subject to corrosion.

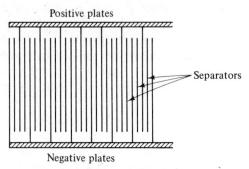

Positive plates

Separators

Negative plates

FIGURE 2-3 *Storage battery.*

Grids are usually made from an antimony alloy of lead, with 5 to 12% antimony being used. Arsenic is a universal impurity in antimony. Since arsenic is harmful to battery operation, it must be removed completely from the antimony used in batteries. The active materials are pastes, with no strength, hence the necessity for supporting them on metallic grids.

Lead has many oxides, including yellow litharge, PbO, and the red oxide Pb_3O_4. The negative paste is produced from litharge with zero to 25% red lead. The positive paste is made of 60 to 80% red lead with litharge. The paste is treated with sulfuric acid to form the finished positive and negative plates.

When the battery is fully charged, all the active material of the positive plates is lead peroxide and of the negative plates sponge lead, and the specific gravity of the electrolyte is at its maximum. During discharge, the acid combines with the active material to produce lead sulfate and water. The amount of acid decreases, the amount of water increases, and the specific gravity falls. The decrease in specific gravity is proportional to the ampere-hours of discharge. But on charging, the increase in specific gravity is not proportional to amp-hours.

Impurities such as iron or copper in the paste or other parts of the battery are harmful to its operation. They may cause a slow discharge of the battery when standing on open circuit, as a result of localized battery action.

Separators located between positive and negative plates prevent metallic conduction while permitting conduction through the electrolyte. Wood separators are often used, the wood being treated to remove soluble matter and to expand its pores. Wood when exposed to sulfuric acid produces acetic acid, which is harmful to positive plates but for some reason unknown enhances the functioning of negative plates. Perforated rubber and glass mat separators are also in use.

The thickness of the separators determines the internal electrical resistance of the cell. Starting batteries for automobiles must deliver large currents and thus must have low electrical resistances. Such batteries use separators $\frac{5}{64}$ in. thick. Batteries for slower discharge rates use thicker separators.

The battery electrolyte is sulfuric acid diluted with distilled water to provide the required specific gravity. Higher specific gravities require a higher acid content and are needed in batteries subjected to low temperatures so that the electrolyte will not freeze as the battery discharges. Batteries used at higher temperatures or in hot climates require a lower specific gravity because of the increased chemical activity at higher temperatures. High acid concentrations increase the capacity of positive plates and reduce the capacity of negative plates at high discharge rates and low temperatures. The following specific gravities are preferred:

Stationary batteries	1.200–1.225
Trucks, tractors, and lift trucks	1.270–1.280
Lighting batteries, tropical use	1.200–1.230
Aviation batteries	1.275–1.285

In the past few years jelly types of electrolyte have been introduced to eliminate spilling. Most of these are made from mixtures of concentrated sulfuric acid and dilute solutions of water glass (sodium silicate).

The open-circuit voltage (that is, no current being drawn from the battery) is given very closely by the relationship:

$$\text{Volts} = \text{sp. gr.} + 0.84$$

But in the case of nickel-iron batteries, the specific gravity of the electrolyte is not an indicator of the state of discharge of the cell.

2-4 THE CAPACITY OF A STORAGE BATTERY

The capacity of any storage battery is expressed in amp-hours, that is, a uniform discharge rate at a certain number of amperes over a number of hours. This rating is a nominal one and depends on the discharge rate in amps. The higher the current drawn from the battery the smaller the amp-hours that it will deliver. The reason for this is in part the internal resistance of the cell. The higher the current, the greater is the internal voltage drop across the cell, and this is wasted energy. Another reason is the inability of the electrolyte to diffuse rapidly enough into the pores of the active material as it becomes exhausted. Usually an eight-hour discharge rate is assumed, though industrial truck batteries are usually based on six hours.

The amp-hour rating is also reduced by lower temperatures than the standard temperature of 77°F. The capacity may be reduced by 50% at a temperature of 0°F. As the temperature is lowered, the internal resistance of the cell increases very rapidly.

Specific gravity has an influence on amp-hour capacity. A difference of 25 points in gravity will change the capacity by 8 to 10%.

A battery may be charged at any rate in amperes that does not produce excessive temperature or gassing. About 110% of the amp-hours discharged must be returned to the battery to bring it to full charge. The voltage of the charging unit must be about 2.5 volts per battery cell. A starting charge of about 20 to 25 amps per 100 amp-hours is used, this current being reduced when the charge is 80% or more complete.

The charging cycle is usually stopped automatically. Fig. 2-4 shows that the battery voltage takes a sharp rise when the charge approaches completion. Charging may be terminated after a fixed period following this voltage rise. The sharp voltage rise triggers a voltage relay to operate a time switch which provides this time delay. For lead-acid batteries in lift truck service, a relay setting of 2.37 volts is used, with a three-hour time delay.

Fig. 2-5 shows how the amp-hour capacity is influenced by the discharge rate. If discharge takes place over an extended period at low current, then the amp-hour capacity increases. Suppose a current of 3 times the nominal discharge current is drawn from the battery. Such a current will discharge the battery in about an hour and a half, and the amp-hour capacity is reduced to 60%.

2-5 ELECTRIC MOTORS

There are many types of electric motors, but only the more common types will receive mention here. Direct-current (d.c.) motors are variable-speed motors while alternating-current (a.c.) motors are basically fixed-speed. The principle is not invariably true: two-speed a.c. motors are not uncommon, and there are types of a.c. motors that permit some speed variation.

The problems of selecting and operating electric motors fall into three groups: environmental, electrical, and mechanical. The motor must be connected to an available electrical service, such as 220 volts, 3-phase. The available service is an electrical consideration in motor selection. If the motor must operate in a dusty area in a foundry, or underwater, then the type of motor must be chosen to suit the environment as well as the electrical supply. Finally the motor must meet the required mechanical characteristics of the load, chiefly speed, horsepower, torque, shaft size, and vertical or horizontal orientation of the shaft. Other mechanical requirements include the location of the electric motor on the machine it is to drive, its mounting arrangements, and the coupling of power transmission devices to it such as couplings and brakes.

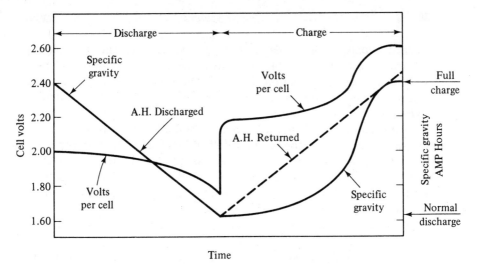

FIGURE 2-4 *Discharge and charge characteristics of a storage battery.*

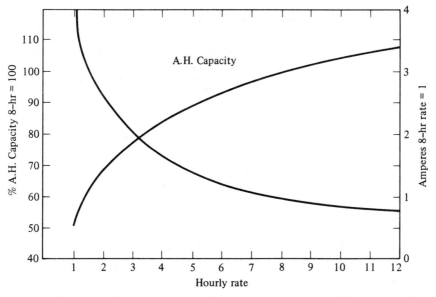

FIGURE 2-5 *Typical amp-hour capacity of a storage battery. If less current is drawn, the amp-hour capacity is increased.*

2-6 DIRECT-CURRENT MOTORS

While the alternating-current motor is basically a fixed-speed motor, its speed being a function of the frequency of the alternating current as discussed below, the direct-current motor is not governed by frequency and is more readily adapted to rotational speed changes. It is therefore used only where variable motor speeds are an operating requirement. In such applications however the d.c. motor has met increasing competition from hydrostatic transmissions, discussed in a later chapter, which are excellent variable-speed devices and are now competitive in price with d.c. motor installations.

A d.c. motor has a rotating armature and a fixed-field winding. These two windings can be connected together in series with each other or in parallel. Most d.c. motors are shunt-wound, that is, the magnetic field windings and the rotating armature windings are in parallel. Speed is controlled by adding or reducing electrical resistance to the field circuit. That is, speed is changed by reducing or increasing the field current, a lower field current providing a higher speed. A maximum speed range of about 8:1 is possible.

In the series d.c. motor the field winding is in series with the armature winding. Since the series field must be able to carry full armature current, it is wound with a few turns of large wire with a very low electrical resistance. The series motor is well suited to driving cranes and winches, where heavy loads must be moved slowly.

In some applications, such as paper-making machines, speed may be controlled by controlling the voltage applied to the armature.

Characteristic performance curves for series and shunt-wound d.c. motors are shown in Fig. 2-6.

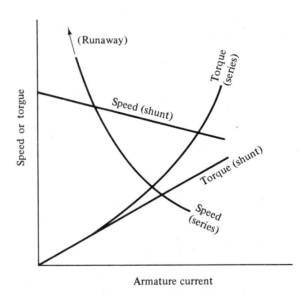

FIGURE 2-6 *Characteristics of shunt-wound and series-wound direct-current motors.*

2-7   MOTOR ENCLOSURES

The environment in which an electric motor must operate dictates the type of enclosure (housing) that must be selected to protect it. An open enclosure for example could not be used on a motor which must be operated while submerged in water. Again, operation in a high-temperature area or in restricted air circulation may call for a specially ventilated enclosure (or special high-temperature insulation for the motor wires). Unusual operating conditions such as chemical fumes, explosive dusts, or salt water require special enclosures. To cope with these problems a wide range of motor enclosures is available. The more usual types of open and enclosed motors are the following.

Open Motors

Most electric motors are open motors. Such motors have ventilation openings to receive cooling air that passes over the motor windings (Fig. 7-5).

Dripproof motors: In a dripproof enclosure the ventilation openings are so designed that drops of liquid falling vertically or nearly so do not enter the motor windings.

Splashproof motors: The splashproof enclosure is another type of open motor with ventilation openings that prevent entrance of drops of water striking at any angle not more than 100 degrees from the vertical.

Guarded motors: These have ventilation openings either of small size or protected by screens.

Weather-protected motors: These are open motors with ventilation openings that minimize the entrance of rain, snow, and airborne particles.

Totally Enclosed Motors

Totally enclosed motors are enclosed so that there is no free exchange of air between the inside and the outside of the enclosure. They are not however airtight.

Totally enclosed nonventilated (TENV) motors: These are not cooled by any means external to the enclosure.

Totally enclosed fan-cooled (TEFC) motors: These have a fan integral with the motor.

Explosion-proof motors: These are constructed to withstand an internal explosion of a gas or vapor and to prevent igniting a vapor surrounding the motor.

Waterproof motors: These are totally enclosed to exclude water.

The open motors are less expensive than enclosed motors. A considerable number of other special enclosures are available, such as lintproof and encapsulated motors. In addition, motors are available for both horizontal and vertical shaft mounting.

2-8 TEMPERATURE RISE

The life of an electric motor depends on its operating temperature. The motor converts electrical energy into mechanical energy, but of course with some inefficiencies. If the motor efficiency is 80%, then 20% of the electrical input is converted into heat, causing a rise in temperature in the windings. The effect of any temperature rise is a steady degradation of the electrical insulation on the windings.

The heat generated in a motor may be considered as approximately proportional to the square of the current which the motor draws, or to the output horsepower squared. Since more current is drawn during motor starts, frequent starts and heavy starting loads impose more severe demands. A stalled motor may draw 5 to 6 times normal running current, which means a heating effect 25 to 36 times that of the rated load.

Open dripproof motors have a service factor of 1.15, which means that they can safely carry a 15% overload continuously. However, it is not recommended that this overload capacity be used in design. TEFC and explosion-proof motors have a service factor of 1.00, that is, no overload capacity.

Motor windings are usually designed for a life of 35,000 hours when operated at rated temperature. There are four classes of insulation in NEMA specifications (National Electrical Manufacturers Association): classes A, B, F, and H. These classes are allowed the following temperature limits:

	A	*B*	*F*	*H*
Temp. rise	105 °C	130 °C	155 °C	180 °C

If the life of the motor is too short, the following expedients may be adopted:

1. Select a motor with a greater horsepower.
2. Select a motor with a higher class of insulation: B, F, or H.
3. Improve the cooling conditions or surroundings of the motor.

2-9 MOTOR SPEEDS

Basically, the rotational speed of an a.c. motor depends only on the frequency or number of cycles per second of the a.c. supply, and the number of magnetic poles in the motor. The speed that is calculated from the frequency and number of poles is called the *synchronous speed,* which is given by the following formula

$$\text{rpm} = \frac{120f}{p}$$

where f = frequency (usually 60-cycle)
          p = the number of magnetic poles

Since poles must occur in pairs, north pole and south pole, p is 2, 4, 6, or 8, etc. Only larger motors have more than 6 poles because larger numbers of poles increase the cost of the motor. For 60-cycle power the fastest motor speed is given by a two-pole motor:

$$\text{Synchronous speed for 2 poles} = \frac{120 \times 60}{2} = 3600 \text{ rpm}$$

On a European frequency of, say 50 cycles, the same motor would have a synchronous speed of 3000 rpm.

Synchronous speeds for 60-cycle power.

Poles	Rpm
2	3600
4	1800
6	1200
8	900
10	600

High-speed motors are cheaper and are selected where possible; they use chain or belt drives to obtain lower speeds.

The synchronous motor rotates at synchronous speeds. The most common type of a.c. motor, however, is the squirrel-cage induction motor. Under no load it runs at approximately synchronous speed, but at rated load has about 4% slip, that is, its motor nameplate speed is 4% less than synchronous.

Induction motor speeds for 60-cycle power.

Poles	Rpm
2	3425
4	1725
6	1160
8	860

The electrical supply across which the motor is connected may be any of the following:

120-volt single-phase

208-volt single-phase

220-volt single-phase

208-volt three-phase

220-volt three-phase

440-volt three-phase

550-volt three-phase

Three-phase power requires three or four wires. Single-phase 110-volt is split from 220 volts. This arrangement may be found for example in the wiring of an electric stove, which has three wires, two "hot" wires across 220 volts and a ground wire splitting 220 into 110 volts to ground. A three-phase 220-volt motor will have three hot wires each 220 volts to ground.

When wiring a three-phase motor the electrician does not know whether the motor will rotate in the right or the wrong direction. If after wiring is completed it is found that the motor runs in the wrong direction, then any two of the three incoming power leads must be interchanged to reverse the direction of rotation.

2-10   THE SQUIRREL-CAGE INDUCTION MOTOR

The simple construction and useful operating characteristics such as high starting torque, of the squirrel-cage induction motor are the reasons why this type of a.c. motor is so commonly selected. Its two basic parts are the stator or primary, which is the stationary winding, and the rotor or secondary which rotates. The stator is connected to the a.c. supply. It is a laminated steel core holding electric coils in its slots. The rotor is not connected to the supply, but like the secondary of a transformer its current is induced in it from the stator or primary, hence the term induction motor.

The rotor construction is quite simple. There is a laminated steel core,

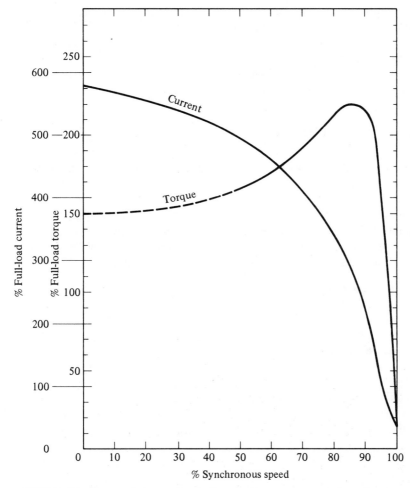

FIGURE 2-7 *Characteristic curves of a low starting current, normal starting torque squirrel case motor.*

with the copper conductors embedded in this core close to the surface and aligned parallel to the shaft or slightly skewed from parallel. Because the rotor currents select the path of least resistance, which is provided by the copper conductors, the conductors are not insulated from the core. At both ends of the rotor the conductors are short-circuited to a solid circular ring. The construction of rotor bars and end rings suggests a revolving squirrel cage, hence the name given to this motor.

The current and torque characteristics of a typical polyphase induction motor are shown in Fig. 2-7. These motors may be assumed to have a starting torque of 150% of running torque, though high-starting-torque types are also available.

Full-load torque is the torque developed by the motor at rated horsepower when rotating at rated full load speed.

Breakdown torque is the maximum torque that the motor will develop without stalling.

Locked rotor torque is the maximum torque which the motor will develop at rest while rated voltage at rated frequency is applied to it.

2-11 SINGLE-PHASE MOTORS

A single-phase squirrel-cage induction motor operated on a single phase only could not start itself, that is, has zero starting torque. Single-phase induction motors therefore are modified for starting by providing a second phase (a split phase as it is called). In addition to the split-phase single-phase induction motor, there are many other kinds of single-phase motors, such as shaded-pole motors and repulsion motors, which will not be discussed.

Split-phase motors are made in the following types:

1. Resistance-start.
2. Reactor-start.
3. Capacitor-start.
4. Split-capacitor.

The resistance-start motor consists of a squirrel-cage rotor and two stator windings, a main winding and a starter winding. A resistance is connected in series with the starter winding, as in Fig. 2-8. By this arrangement a two-phase rotating magnetic field is produced for starting the motor. When the

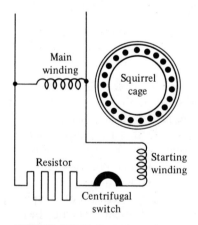

FIGURE 2-8 *Split-phase resistance start a.c. motor.*

motor reaches about 75% of its rated speed a centrifugal switch opens to disconnect the starter winding from the line. If this type of motor is so heavily loaded that it cannot approach its operating speed, then the centrifugal switch does not open. The starter winding then remains in the circuit and burns out. The motor will still run, but must be started by some other means. The resistance-start motor has a low starting torque and is not suited to heavy-duty starts; for such applications the capacitor-start motor is required.

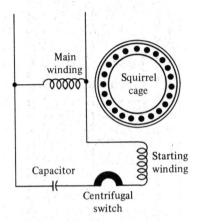

FIGURE 2-9 *Split-phase capacitor start motor.*

The capacitor-start motor of Fig. 2-9 also has a running and a starting winding, but a capacitor substitutes for a resistor in the starting circuit. The capacitor is usually mounted in a small housing on top of the motor. This motor provides a high starting torque.

The reactor-start and split-capacitor motors are variants of the capacitor-start motor. All these single-phase motors may be reversed by reversing the connections to either the main or the starter winding.

2-12 MOTOR CONTROLS

Motor controls may have many functions, but the more important are:

1. Starting and stopping the motor.
2. Protection of the motor from burning out.
3. Limiting the starting current.

Motor starters which apply full voltage directly to the motor terminals are either of the manual or magnetic type. A starter for a simple motor of small horsepower is usually a manual starter. This is a hand-operated mechanism to make or break the motor circuit. A thermal overload device in the starter gives protection against excessive currents.

The magnetic starter also contains a mechanism to make or break the motor circuit and a thermal overload device. This starter however uses an electrical signal to make the contacts open or close. The contacts are operated by an electromagnet. Magnetic starters are often controlled by such pilot devices as limit switches, relays, timers, pressure switches, or remote pushbuttons.

2-13 GEAR MOTORS

A gear motor is a parallel or right-angle gear reduction unit combined with an electric motor in a unified housing and mounting base. The chief advantage of the gear motor is that the final driven shaft may be coupled directly to the driving shaft of the gear motor, thus eliminating gearing, belts, pulleys, drive chain, or other components.

In a gear motor, gear friction is a maximum at the instant of starting. For a gear motor using worm gearing, this gear starting torque is especially high.

Overhung loads are applied to gear motors when they are connected to driven shafts by drive chains, belts, or gears. An overhung load limits the torque output of the gear motor, since such a load imposes heavier stresses on the gear motor shaft and bearings. The allowable capacity for an overhung load is found from the manufacturer's catalogue information on the gear motor.

Clutch and brake motors combine in unit construction an electric motor with a clutch or brake. These units are used when load engagement and disengagement are frequent or stopping is frequent and fast.

2-14 FRAME NUMBERS AND DIMENSIONS

Standard dimensions and frame numbers of electric motors are given in the following tables.

FRAME SIZE (2) (5)

HP	SYNCH SPEED RPM	DRIPPROOF	TOTALLY-ENCLOSED (4)
1/4	1800	F48	F48
1/3	1800	F48	G48
1/2	1800	H56	H56
3/4	1800	J56	J56
1	3600	J56	J56
1	1800	143T	143T
1	1200	145T	145T
1 1/2	3600	143T	143T
1 1/2	1800	145T	145T
1 1/2	1200	182T	182T
2	3600	145T	145T
2	1800	145T	145T
2	1200	184T	184T
3	3600	145T	182T
3	1800	182T	182T
3	1200	213T	213T
5	3600	182T	184T
5	1800	184T	184T
5	1200	215T	215T
7 1/2	3600	184T	213T
7 1/2	1800	213T	213T
7 1/2	1200	254T	254T
10	3600	213T	215T
10	1800	215T	215T
10	1200	256T	256T
15	3600	215T	215T
15	1800	254T	254T
15	1200	284T	284T

FRAME SIZE (2) (3) (5)

HP	SYNCH SPEED RPM	DRIPPROOF	TOTALLY-ENCLOSED
20	3600	254T	256T
20	1800	256T	256T
20	1200	286T	286T
25	3600	256T	284TS
25	1800	284T	284T
25	1200	324T	324T
30	3600	284TS	286TS
30	1800	286T	286T
30	1200	326T	326T
40	3600	286TS	324TS
40	1800	324T	324T
40	1200	364T	364T
50	3600	324TS	326TS
50	1800	326T	326T
50	1200	365T	365T
60	3600	326TS	364TS
60	1800	364T	364T
60	1200	404T	404T
60	900	405T	405T
75	3600	364TS	365TS
75	1800	365T	365T
75	1200	405T	405T
75	900	444T	444T
100	3600	365TS	405TS
100	1800	404T	405T
100	1200	444T	444T
100	900	445T	445T
100	720	9506	—
100	600	9508	—

FRAME SIZE (2) (3) (5)

HP	SYNCH SPEED RPM	DRIPPROOF	TOTALLY ENCLOSED
125	3600	404TS	444TS
125	1800	405T	444T
125	1200	445T	445T
125	900	9506	—
150	3600	405TS	445TS
150	1800	444T	445T
150	1200	445T	—
150	900	9506	—
150	720	9508	—
200	3600	444TS	—
200	1800	445TS	—
200	1200	9506	—
200	900	9508	—
200	720	9508	—
250	3600	445TS	—
250	1800	9506S	—
250	1200	9508	—
250	900	9508	—
250	720	9510	—
300	1800	9506S	—
300	1200	9508	—
300	900	9510	—
350	1800	9508S	—
350	1200	9510	—
400	1800	9508S	—
400	1200	9510S	—
450	1800	9508S	—
500	1800	9510S	—
600	1800	9510S	—

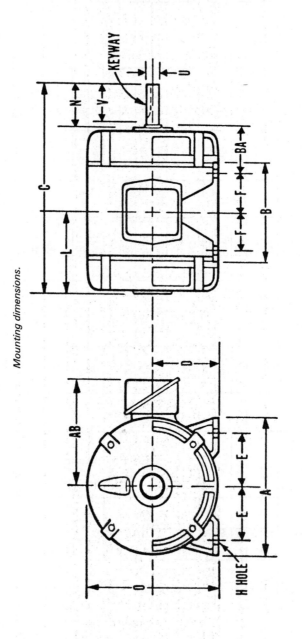

Mounting dimensions.

FRAME SIZE	NET WEIGHT (LBS.)	KEYWAY WIDTH	KEYWAY DEPTH	A	B	BA	C	D	E	F	H	L	N	O	U	V	AB
F48	17	3/64	Flat	5.63	3.63	2.50	9.44	3.00	2.13	1.38	11/32x11/32 Slot	4.06	1.56	5.88	.500	1.50	—
G48	19						9.94					4.56					
H56	23	3/16	3/32	6.50	4.00	2.75	10.07	3.50	2.44	1.50	11/32 x 11/32 Slot	3.94	1.94	6.75	.625	1.88	—
J56	28						11.07						4.94				
K56	32						11.44						5.31				
L56	35						12.19						6.06				
143T	33	3/16	3/32	7.00	5.00	2.25	10.69	3.50	2.75	2.00	11/32	4.19	2.31	7.00	.875	2.00	5.76
145T	44				6.00		11.69			2.50		4.69					
182T	71	1/4	1/8	9.00	5.75	2.75	12.69	4.50	3.75	2.25	13/32	4.94	2.81	9.00	1.125	2.50	8.12
184T	82				6.75		13.69			2.75		5.44					
213T	124	5/16	5/32	10.50	7.00	3.50	15.75	5.25	4.25	2.75	13/32	6.13	3.50	10.56	1.375	3.13	8.76
215T	144				8.50		17.25			3.50		6.88					
254T	185	3/8	3/16	12.38	10.50	4.25	20.50	6.25	5.00	4.13	17/32	8.13	4.25	12.50	1.625	3.75	9.76
256T	214				12.25		22.25			5.00		9.00					
284T	266	1/2	1/4	13.88	12.25	4.75	23.38	7.00	5.50	4.75	17/32	9.25	4.88	14.00	1.875	4.38	11.19
284TS		3/8	3/16		12.25		22.00			4.75		9.25	3.50		1.625	3.00	
286T	310	1/2	1/4		13.75		24.88			5.50		10.00	4.88		1.875	4.38	
286TS		3/8	3/16		13.75		23.50			5.50		10.00	3.50		1.625	3.00	
324T	404	1/2	1/4	15.88	13.75	5.25	26.00	8.00	6.25	5.25	21/32	10.25	5.50	16.00	2.125	5.00	14.00
324TS					13.75		24.50			5.25		10.25	4.00		1.875	3.50	
326T	452				15.25		27.50			6.00		11.00	5.50		2.125	5.00	
326TS					15.25		26.00			6.00		11.00	4.00		1.875	3.50	
364T	620	1/2	1/4	17.75	15.00	5.88	28.63	9.00	7.00	5.63	21/32	11.25	6.13	18.00	2.375	5.63	16.06
364TS					15.00		26.50			5.63		11.25	4.00		1.875	3.50	
365T	680				16.00		29.63			6.13		11.75	6.13		2.375	5.63	
365TS					16.00		27.50			6.13		11.75	4.00		1.875	3.50	
404T	869	1/2	1/4	19.75	16.00	6.63	32.50	10.00	8.00	6.13	13/16	12.50	7.50	20.06	2.875	7.00	19.22
404TS					16.00		29.50			6.13		12.50	4.50		2.125	4.00	
405T	938				17.50		34.00			6.88		13.25	7.50		2.875	7.00	
405TS					17.50		31.00			6.88		13.25	4.50		2.125	4.00	
444T	1196	7/8	7/16	21.75	18.25	7.50	37.63	11.00	9.00	7.25	13/16	14.38	8.87	22.00	3.375	8.25	20.28
444TS		5/8	5/16		18.25		33.88			7.25		14.38	5.12		2.375	4.50	
445T	1356	7/8	7/16		20.25		39.63			8.25		15.38	8.87		3.375	8.25	
445TS		5/8	5/16		20.25		35.88			8.25		15.38	5.12		2.375	4.50	
9506	1930	7/8	7/16	24.50	25.00	8.50	46.75			10.00		18.13		25.00	3.375	9.88	
9506S		3/4	3/8				42.38								2.875	5.50	
9508	2500	1	1/2		30.00	8.50	53.63	12.50	10.00	12.50	15/16	20.63	12.37		4.000	11.75	22.81
9508S	2470	3/4	3/8				47.38						6.12		2.875	5.50	
9510	3300	1	1/2		37.00		60.63	12.50		16.00		24.13	12.37		4.000	11.75	
9510S	3265	1	3/8				54.38						6.12		2.875	5.50	

QUESTIONS

2-1. Explain why the following prime movers are selected for the function given:
   (a) a diesel engine to drive a large electric generator.
   (b) a gasoline engine for a small farm tractor.
   (c) an electric motor for an engine lathe or drill press.
   (d) a hydraulic motor for driving a bulldozer.

2-2. Compare the advantage and disadvantages of propane versus gasoline as a fuel.

2-3. How many cells in series are required to produce 24 volts, using
   (a) lead-acid batteries?
   (b) nickel batteries?

2-4. Why must a storage battery from which large currents are drawn have a low internal resistance?

2-5. **(a)** Why is a higher electrolyte specific gravity required for low-temperature operation of a storage battery?
   (b) Why is a lower electrolyte specific gravity required for high-temperature operation of a storage battery?

2-6. How do the following factors influence the amp-hour capacity of a storage battery:
   (a) specific gravity.
   (b) the current drawn from the battery.

2-7. How is the rotation of a three-phase motor reversed?

2-8. What is the difference between full-load and breakdown torque in an electric motor?

3

GEARING

Gearing transmits rotary motion from one shaft to another at a fixed ratio of shaft angular velocities. The mating gear teeth acting against each other are actually cams which provide this constant ratio.

Spur gears are those gears with teeth parallel to the axis of the gear. Such gearing can transmit power between parallel shafts only. Other types of gears such as helical or bevel gears have teeth which are not parallel to the shaft. These other types are used for a range of special requirements, including nonparallel shafts.

The small gear in a pair of mating gears is termed the *pinion.*

3-1 GEAR GEOMETRY

The shape of the gear tooth is a special curve known as an *involute,* though a few gears use curves other than the involute. As shown in Fig. 3-1, the involute is the curve traced by a point on a tight cord as the cord is unwound from a circle.

Certain definitions must be understood in order to comprehend the design and function of gears.

Pitch circle: A pinion and mating gear make contact at the pitch circle. The diameter of this circle is called the *pitch diameter;* this is the effective diameter of the gear. Pitch diameter is designated by D (Fig. 3-2).

Pitch: The pitch measures the size or the spacing of gear teeth around the pitch circle.

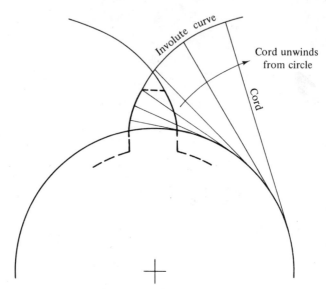

FIGURE 3-1 *The involute curve.*

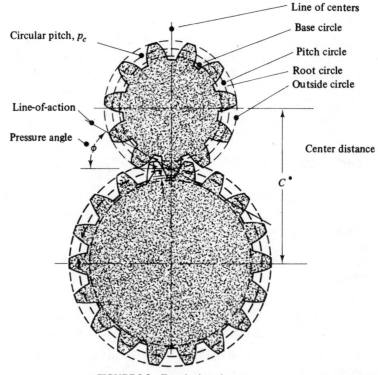

FIGURE 3-2 *Terminology for spur gears.*

Circular pitch: The circular pitch, p_c, is the distance measured along the pitch circle between the same points on two adjacent teeth.

$$p_c = \frac{\text{pitch circle length}}{\text{number of teeth}} = \frac{\pi D}{N}$$

Diametral pitch: This is the number of teeth per inch of pitch diameter, symbolized by p_d. Any two mating gears must have the same diametral pitch. See Fig. 3-3 for sizes of teeth of varying diametral pitch. Note that a large diametral pitch indicates a small tooth size.

The product of the circular pitch and the diametral pitch is π .

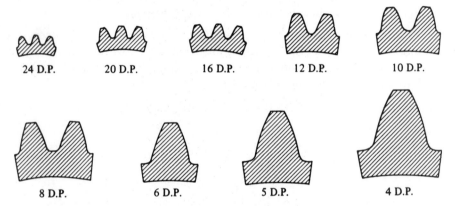

| 24 D.P. | 20 D.P. | 16 D.P. | 12 D.P. | 10 D.P. |

| 8 D.P. | 6 D.P. | 5 D.P. | 4 D.P. |

FIGURE 3-3   *Actual sizes of gear teeth in a range of diametral pitches.*

Center distance: The center distance is the sum of the radii of the two mating gears. It can be expressed in terms of the number of teeth in the gears:

$$\text{Center distance} = C = \frac{D_1 + D_2}{2} = \frac{1}{2}\left(\frac{N_1}{pd} + \frac{N_2}{pd}\right) = \frac{N_1 + N_2}{2pd}$$

Velocity ratio: This is the ratio Z of angular velocities n_1 and n_2 rpm.

$$Z = \frac{n_1}{n_2} = \frac{D_2}{D_1} = \frac{N_2}{N_1}$$

Pressure angle: This is the angle the tooth profile makes with a radial line at the pitch circle. See Fig. 3-2. For power transmission gearing, the pressure angle is 14½ or 20 degrees, for gear pumps it is often 28 degrees. Mating gears must use the same pressure angle as well as the same diametral pitch.

Addendum: The height of a tooth, measured from the pitch radius to the outside radius of the gear.

$$\text{Addendum} = A = \frac{1}{P_d}$$

Dedendum: The depth of a tooth, measured from the pitch circle to the root circle of the gear.

Whole depth of tooth: The total height of the gear tooth; the sum of addendum and dedendum.

Clearance: The space between the outside circle of one mating gear and the root circle of the other gear.

Backlash: The difference between a tooth space and the thickness of a tooth. See Fig. 3-4. Some backlash is needed to allow for thermal expansion, lubrication, and tooth and shaft deflection. Backlash may be designed into the gears or introduced by a slight increase in center distance.

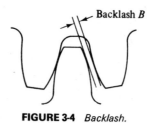

FIGURE 3-4 *Backlash.*

TABLE 3-1

Standard gear systems.

	$14\frac{1}{2}°$ *and* $20°$ *Full-depth* *(ASA B.6)*	$20°$ *Stub* *(ASA B.6)*	$20°$ *and* $25°$ *Full-depth Coarse-pitch* *19.99 and Coarser* *(AGMA 201.03)*	$14\frac{1}{2}°, 20°$ *and* $25°$ *Full-depth, 20-pitch and Finer* *(AGMA 207.05)*
Addendum	$\dfrac{1.000}{P_d}$	$\dfrac{0.800}{P_d}$	$\dfrac{1.000}{P_d}$	$\dfrac{1.000}{P_d}$
Dedendum	$\dfrac{1.157}{P_d}$	$\dfrac{1.000}{P_d}$	$\dfrac{1.250}{P_d}$	$\dfrac{1.200}{P_d} + 0.002$
Clearance	$\dfrac{0.157}{P_d}$	$\dfrac{0.200}{P_d}$	$\dfrac{0.250}{P_d}$	$\dfrac{0.200}{P_d} + 0.002$

Table 3-1 above gives the tooth proportions for the standard systems adopted by the ASA (American Association Standards) and the AGMA (American Gear Manufacturers Association). Molded and sintered gears tend to adopt the 25-degree system. Gearing with higher pressure angle generates somewhat less noise than 14½-degree systems but produce slightly higher forces against the bearings of the shaft.

The fine pitches are used in instrument systems such as computers and timers.

The following are the commonly used and preferred diametral pitches.

Coarse			Fine		
½	3	12	20	64	128
1	4	14	24	72	150
2	6	16	32	80	180
2.25	8	18	40	96	200
2.5	10		48	120	

EXAMPLE 3-1:   Consider a 12-DP spur pinion of 15 teeth rotating at 1725 rpm driving a gear rotating at 720 rpm. Find:

(a)   the number of teeth in the gear.

(b)   the pitch diameter of the pinion.

(c)   the pitch diameter of the gear.

(d)   the center distance of the two gears.

(e)   the O.D. of the larger gear.

SOLUTION:

(a) $\dfrac{1725}{720} \times 15 \text{ teeth} = 36 \text{ teeth in gear}$

(b)   Diametral pitch $= \dfrac{N}{D}$

$$12 = \frac{15}{D}$$

$$D = 1.250 \text{ in.}$$

(c) $D = \dfrac{36}{12} = 3.000 \text{ in.}$

(d)   Center distance $= \dfrac{1}{2}$ (sum of pitch diameters) $= \dfrac{3.000 + 1.250}{2} = 2.125 \text{ in.}$

(e)   O.D. = pitch diameter plus two addendums

$$A = \frac{1}{P_d} = \frac{1}{12} \; 0.0833 \text{ in.}$$

O.D. $= 3.000 + 2 \times 0.0833 = 3.167 \text{ in.}$

EXAMPLE 3-2: A 20-tooth 6-DP pinion meshes with a 72-tooth gear. The pinion has an angular velocity of 1200 rpm. Find:

(a)   the angular velocity of the gear.

(b)   the center distance.

(c)   the pitch diameter of the mating gears.

SOLUTION:

(a)   Gear rpm $= 20/72 \times 1200 = 333$ rpm

(b)   Center distance $= \dfrac{1}{2}\left(\dfrac{N_1 + N_2}{Pd}\right) = \dfrac{1}{2}\left(\dfrac{20 + 72}{6}\right) = 7.667$

(c) $D = \dfrac{N}{Pd} \qquad \dfrac{N_1}{Pd} = \dfrac{20}{6} = 3.333$ in.

$$\dfrac{N_2}{Pd} = \dfrac{72}{6} = 12.000 \text{ in.}$$

When a pinion has fewer than a certain number of teeth there is interference between the meshing teeth of the gears. Such interference occurs at the bottom of the pinion teeth as shown in Fig. 3-5. The least number of teeth that provides no interference or required undercutting of the teeth is 32 for a 14½° pressure angle and 18 for a 20° pressure angle. For a 20° pressure angle and stub teeth the minimum number is 14 teeth. If fewer teeth than these minimums must be used, then the teeth of the pinion must be undercut in manufacture.

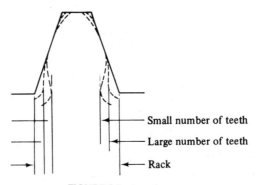

Small number of teeth

Large number of teeth

Rack

FIGURE 3-5   *Interference.*

If a gear must be keyed to a shaft, the minimum pitch diameter must be twice the shaft diameter.

In order to mate, the two gears must meet the following requirements:

1.   Identical pitch.

2. Identical pressure angle.
3. Identical addendum and dedendum.

Metric Gearing

In the S.I. system the module m is used rather than the diametral pitch p_d.

$$\text{Module} = m = \frac{1}{p_d} = \frac{D}{N} \text{ millimeters}$$

For diametral pitch, p_d is replaced by $25.4/m$.

The following formulas, based on m, then become reasonably obvious and therefore need not be discussed. Refer back to the earlier definitions in this section where necessary.

$$\text{Pitch diameter} = D = mN$$
$$\text{Circular pitch} = m\pi = \frac{\pi D}{N}$$
$$\text{Number of teeth} = N = \frac{D}{M}$$

From previous definitions:

$$\text{Addendum} = \frac{1}{p_d} = m$$
$$\text{O.D. of gear} = D + 2m = m(N + 2) \text{ mm}$$
$$\text{Center distance} = C = \tfrac{1}{2}m(N_1 + N_2) \text{ mm}$$

EXAMPLE 3-3: A pair of mating metric gears of module 1.25 have 28 and 38 teeth. Find the center distance, the pitch diameters, and the addendum.

SOLUTION:

$$C = \tfrac{1}{2}m(N_1 + N_2)$$
$$= \tfrac{1}{2}(1.25)(28 + 38) = 41.25 \text{ mm}$$
$$D = 1.25 \times 28 \text{ and } 1.25 \times 38 \quad \text{or} \quad 35 \text{ and } 47.5 \text{ mm}$$
$$A = m = 1.25$$

3-2 FORCES IN GEARS

Forces in gears may be resolved into three components:

1. A tangential component of force, tangential to the pitch circle.

2. A radial force tending to separate the gears.

3. A thrust force axial to the shaft. For straight spur gears there is no thrust.

These forces must be known in order to select suitable bearings for the shaft. Figure 3-6 shows a mating gear and pinion. The forces between the mating teeth occur at the pitch circle along the pressure line at angle θ , the pressure angle. The force F, equal to the force between mating teeth, is transmitted to the bearings of the shaft.

In Fig. 3-7 the forces F and W are resolved into tangential and radial components. The torque transmitted by gear or pinion is

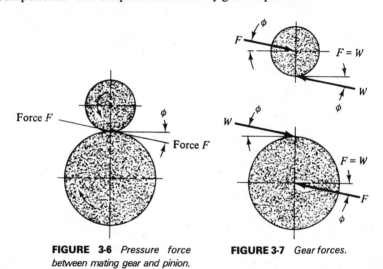

FIGURE 3-6 *Pressure force between mating gear and pinion.*   **FIGURE 3-7** *Gear forces.*

$$T = W_t R$$

Where R = radius of the pitch circle

If V is the pitch circle velocity in fpm, then

$$HP = \frac{W_t V}{33,000}$$

from which W_t may be calculated if the horsepower is known.

EXAMPLE 3-4: Suppose the two gears of Example 3-2 transmit 5 HP. Determine the pitch line velocity and the force between the mating teeth. It is assumed that only one tooth of each gear transmits power at any instant.

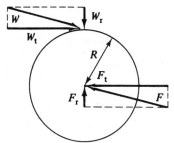

FIGURE 3-8 *Radial and tangential components of gear forces.*

SOLUTION:

Both gears have the same pitch line velocity. For ease of calculation, use the gear to determine this velocity.

$$V = \frac{\pi D \,(\text{rpm})}{12} = \frac{\pi \,(12)\,333}{12} = 1043 \text{ fpm}$$

$$\text{HP} = 5 = \frac{W_t V}{33{,}000} = \frac{1043}{33{,}000} \, W_t$$

$$W_t = 158 \text{ lb}$$

If the pressure angle is 20°, then the force between gear teeth is

$$\frac{W_t}{\cos} \, 20° = \frac{158}{0.94} = 168 \text{ lb}$$

3-3 HELICAL GEARS

Helical gears, like spur gears, are cut from a cylindrical gear blank, but with teeth at some helix angle to the axis of the gear. This helix angle is measured at the pitch circle. Helical gears may substitute for spur gears driving parallel shafts, but may also be applied to shafts at an angle to each other. For shafts at 90 degrees they provide only a point contact between the two gears and therefore can transmit only small amounts of power. Helical gears are preferred if the width of the gear is large, since in the case of helical gears the whole width of the tooth does not engage at once. This action reduces shock and makes such gearing adaptable to heavy loads, high speeds, and low noise levels. Helical gears use the involute tooth shape and the usual pressure angles.

The hand of the helix must be selected correctly. If the two mating helical gears drive parallel shafts, one of the pair must have a left-hand helix and the other a right-hand helix, as in Fig. 3-9. The two gears must have identical helix angles.

Because of the helix, there is an axial force component parallel to the shaft. A double helical gear or herringbone gear is the equivalent of two helical gears of opposite hand mounted together to produce opposing thrusts which cancel each other out.

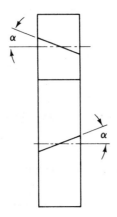

FIGURE   **3-9**   *Mating helical gears, one left hand, the other right hand.*

3-4 BEVEL GEARS

The two shafts of a bevel gear drive are at an angle to each other, usually 90 degrees, and intersect (Fig. 3-10). The point of intersection of the two shafts is usually the apex of both pitch cones. If two spur tooth bevel gears intersect at right angles and both gears have the same number of teeth, they are referred to as miter gears. Terminology for bevel gears is given in Fig. 3-10.

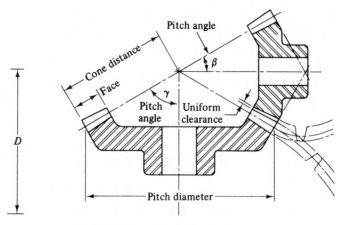

FIGURE 3-10   *Right-angle bevel gear drive.*

The tooth section gradually becomes smaller as the apex of the pitch cone is approached. Only a length of cone close to its base is used for the teeth, actually not more than one-third of the full length of the cone. All such dimensions as pitch diameter, diametral pitch, addendum, and dedendum are measured at the large diameter of the bevel gear.

FIGURE 3-11 *Spiral bevel gears.*   **FIGURE 3-12** *Zero-bevel gears.*

Besides the straight-tooth bevel gear, other variants are used, including helical bevel gears, hypoid, skew, and zerol types. Spiral or helical bevel gears are selected when low noise levels are a requirement. Hypoid gears resemble spiral bevel gears but the two shafts of the drive do not intersect. Hence the two shafts can be extended beyond the gears without interfering with each other. The hypoid gear was originally developed for automobile rear ends, because it allowed the drive shaft to be lower than the rear axle and permitted a lower floor level in the vehicle. Because there is less taper, hypoid drives are better suited to high horsepower requirements, but since this gear slides as well as rolls, it requires an extreme pressure lubricant.

The spiroid gear uses a tapered worm for a pinion (Fig. 3-14). It has the advantage of backlash control (by axial movement of the pinion) and shock

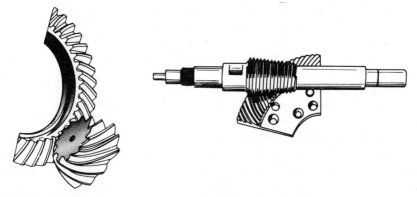

FIGURE 3-13 *Hypoid gears.*   **FIGURE 3-14** *Spiroid gearing.*

resistance. Several teeth are simultaneously in contact. The spiroid gear is found in many portable power tools, including hedge trimmers, portable grinders, portable drills, electric can openers, etc.

3-5 WORM DRIVES

The terminology for worm drives is given in Fig. 3-15. These drives are used to obtain large speed reductions up to a maximum of perhaps 80:1 in a small space. Higher reductions, however, are less efficient than smaller reduction ratios. The two shafts are usually at right angles to each other. The worm is a special case of a helical or spiral gear in that the helix wraps completely around the worm like a screw thread. Indeed, the worm teeth are referred to as threads.

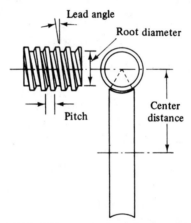

FIGURE 3-15   *Terminology of a worm drive.*

Because of considerable sliding friction there is the problem of heat generation in a worm drive. Selection of the lubricant is more critical than in other types of gearing. While most types of mating gears have efficiencies from 96 to 99%, the efficiency of a worm drive is much lower. To prevent seizure of worm to gear, the worm is usually a hardened steel and the gear a bronze.

For a single-thread worm the speed reduction is the number of teeth in the gear. A double-thread worm will give a speed reduction of half the teeth in the gear. The number of threads also determines whether the drive is self-locking. A single-thread worm has the smallest helix angle and is always self-locking, that is, the worm cannot be turned by the gear. Multithread worms however are more common than single-threads because of higher efficiency. Self-locking worms do not require brakes.

The American Gear Manufacturers Association (AGMA) recommends the following relationships in worm drives:

$$p_d \text{ of worm } = \frac{C}{2.2}$$

where C = the center distance between shafts.

Face width of gear = 0.72 × worm pitch diameter approximately

Axial length of worm = $(4.5 + N_g/50)\, p_c$

where N_g = the number of gear teeth

The maximum input horsepower of a worm gear unit is limited by the problem of dissipating the friction heat that is generated. This maximum input horsepower can be estimated from

$$HP = \frac{9.50^{1.7}}{R + 5}$$

where R = the reduction ratio
            C = the center distance

Note that in the worm the *pitch* is the axial distance from a point on a thread to the same point on the next thread. The *lead* is the distance a screw thread advances axially in one turn; for a double-threaded worm the lead is twice the pitch.

3-6 GEAR LUBRICATION

There are five possible mechanisms of wear in gear teeth:

1. Seizing: welding of the teeth due to high local pressure in the absence of lubrication.
2. Scuffing: plastic flow of material near the pitch line.
3. Pitting: due to compressive fatigue stress resulting from repeated applications of force. A hard tooth surface reduces scuffing.
4. Abrasion: scoring of the teeth by foreign matter.
5. Scoring: due to sharp edges on the teeth; not a problem in quality gearing.

Scuffing and seizing are prevented by proper lubrication. The type of gear and the loading conditions dictate the type of lubricant. A spur gear rolls, but a hypoid or worm gear also slides, and different lubricants are needed for these different conditions. Most gears with moderate loads will perform satisfactorily with a rust and oxidation inhibited (R & O) mineral oil; for heavier loads extreme pressure lubricants are preferred. Sliding gears such as worm gears require lubricants with special additives to reduce friction and supply resistance to scoring.

Five groups of gear lubricant are in common use:

1. R & O oil: rust and oxidation inhibited mineral oil.

2. EP (extreme pressure) oil: contains chemical additives that react with gear materials at high contact temperatures to produce a protective film that reduces metal-to-metal contact.

3. Compounded oil: usually a cylinder oil with a few percent of animal fat to reduce friction.

4. Heavy-bodied open-gear oil: these are heavy, sticky oils, applied by hand, dip, or intermittent spray. They are available with or without an EP additive.

5. Grease: a grease is a fluid thickened by an agent to reduce the tendency to flow away from the region being lubricated.

Lubrication requirements for spur, helical, and bevel gearing are identical. R & O oils are used, but EP oils are substituted for heavy and shock loads. For worm gears, EP and compounded oils are preferred. Hypoid gears require EP oils.

3-7 GEAR TRAINS

A power transmission system consisting only of gears is called a gear train or gear transmission. Gear trains are of several types: simple, compound, reverted, and planetary (epicyclic). In the planetary train at least one of the gear axes must rotate.

In a *simple gear train* each shaft carries only one gear. The compound gear train contains one or more shafts carrying more than one gear. Consider the simple gear train of Fig. 3-16, where gear A is the driving gear. Speed ratios are set by the number of teeth, hence

$$\frac{\omega_B}{\omega_A} = \frac{N_A}{N_B} \qquad \frac{\omega_C}{\omega_B} = \frac{N_B}{N_C} \qquad \frac{\omega_D}{\omega_C} = \frac{N_C}{N_D}$$

$$\frac{\omega_B}{\omega_A} = \left(\frac{\omega_B}{\omega_A}\right)\left(\frac{\omega_C}{\omega_B}\right)\left(\frac{\omega_D}{\omega_C}\right) = \frac{N_A \, N_B \, N_C}{N_B \, N_C \, N_D} = \frac{N_A}{N_D}$$

where ω = rpm or angular velocity
N = number of teeth.

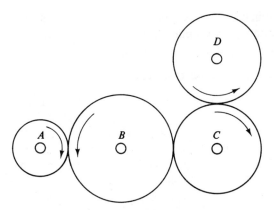

FIGURE 3-16 *Simple gear train of four gears.*

Thus the intermediate gears, called idler gears, do not influence the overall velocity ratio. Such a simple gear train may be used to fill up a large center distance between driving and driven shafts, to reverse the direction of rotation of the driven shaft, or for taking power off the intermediate gears.

A compound gear train is illustrated in Fig. 3-17. Speed ratios are:

$$\frac{\omega_B}{\omega_A} = \frac{N_A}{N_B} \qquad \frac{\omega_D}{\omega_C} = \frac{N_C}{N_D} \qquad \frac{\omega_F}{\omega_E} = \frac{N_E}{N_F}$$

Overall speed ratio $= \dfrac{\omega_F}{\omega_A} = \dfrac{\omega_B}{\omega_A}\,\dfrac{\omega_D}{\omega_C}\,\dfrac{\omega_F}{\omega_E}$

where $\omega_B = \omega_C$ and $\omega_D = \omega_E$
Substituting tooth numbers:

$$\frac{\omega_F}{\omega_A} = \left(\frac{N_A}{N_B}\right)\left(\frac{N_C}{N_D}\right)\left(\frac{N_E}{N_F}\right)$$

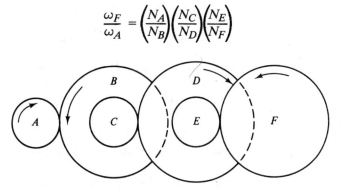

FIGURE 3-17 *Compound gear train.*

All the gears influence the overall speed ratio. Note that in this speed ratio equation the numerator is the product of all the driver teeth ($N_A \times N_C \times N_E$)

65

and the denominator is the product of all the driven teeth ($N_B \times N_D \times N_F$). These same relationships apply to belt drives and chain drives as well as to gears, using the pitch diameters of pulleys and sprockets.

Design of a Compound Gear Train

To understand the design of a compound gear train, consider the following example.

A small precision compound gear train requires a speed reduction of 1:15. Standard 20-degree full-depth spur gears with a diametral pitch of 24 are selected. A maximum pitch diameter of 3 in. is desired, and to avoid undercutting, not less than 18 teeth should be used.

Given the requirements, it is clear that a single pair of gears cannot be used, because the number of teeth on the large gear would be 18 × 15, giving too large a pitch diameter. Eighteen is the smallest number of teeth allowed in the pinion, and 15 is the reduction ratio. Therefore to begin the design, try two equal speed reductions:

$$\frac{\omega_{out}}{\omega_{in}} = \frac{1}{15} = \frac{1}{3.88}\frac{1}{3.88}$$

where $3.88^2 = 15$, and each reduction is to be 1:3.88

Next change one of the 3.88's to a number close to 3.88 but which can be converted into a reasonably simple fraction. Change 3.88 to 3.875, which is 31/8. This alters the speed ratio equation to:

$$\frac{1}{15} = \left(\frac{1}{\frac{31}{8}}\right)\left(\frac{\frac{31}{8}}{15}\right) = \frac{8}{31}\left[\frac{31}{8 \times 15}\right] = \frac{8}{31} \times \frac{31}{120}$$

A reduction of 8:31 then 31:120 (tooth numbers) will give the required ratio of 1:15, but the last gear would have 120 teeth and a pitch diameter of 5 in. The first gear would have only 8 teeth, an insufficient number. If the number of teeth in the first reduction is doubled to 16:62, then 16 teeth are still too few.

Try a larger reduction in the first pair of gears, say 1:4.

$$\frac{1}{15} = \frac{1}{4} \times \frac{4}{15} = \frac{18}{72} \times \frac{20}{75}$$

Eighteen teeth is the smallest number of teeth allowable and is acceptable, however 75 teeth gives a pitch diameter slightly over 3 in., but is probably acceptable.

For a second case, consider a gear reducer which is to reduce an electric motor speed of 1725 rpm to 200 rpm. No gear is to have less than 20 or more than 50 teeth. Determine the number of gear pairs and the tooth numbers.

The speed ratio is $^{1725}\!/_{200}$ or 8.625. Using the smallest and largest gears allowed, 20 and 50 teeth, the maximum speed reduction is 50/20 or 2.50. Using two pairs it is 50/20 × 50/20 or 6.25. This is still less than the required 8.625. Therefore three combinations of gears will be required.

Since three combinations are needed, first take the cube root of 8.625, which is 2.05. Ideally, the reductions would be

$$\frac{2.05}{1} \times \frac{2.05}{1} \times \frac{2.05}{1} = 8.625$$

Suppose we change two of the three ratio to 2/1 and then alter the third ratio to suit:

$$2.0 \times 2.0 \times 2.15625 = 8.625$$

For the first two reductions use tooth numbers of 40 and 20. For the last reduction, if 20 teeth are given to the driving gear, then the final driven gear will have 43 teeth (20 × 2.15).

The Reverted Gear Train

A reverted gear train is a compound train in which both input and output shafts have the same line as axis. With this requirement, it will be seen that the center distance must be the same for all pairs of gears in the train. See Fig. 3-18.

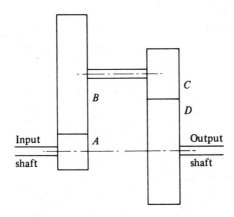

FIGURE 3-18 *Reverted gear train of four gears.*

If C is the center distance, then

$$2C = D_A + D_B = D_C + D_D$$

But since

$$D = \frac{N}{p_d} \quad \text{then} \quad 2C = \frac{N_A}{p_1} + \frac{N_B}{p_1} = \frac{N_C}{p_2} + \frac{N_D}{p_2}$$

where p_1 and p_2 are two diametral pitches. If a single diametral pitch is used in the reverted gear train, then

$$2Cp_d = N_A + N_B = N_C + N_D$$

and thus the same number of teeth must be used in each pair of gears.

To design a reverted gear train, the following example can be used. The speed ratio between input and output shafts is to be a reduction of 1:6. No gear is to have less than 18 teeth or more than 96, and a uniform diametral pitch will be used.

The maximum ratio for one pair of gears is $^{18}\!/_{96}$ or $^{3}\!/_{16}$, and for two pairs $^{9}\!/_{64}$. A ratio of 1:6 falls between these two numbers, so two reductions are required. Begin as with previous gear train designs by taking the square root of 1/6, which is $(1/2.45) \times (1/2.45)$.

Try $^{1}\!/_{2.5}$ for the first ratio and alter the second ratio to suit:

$$\frac{1}{6} = \frac{1}{2.5}\frac{2.5}{6}$$

But the sums of numerator and denominator are $(1 + 2.5)$ and $(2.5 + 6)$; these sums are not equal and therefore neither will the number of teeth be equal in the two combinations.

$$\frac{1}{2.5}\frac{2.5}{6} = \frac{2}{5}\frac{5}{12}$$

with sums of 7 and 17. Now multiply the first fraction by $^{17}\!/_{7}$, the sum of $5 + 12$, and the second fraction by $^{7}\!/_{7}$, the sum of $2 + 5$:

$$\left(\frac{2}{5} \times \frac{17}{17}\right) \left(\frac{5}{12} \times \frac{7}{7}\right) = \frac{34}{85}\frac{35}{84}$$

The tooth totals are now equal. Neither too large nor too small a number of teeth has been used.

3-8 THE PLANETARY OR EPICYCLIC GEAR TRAIN

PLANET

A simple type of planetary gear train is shown in Fig. 3-19. The distinguishing characteristic of this type of gear train is the rotating arm or planet carrier. If we assume the sun gear to be stationary and the arm to rotate clockwise about its axis *O,* then the planet gear also rotates clockwise about its center *C.* Alternatively, the ~~ring~~ gear could be the stationary member. If the arm is stationary and both sun and planet gear rotate, then the planetary train becomes a standard gear train. In an epicyclic or planetary gear train one or more gears rotate about a moving axis.

Figure 3-20 shows a planetary train with two planet pinions. The number of pinions has no influence on the speed ratio, but allows more torque to be transmitted through an increased number of planet gears.

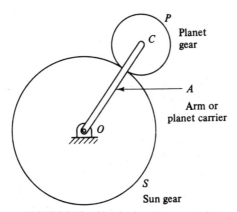

P

C   Planet gear

A

Arm or planet carrier

O

S

Sun gear

FIGURE 3-19   *Simple planetary gear train.*

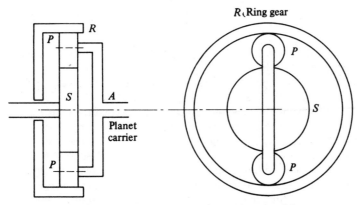

R Ring gear

P

R

S   *A*

Planet carrier

P

P

S

P

FIGURE 3-20   *Epicyclic gear train with two planetary pinions.*

The gear speeds of the epicyclic train of Fig. 3-20 can be determined from the equation

$$\omega_S = \left(1 + \frac{N_R}{N_S}\right)\omega_A - \left(\frac{N_R}{N_S}\right)\omega_R$$

where ω_S = rpm of sun gear
            ω_A = rpm of planet carrier arm
            ω_R = rpm of ring gear
            N_R = number of teeth on the ring gear
            N_S = number of teeth on the sun gear

EXAMPLE 3-5:   The following information applies to the train of Fig. 3-20:

$$\omega_S = 1200 \text{ rpm clockwise}$$
$$N_S = 96$$
$$N_P = 24$$
$$N_R = 144$$

Find the planet carrier shaft speed if the sun gear is the input, the ring gear is fixed, and the planet carrier is the output.

SOLUTION:

$$\omega_S = \left(1 + \frac{N_R}{N_S}\right)\omega_A - \left(\frac{N_R}{N_S}\right)\omega_R$$

$$1200 = \left(1 + \frac{144}{96}\right)\omega_A - 0$$

$$= 2.5\,\omega_A$$

$$\omega_A = +\,480 \text{ rpm}$$

The direction of rotation of the carrier is the same as that of the sun gear, since the answer is positive.

A useful method of analyzing planetary trains requires a tabulation of separate motions. The former example will be worked by this tabular method.

In this method we lock the planetary train so that the gears cannot rotate, and rotate the arm and the whole train one positive turn. Then the arm, the sun, the planet, and the ring gear have all been rotated one positive turn. But in the above example the ring gear is actually fixed and should not have turned. This correction is made by rotating the ring gear one negative turn to bring it back to zero rotation. In doing so the planet and sun gears must also rotate the required number of turns given by their tooth numbers. All this tabulates as follows:

	Arm	Ring	Planet	Sun
Lock train and rotate arm	+ 1	+ 1	+ 1	+ 1
Rotate ring one negative turn	0	− 1	$-\dfrac{144}{24}$	$+\dfrac{144}{46}$
Total rotations	+ 1	0	− 5	+ 2.5

Then the sun gear to arm speed ratio is 2.5:1, and the arm rotates ⅖ × 1200 or 480 rpm in the same direction as the sun gear.

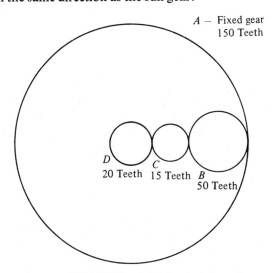

A — Fixed gear
150 Teeth

D
20 Teeth C 15 Teeth B
50 Teeth

FIGURE 3-21 *Epicyclic example.*

EXAMPLE 3-6:   In the planetary train of Fig. 3-21, the internal gear A is fixed. Find the ratio of turns of gear D to the arm.

SOLUTION: As in the previous case, the gear train is first assumed to be locked and the whole train, including A, is rotated one positive turn. This rotates the arm one turn, but the gears have not rotated and A, actually a fixed gear, has made a rotation. Next A is given a negative turn to cancel out the positive turn, with the arm fixed and the gears rotating.

	Arm	A	B	C	D
Train locked, one positive turn	+ 1	+1	+ 1	+ 1	+ 1
Arm fixed, gear A one negative turn	0	− 1	$-\dfrac{150}{50}$	$+\dfrac{150}{50}\times\dfrac{50}{15}$	$-\dfrac{150}{50}\times\dfrac{50}{15}\times\dfrac{15}{20}$
Relationship of turns	+ 1	0	− 2	+ 11	− 6½

3-9 THE DIFFERENTIAL

The differential of Fig. 3-22 is most familiar as the final element in the power transmission train to the rear wheels of vehicles and tractors. The basic bevel gear differential is a planetary train: the two bevel gears mounted on the spider arm are the planet gears, either of the side gears is the sun gear and the other side gear is the ring gear. The large ring gear of the figure rotates only the arm; it is not fixed to the left axle.

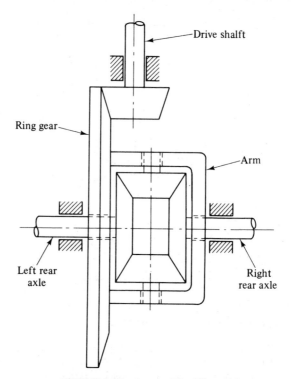

FIGURE 3-22 *Automobile differential.*

The basic principle of the differential is a simple one: the sum of the rotational speeds of the two output shafts is equal to twice the rotational speed of the spider. That is

$$\text{rpm}_1 + \text{rpm}_2 = 2(\text{rpm}_{\text{arm}})$$

If both axles rotate at identical speeds, as in the case of a car moving along a straight highway, then

$$\text{rpm}_1 = \text{rpm}_2 = \text{rpm}_{\text{arm}}.$$

Examination of the differential shows that this must be so because the two axles will carry the spider arm around with them. The whole differential rotates as a unit. Again, if the two axles have the same speed but opposite rotations, then the arm does not rotate.

When the vehicle makes a turn, the outside rear axle increases speed and the inside wheel decreases speed by the same amount, so that the wheels do not slip when traversing a cruve. As is familiar from experience, if one rear wheel slips on ice or snow while the opposite wheel is on pavement, the wheel on pavement does not rotate, while the wheel on ice rotates at twice the speed of the arm.

The spider torque is always twice the torque of either side gear and the torques of the two side gears are always equal:

$$\frac{T_{\text{arm}}}{2} = T_1 = T_2$$

If one rear wheel is one ice and the other on pavement, the torque of the wheel on pavement is limited to the torque delivered by the wheel on ice, which may be so little that the vehicle cannot move. To prevent this loss of torque when one wheel loses traction, differential locks are sometimes used to lock out the differential and thus to keep the vehicle or tractor moving. The lock causes the whole differential to rotate as a unit.

These speed and torque characteristics of the differential are independent of the tooth numbers.

3-10   GEAR CHANGE TRANSMISSIONS

Speed change gear boxes, also called transmissions, are employed to obtain a range of output speeds from an electric motor or an internal combustion engine. Such transmissions are familiar in tractors, trucks, and machine tools such as lathes. If the prime mover is an internal combustion engine, then the gear box must provide a reverse gear. If the prime mover is an electric motor, it is cheaper and more convenient to provide a reversing switch for the motor than a reverse gear in the transmission.

Figure 3-23 shows a common type of gear change transmission. This transmission provides six speeds but no reverse gear. Gears 1 and 2 on the input shaft and gears 5, 6, and 7 on the intermediate or countershaft are fixed in position on their shafts. Gears 3 and 4 and also 8, 9, and 10, slide axially on splined shafts to engage the fixed gears as required. Two speeds of the countershaft are available by engaging either gear 3 or gear 4 with the input shaft. Three gear ratios are available between countershaft and output shaft.

A configuration of three parallel shafts as shown makes for an incon-

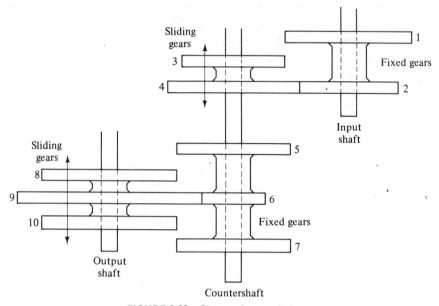

FIGURE 3-23 *Six-speed transmission.*

veniently wide gear box. The transmission is made more compact by combining the three shafts in a reverted train as in Fig. 3-24. As with any reverted train, the fixed center distance places restrictions on the number of teeth of each pair of gears.

If the input speed is 1000 rpm and the tooth numbers are as given below then the output speeds are readily determined.

Gear	Teeth
1	65
2	30
3	65
4	100
5	65
6	40
7	52
8	65
9	90
10	78

The tooth number in each pair is 130, suggesting a uniform diametral pitch.

A planetary gear system can be used as a gear change transmission. Suppose in Fig. 3-20 that the input is to the sun gear and the output is from the planet arm. A high-speed direct drive is produced by locking the planet

74

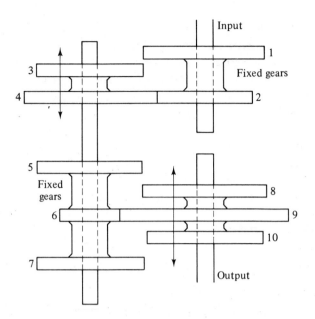

FIGURE 3-24 *Six-speed transmission reverted.*

carrier and the sun gear together by means of a clutch. This causes the input and output shafts to rotate together. For the low-speed drive, the direct-drive clutch is released and the ring gear is held stationary by a brake. This causes the rotating sun gear to turn the planet pinions against the fixed ring gear so that the planet carrier rotates at slow speed in the same direction as the sun gear.

QUESTIONS

3-1. Give the pitch diameter of the following spur gears:

    (a) 8 pitch, 18 teeth.

    (b) 1½ pitch, 120 teeth.

    (c) 12 pitch, 16 teeth.

    (d) 6 pitch, 37 teeth.

3-2. A small gear of 12 diametral pitch, specification ASA B.6, has 11 teeth. For this gear determine:

    (a) pitch diameter.

    (b) addendum.

    (c) dedendum.

    (d) outside diameter.

3-3. What is the difference between:

    (a) pitch diameter and diametral pitch?

    (b) diametral pitch and circular pitch?

3-4. A full-depth spur gear has an O.D. of 3.250 in., a pitch diameter of 3.000 in., and 24 teeth. Find:

    (a) addendum.

    (b) diametral pitch.

3-5. A spur gear of 8 diametral pitch has 11 teeth. Determine:

    (a) pitch diameter.

    (b) outside diameter of the gear.

3-6. For a 20° full-depth gear, specification AGMA 201.02, ½-pitch and 180 teeth, find:

    (a) pitch diameter.

    (b) outside diameter.

3-7. A 12-pitch pinion with 36 teeth rotates at 1800 rpm driving a gear at 540 rpm. Find:

    (a) number of teeth in the gear.

    (b) center distance of the mating gears.

3-8. The accompanying sketch shows two spur gears transmitting 20 HP. The force exerted by one gear against the other is 215 lb. Determine the force on each of the four bearings.

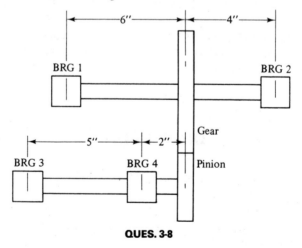

QUES. 3-8

3-9. Differentiate between the pitch and the lead of a worm.

3-10. A welding turntable is driven by the belts and gearing shown, with power input supplied by an infinitely variable-speed motor. A fillet weld is to be deposited around the circumference of a 6.00 in. diameter steel tube rotated by the turntable at a welding speed of 16 in. per min. What must be the speed of the driving motor?

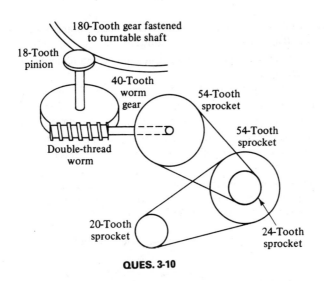

QUES. 3-10

3-11. Design a compound gear train for a speed reduction of 1:20, using not less than 18 teeth or more than 96 teeth in any gear. Determine the number of teeth in each gear and the center distances. All gears are 12-pitch.

3-12. Design a compound gear train for a speed reduction of 1:11. The maximum number of teeth in any gear must not exceed 54 and the minimum must not be fewer than 18.

3-13. A pair of mating gears have a diametral pitch of 8. The driving gear rotates at 1800 rpm and the output speed of the driven gear must be as close to 700 rpm as possible. Center distance must be 4.500 in. closely. Find the number of teeth in each gear, the output speed, and the center distance.

3-14. The gear reducer train shown is driven by the first 26-tooth gear on the left at 1750 rpm. Determine the rpm of the output gear.

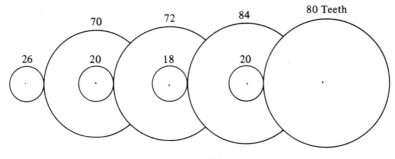

QUES. 3-14

3-15. Design reverted gear trains to the following specifications. State the number of teeth in all gears and given center distances.

(a) Minimum and maximum number of teeth 20 and 100, center distance 3.20 in. closely, speed reduction 1:10.

(b) Speed reduction 2:25, minimum and maximum number of teeth 18 and 120, diametral pitch 12.

3-16. For the planetary train of Fig. 3-20 the sun gear rotates at 500 rpm and the arm at 300 rpm, both counterclockwise. Numbers of teeth are as follows: ring 108, planet 18, sun 72. Determine the rpm and direction of the ring gear.

3-17. For the planetary train of Fig. 3-20, find the number of teeth in the sun and planet gears, given the following data: ring gear 120 teeth; ring gear is fixed; sun gear 80 rpm clockwise; arm 20 rpm clockwise.

3-18. Find the speed of rotation of the sun gear in the planetary train shown, given the following data: ring gear 100 teeth, 25 rpm clockwise; planet 20 teeth; sun gear 60 teeth. Planet carrier rotates at 50 rpm clockwise.

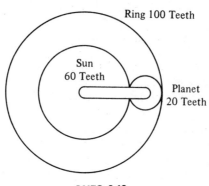

QUES. 3-18

4

BELT AND CHAIN DRIVES

4-1 BELTING MATERIALS

Flat belts have been used in power transmission for many centuries. Belts of earlier times were either leather or rope. While the rope belt no longer has a role in modern power transmission, the leather belt is still a most successful power transmission device and it is not easy to develop synthetic belting materials that can match leather's range of useful characteristics and its versatility. Synthetic rubber belting has been the most successful competitor to leather.

A belt is subject to tension, bending, and centrifugal forces. A suitable belt must be strong in tension, yet pliable for bending about pulleys, light in weight, and must provide sufficient friction against pulleys. Many belts are subject to shock loadings when drive motors are started, and a successful belt must have elasticity to absorb such shocks without breaking. Four classes of belting materials have suitable characteristics: leather, fabric, rubber, or synthetics (plastics).

Leather has a high coefficient of friction against pulleys, excellent flexibility, long life, and outstanding ability to hold belt splices. Leather belts are available in single-, double-, or triple-ply, and in light, medium, or heavy weights. Since leather is not a woven material but a hide, it does not unravel or become frayed. The absence of a weave also makes it more receptive to belt fasteners. A leather belt has a higher capacity for overloading than other belting materials. If installed with excessive tension, it stretches somewhat to reduce such tension.

Leather belts are tanned by immersion in solutions that are termed "tan liquors." Tan liquors are extracts of vegetable tanning materials such as oak bark, quebracho, and others. A belt tanned in such materials is termed "vegetable-tanned" or "oak-tanned." This is the treatment given to most belts. An alternative is to use tanning solutions that contain mineral salts, usually chromic acid. Such a belt is termed "mineral-tanned" or "chrome-tanned." Oak-tanned leather is firmer and less pliable than a chrome-tanned leather, but has a lower friction coefficient and a lower resistance to water.

A leather belt must be lubricated occasionally with a suitable belt dressing, otherwise its life is shortened due to hardening and cracking on the pulley side of the belt. Also, since the belt dressing maintains the leather in pliable condition, a high coefficient of friction with pulleys is maintained. Suitable belt dressings contain beef tallow, vegetable waxes, fish oils, or stearines, but the mineral oils and waxes that lubricate other power transmission devices such as bearings are not suitable for leather.

Rubber has become a commonly used belting material. It has a lower coefficient of friction than leather and thus requires more tension. Rubber belts, however, do not stretch as much as leather. The rubber belt has a core of canvas, cotton duck, or cords enveloped in rubber. The core material takes the tension stress in the belt, while the rubber provides resilience, elasticity, and surface friction against pulleys. Basic types of construction for such belts are raw-edge, folded-edge, and cord: these are illustrated in Fig. 4-1.

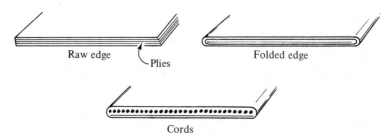

Raw edge ⎸ Plies   Folded edge

Cords

FIGURE 4-1 *Types of rubber belting for power transmission.*

Woven cotton and canvas, often impregnated with rubber, is available in various grades. Synthetic materials have become more widely used in belting including polyester and nylon. Various combinations are in use, such as a nylon core with a leather surface for good grip.

4-2 FLAT-BELT DRIVES

Power transmission by a flat belt is possible only with sufficient friction between the belt and its pulleys. As a result of friction effects, there will be a difference between the tight-side tension T_1 and the slack-side tension T_2. If the belt is on the verge of slipping the relationship between these two belt tensions is given by

Mis-Print

$$\frac{T_1}{T_2} = e^{\mu\beta}$$

where $e = 2.718$
     μ = coefficient of friction between belt and pulley
     β = contact angle of belt in radians (1 radian = 57.3°)
     $T_1 T_2$ = tight-side and slack-side tension forces in the belt, in units of force, usually pounds. Values of c^x are given in Table 4-1.

At high velocities the belt will tend to leave the pulley due to centrifugal effects, thus reducing friction force. To take account of such centrifugal effects, the above equation is thus modified:

$$\frac{T_1 - T_c}{T_2 - T_c} = e^{\mu\beta} \qquad \text{Mis Print}$$

$$T_c = \frac{wV^2}{3600g}$$

where w = belt weight in pounds per lineal foot
     V = belt speed in fpm
     g = gravitational acceleration = 32.2 fps/s

The difference between tight-side and slack-side tensions in the belt produces a torque T:

$$T = (T_1 - T_2)r$$

or if centrifugal force is significantly large

$$T = [(T_1 - T_c) - (T_2 - T_c)]R = (T_1 - T_2)\, r$$

where r = pitch radius of the belt.

Horsepower and belt torque T are related by the equation

$$HP = \frac{TV}{33,000\, r} = \frac{(T_1 - T_2)V}{33,000} = \frac{T * RPM}{5250}$$

(ft-lb)

TABLE 4-1

x	c^x	x	c^x	x	c^x
0·02	1·0202	0·25	1·2840	0·45	1·5683
0·04	1·0408	0·26	1·2969	0·46	1·5841
0·06	1·0618	0·27	1·3100	0·47	1·6000
0·08	1·0833	0·28	1·3231	0·48	1·6161
		0·29	1·3364	0·49	1·6323
0·10	1·1052	0·30	1·3499	0·50	1·6487
0·11	1·1163	0·31	1·3634	0·56	1·8221
0·12	1·1275	0·32	1·3771	0·57	2·0138
0·13	1·1388	0·33	1·3910	0·58	2·2255
0·14	1·1505	0·34	1·4050	0·59	2·4596
0·15	1·1618	0·35	1·4191	1·0	2·7183
0·16	1·1735	0·36	1·4333	1·1	3·0042
0·17	1·1835	0·37	1·4477	1·2	3·3201
0·18	1·1972	0·38	1·4623	1·3	3·6693
0·19	1·2092	0·39	1·4770	1·4	4·0552
0·20	1·2214	0·40	1·4918	1·5	4·4817
0·21	1·2337	0·41	1·5068	1·6	4·9530
0·22	1·2461	0·42	1·5220	1·7	5·4739
0·23	1·2586	0·43	1·5373	1·8	6·0497
0·24	1·2712	0·44	1·5527	1·9	6·6859
				2·0	7·3891

where V = the belt speed in fpm

          r = the pitch radius of the belt in feet

EXAMPLE 4-1:   A flat belt with 200 degrees of wrap on the driving pulley transmits 25 HP to the driven shaft at a lower speed. Diameter of driving pulley is 18 in., coefficient of friction between belt and pulleys is 0.35, and belt speed is 100 fpm. Determine the tight-side force T_1.

SOLUTION:

$$\frac{T_1}{T_2} = e^{\mu\beta} = e^{0.35}$$

$$\beta = 200° = \frac{200}{57.3} \text{ radians}$$

Then

$$\mu\beta = e^{0.35 \times 3.49} = e^{1.22} = 3.39$$

$$T_1 = 3.39\, T_2$$

$$HP = \frac{(T_1 - T_2)V}{33,000)} = \frac{\left(T_1 - \dfrac{T_1}{3.39}\right)}{33,000} \times 1000 = 25$$

$$T_1 = 1190 \text{ lb}$$

Note that these relationships hold only if the belt is on the verge of slipping and if the stated horsepower is actually being transmitted—not merely a rated horsepower.

For an approximation, the tension in the tight side of the belt can be taken as twice the tension in the slack side. Since the effective tension for power transmission equals the tight-side tension minus the slack-side tension, the driving force is equal to the slack-side tension, using this approximation.

4-3 ANGLE OF WRAP AND BELT LENGTH

A belt transmits power by means of friction against its pulley. Therefore the two most important factors in determining the maximum power that can be transmitted are the coefficient of friction and the angle of wrap or contact angle. Suppose we compare two angles of wrap, one of 40° and one of 180°, with the smaller angle of wrap transmitting 1 HP. If all other conditions are the same, the larger angle of 180° can transmit 2.73 HP. Small angles therefore are undesirable, such as are produced by mounting a small pulley very close to a large pulley.

Belt length is determined from the center distance and diameter of the pulleys. For the open-belt drive of Fig. 4-2 the length of the belt is computed as follows:

$$\sin \theta = \frac{D - d}{2C}$$

$$\beta_1 = 180° + 2\theta = 180° - 2 \sin^{-1} \frac{D - d}{2C}$$

$$\beta_2 = 180° - 2\theta = 180° - 2 \sin^{-1} \frac{D - d}{2C}$$

$$\text{Exact length} = 2C \cos \theta + \frac{\pi}{2} (D + d) + \frac{\pi \theta°}{180°} (D + d)$$

$$\text{Approximate length} = 2C + 1.57 (D + d) + \frac{(D - d)^2}{4C}$$

For the crossed belts of Fig. 4-3, β_1, β_2 and length L are given by

$$\sin \theta = \frac{D + d}{2C}$$

$$\beta_1 = \beta_2 = 180° + 2\theta = 180° + 2 \sin^{-1} \frac{D + d}{2C}$$

$$L \text{ exact} = 2C \cos \theta + \frac{(90° + \theta°) (D + d)}{180°}$$

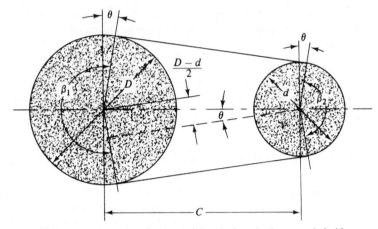

FIGURE 4-2 *Dimensions for determining the length of an open belt drive.*

EXAMPLE 4-2: In the open-belt drive of Fig. 4-2, $D = 40$ in., $d = 10$ in., and $C = 30$ in. Find (a) the contact angles β_1 and β_2; (b) the difference in the calculated belt lengths for the exact and the approximate formulas.

SOLUTION:

(a) $\dfrac{\dfrac{D-d}{2}}{C} = \sin \theta = \dfrac{\dfrac{40-10}{2}}{30} = 0.5 \qquad \theta = 30°$

$\beta_1 = 180° + 2\theta = 240° \qquad \beta_2 = 180° - 2\theta = 120°$

(b) $L_{\text{exact}} = 2C \cos \theta + \dfrac{\pi}{2}(D + d) + \dfrac{\pi}{180}\theta(D - d)$

$= 2 \times 30 \times 0.866 + 1.57(40 + 10) + \dfrac{\pi 30}{180}(40 - 10)$

$= 146.2$ in.

$L_{\text{approx}} = 2C + 1.57(D + d) + \dfrac{(D - d)^2}{4C}$

$= 60 + 1.57 \times 50 + \dfrac{30^2}{120} = 146.0$ in.

The difference in length by these two calculations is 0.2 in.

Note that in this belt drive that the angle of wrap for the large pulley is twice that for the small pulley. A larger center distance would make the angle θ smaller and therefore increase the angle of wrap of the small pulley.

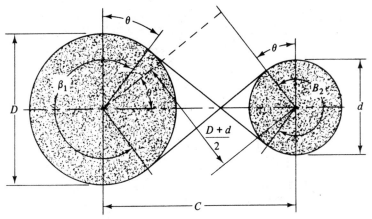

FIGURE 4-3 *Dimensions for determining the length of a crossed belt drive.*

4-4 BELT INSTALLATIONS

The use of an idler pulley located near the small-diameter pulley will increase the angle of wrap and reduce the belt tension required for a given horsepower. If idlers are not used, then one set of bearings must be adjustable to allow for taking up slack as the belt stretches and to slack off the belt when it must be repaired, spliced, or replaced.

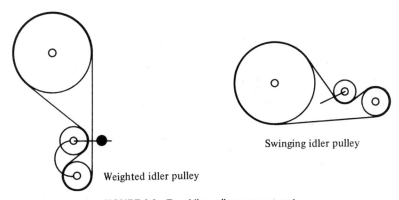

Swinging idler pulley

Weighted idler pulley

FIGURE 4-4 *Two idler pulley arrangements.*

A flat belt on a conical pulley tends to move higher and higher up the cone. This tendency is put to use to keep the belt in position by crowning the pulley as shown in Fig. 4-5. A crown of ⅛ inch per foot of pulley width is usual. The crowning of only one pulley is sufficient, and idlers are not usually crowned.

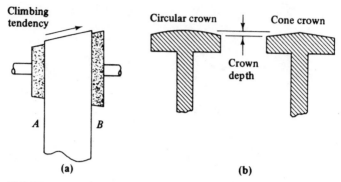

FIGURE 4-5 *Crowning of pulleys for flat belts: (a) the belt tends to move to the high point of the pulley; (b) circular and cone crown.*

Speed ratios in belt drives rarely exceed 6:1. Large ratios require long center distances to obtain sufficiently large angles of wrap in the small pulley. The belt is flexed more severely when passing around a small pulley, and the result is a drastic reduction in belt life.

Belt speed should not exceed 5000 fpm. Above this speed centrifugal force causes excessive slippage of the belt.

Belts are preferably made of endless construction. An endless belt is uniform in strength, and the noise, wear, and jarring of fasteners passing

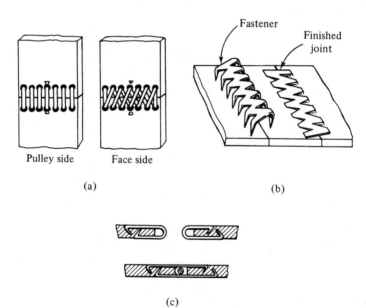

FIGURE 4-6 *Belt fasteners: (a) lacing; (b) steel fastener; (c) hinged joint.*

over pulleys is avoided. However, it is not always possible to employ an endless belt, and belt fasteners are necessary to join the ends of the belt. Both belt lacing and hinges are in use for joining lighter sizes of belt, while plates are used for heavier loads.

The link belt of Fig. 4-7 should be considered for belt drives subject to slippage. In this type of belt the grain of the leather is at right angles to the face of the belt. This characteristic together with the many linkages gives a flexible belt that can use smaller pulleys, has excellent resistance to wear, and can slip without burning. It does not require a crowned pulley.

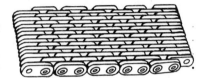 

FIGURE 4-7   *Link belt.*

4-5 SERVICE FACTORS FOR FLAT BELTS

When selecting a flat belt for an application at a rated horsepower or design horsepower, the service factors of Table 4-2 are applied to the given horsepower as in the example below. For certain special conditions, these service factors are increased as follows:

Continuous operation	0.2
Frequent starts, stops, and reverses	0.1
Speed-up drives	0.2
Wet conditions	0.1

EXAMPLE 4-3: A hammermill used in the preparation of animal feeds is rated at 5 HP. Operation is continuous. Determine the required horsepower rating for the belt driving the hammermill. The prime mover is a squirrel-cage motor.

SOLUTION: From Table 4-1 the service factor is 1.4, to which must be added 0.2 for continuous operation.

$$\text{Required horsepower rating} = 5 \times 1.6 = 8\,\text{HP}$$

4-6 V-BELT DRIVES

The peculiar advantage of the V-belt drive is the wedging effect produced by the rubber belt in the sheave or pulley. The wedge increases the normal

TABLE 4-2

Flat-belt service factors.

FLAT BELT SERVICE FACTORS[1]

Driven machine		Driver						
		A-C motors						Engines Gas or diesel
		Squirrel cage			Wound rotor (slip ring)	Synchronous		
		Normal torque		High torque		Normal torque (150% to 249%)	High torque (250% to 400%)	
General type	Specific type	Line start	Compensator start					
Agitators	for liquids	1.0	1.0	1.2	–	–	–	–
	for semi-liquids	1.2	1.0	1.4	1.2	–	–	–
Bakery machinery	–	1.2	–	–	–	–	–	–
Brick and clay machinery	de-airing machine, granulator auger, cutting table, rolls	–	1.2	1.4	1.4	–	–	–
	mixer, dry press	–	1.2	1.6	1.4	–	–	–
	pug mill	1.5	1.3	1.8	1.5	–	–	–
Compressors	centrifugal, rotary	1.2	1.2	–	1.4	1.4	–	–
	reciprocating, 1 or 2 cyl.	1.4	1.4	–	1.5	1.5	–	–
	reciprocating, 3 or more cyl.	1.2	1.2	–	1.4	1.4	–	–
Conveyors	apron, bucket, pan, elevator	–	1.4	1.6	–	–	–	–
	belt (ore, coal, sand, etc.)	–	1.2	1.4	–	–	–	–
	flight	–	1.6	1.8	–	–	–	–
	oven, belt (light package)	–	1.0	1.1	–	–	–	–
Crushing machinery	jaw, cone crushers, crushing rolls gyratory, ball, pebble, tube mills	–	1.4	1.6	1.4	1.4	1.6	1.4
Fans, blowers	centrifugal, induced draft, exhausters	1.2	1.2	–	1.4	–	–	1.4
	propeller, mine fans	1.6	1.6	1.6	1.6	–	1.8	1.6
	positive blowers	1.6	1.6	–	2.0	2.0	1.8	1.6
Flour, feed, cereal mill machinery	bolters, sifters, separators	1.0	1.0	–	–	–	–	–
	grinders, purifiers, reels mainline shaft, hammermills	1.4	1.4	1.6	1.4	1.4	–	1.8
Generators, exciters	–	1.2	–	–	–	–	–	1.2
Line shafts	–	1.4	1.4	–	1.4	1.4	2.0	1.6
Machine tools	grinders, milling machines boring mills, planers, shears	1.2	–	–	1.4	–	–	–
	lathes, screw machines, cam cutters shapers, drill press, drop hammers	1.0	–	–	1.2	–	–	–
Mills	pebble, rod, ball, roller	–	1.4	1.6	1.4	–	–	–
	flaking mills, tumbling barrels	–	1.6	1.6	1.4	–	–	–
Oil-field machinery	–	1.2	1.2	1.4	–	–	–	1.4
Paper machinery	jordan engines	1.5	1.3	1.8	1.5	1.6	1.8	–
	beaters, paper machines	1.4	1.4	–	1.5	–	–	–
	calenders, agitators, dryers	1.2	1.2	1.4	1.2	–	–	–
Printing machinery	–	1.2	1.2	–	1.2	–	–	–
Pumps	centrigugal, gear, rotary	1.2	1.2	1.4	1.4	–	–	1.2
	reciprocating, 1 or 2 cyl	1.4	1.4	–	1.6	1.6	1.8	2.0
	3 or more	1.2	1.2	–	1.4	1.4	1.6	1.8
Rubber plant machinery	–	1.4	1.4	1.4	1.4	–	1.8	–
Sawmill machinery	log canter, log jack, cutoff saws trimmers, slashers, swing saws	1.4	1.4	–	1.4	–	–	–
	brand mill, circular, hogs, resaw	2.0	1.6	–	1.8	–	1.6	–
	planers	1.2	1.2	–	1.2	–	–	–
	edgers	1.6	1.6	–	1.6	–	1.6	–

force P_n between the belt and the groove in the pulley by an amount equal to (see Fig. 4-8):

$$P_n = \frac{P}{2 \sin \emptyset}$$

Here $\emptyset$ is one half of the wedge angle. For the friction force F

$$F = 2\mu \, P_n = \frac{2\mu \, P}{2 \sin \emptyset} = \frac{\mu P}{\sin \emptyset} = \mu_e P$$

where $\mu_e = \dfrac{\mu}{\sin \emptyset}$, the equivalent coefficient of friction.

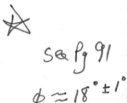

$S \otimes \, P_g \, 91$

$\phi \simeq 18° \pm 1°$

Wedge angle
2φ

(a)   (b)

FIGURE 4-8   *V-belt and sheave.*

$\dfrac{T_1}{T_2} = (\in)^{\mu_e * \beta}$

The flat-belt-drive equations previously given may be applied to V-belts if μ_e is substituted for μ. Because of the increased friction resulting from wedging action, V-belts can operate successfully on short center distances and small angles of wrap.

The construction of a V-belt requires fabric, cords, and rubber compounds. Fabric is a woven material used for the cover stock and impregnated with rubber. The cords that sustain the tension in the belt in one or more plies are made of synthetic textiles such as polyester or nylong.

4-7 INDUSTRY STANDARDS FOR V-BELTS

V-belts are made in industrial, automotive, agricultural, and fractional horsepower types. The Rubber Manufacturers Association (RMA) and the Mechanical Power Transmission Association (MPTA) have developed standards for dimensions, tolerances, sheaves, and horsepower ratings for the convenience of users of V-belts.

Figure 4-9 gives the nominal dimensions of the five industrial V-belt sections A to E and their recommended tight-side tensions. Table 4-3 provides standard groove dimensions for sheaves. The pitch diameter is measured to that plane in the belt that does not change in length as the belt is bent around the sheave. Pitch diameter must be used in any calculations involving belt length and contact angle.

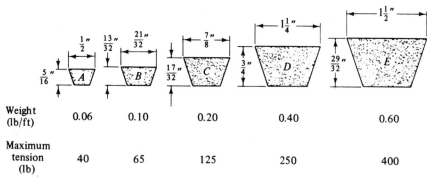

Weight (lb/ft)	0.06	0.10	0.20	0.40	0.60
Maximum tension (lb)	40	65	125	250	400

FIGURE 4-9 *Dimensions of standard V-belts.*

The following equations are used to calculate belt length if center distance is known and center distance if belt length is known:

$$L = 2C + 1.57\,(D' + d') + \frac{(D' - d')^2}{4C}$$

$$C = \frac{b + \sqrt{b^2 - 32\,(D' - d')^2}}{16}$$

where
$b = 4L - 6.28(D' + d')$
$D' = $ pitch diameter of large sheave in inches
$d' = $ pitch diameter of small sheave in inches
$L = $ pitch length of belt
$C = $ center distance in inches

In a multiple V-belt drive the belts of two different manufacturers must not be combined. Industry standards permit plus and minus tolerances, and if two brands of belts are installed in a multiple drive, some of the belts will be shorter than the others and will be forced to carry the full horsepower.

Narrow V-belts have a different cross-section from the industrial belts. Dimensions of narrow V-belts are given in Fig. 4-10.

Since these have different profile, they also require a different type of sheave. As with industrial V-belts, all 3V, 5V, and 8V belts and sheaves of

TABLE 4-3

V-belt pulley dimensions.

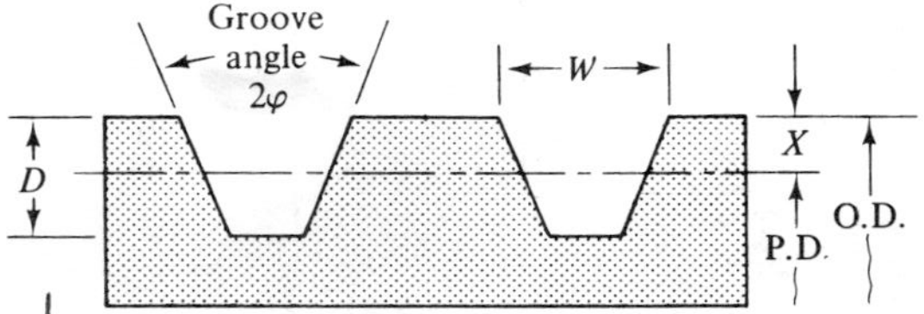

Belt	Pitch diameter (inches)		Groove angle (±½°)	Standard groove dimensions			Deep groove†† dimensions		
	Minimum	Range		W	D (±0.031)	X†	W	D (±0.031)	X†
A	3.0	2.6 to 5.4	34°	0.494 ±0.005	0.490	0.125	0.589 ±0.005	0.645	0.280
		Over 5.4	38°	0.504 ±0.005			0.611 ±0.005		
B	5.4	4.6 to 7.0	34°	0.637 ±0.005	0.580	0.175	0.747 ±0.005	0.760	0.355
		Over 7.0	38°	0.650 ±0.005			0.774 ±0.005		
C	9.0	7.0 to 7.99	34°	0.879 ±0.007	0.780	0.200	1.066 ±0.007	1.085	0.505
		8.0 to 12.0	36°	0.887 ±0.007			1.085 ±0.007		
		Over 12.0	38°	0.895 ±0.007			1.105 ±0.007		
D	13.0	12.0 to 12.99	34°	1.259 ±0.007	1.050	0.300	1.513 ±0.007	1.465	0.715
		13.0 to 17.0	36°	1.271 ±0.007			1.541 ±0.007		
		Over 17.0	38°	1.283 ±0.007			1.569 ±0.007		
E	21.0	18.0 to 24.0	36°	1.527 ±0.010	1.300	0.400	1.816 ±0.010	1.745	0.845
		Over 24.0	38°	1.542 ±0.010			1.849 ±0.010		

[handwritten: Avg ≈ 36° (2φ)]

[handwritten: 18° = φ]

†Add 2 X to pd to get OD.

††Deep groove sheaves are intended for quarter-turn drives and for long center vertical shaft drives. They may also be necessary for such applications as car shakers, vibrating screens and certain types of crushers where oscillations in the center distance may occur.

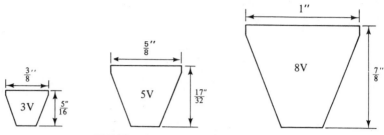

FIGURE 4-10 *Dimensions of narrow V-belts.*

all manufacturers are interchangeable, but as usual different brands of these belts must not be combined in a multiple V-belt drive.

For light-duty applications, the fractional horsepower belts of Fig. 4-11 may be used. The L in the designation stands for "light duty," and the number indicates the top width of the belt in eighths of an inch. Belt length is designated in tenths of an inch. Thus a 4L215 belt has a top width of ½ in. and a length of 21.5 in.

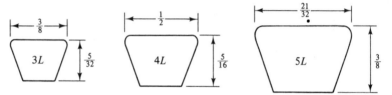

FIGURE 4-11 *Dimensions of light-duty V-belts.*

V-belts made to metric standards will presumably be designated using the following code:

$$00 \text{ X } 0000 \quad \text{that is, 2 digits, 1 letter, 4 digits.}$$

The first two digits will designate the top width of the belt in millimeters and will be followed by a letter giving the type of belt. The last four digits will be the pitch length of the belt in millimeters.

4-8 DESIGN METHODS

Service factors for a range of V-belt operations are given in Table 4-4. Design horsepower for selection of a suitable belt is found by multiplying the theoretical horsepower or rated horsepower by the service factor. While it is usual to consult the manufacturer's catalogue information when designing V-belt drives, the graphs and tables that follow are typical.

Suitable V-belt cross-sections for various combinations of design horsepower and small sheave rpm can be found from Fig. 4-12, and maximum horsepower ratings in terms of belt speed for multiple V-belt drives are given in Figs. 4-13 to 4-17.

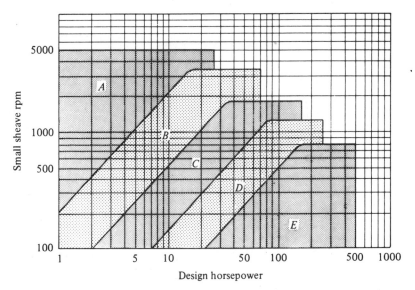

FIGURE 4-12 *Selection chart for V-belts.*

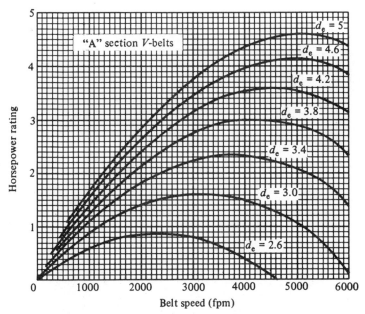

FIGURE 4-13 *Horsepower ratings for "A" belts.*

TABLE 4-4

Service factors for V-belts.

V-BELT SERVICE FACTORS[1]

Driven Machine Types		Driver Types					
Driven Machine Types noted below are representative samples only. Select a category most closely approximating your application from those listed below. If idlers are used, add the following to the service factor. Idler on slack side (inside) — None Idler on slack side (outside) — 0.1 Idler on tight side (inside) — 0.1 Idler on tight side (outside) — 0.2		Electric Motors: AC Normal Torque Squirrel Cage and Synchronous AC Split Phase DC Shunt Wound Internal Combustion Engines			Electric Motors: AC Hi-Torque AC Hi-Slip AC Repulsion-Induction AC Single Phase Series Wound AC Slip Ring DC Compound Wound		
		Intermittent service	Normal service	Continuous service	Intermittent service	Normal service	Continuous service
Agitators for Liquids Blowers and Exhausters Centrifugal Pumps and Compressors Fans up to 10 HP Light Duty Conveyors		1.0	1.1	1.2	1.1	1.2	1.3
Belt Conveyors for Sand, Grain, etc. Dough Mixers Fans Over 10 HP Generators Line Shafts Laundry Machinery Machine Tools Punches-Presses-Shears Printing Machinery Positive Displacement Rotary Pumps Revolving and Vibrating Screens		1.1	1.2	1.3	1.2	1.3	1.4
Brick Machinery Bucket Elevators Exciters Piston Compressors Conveyors (Drag-Pan-Screw) Hammer Mills Paper Mill Beaters Piston Pumps Positive Displacement Blowers Pulverizers Saw Mill and Woodworking Machinery Textile Machinery		1.2	1.3	1.4	1.4	1.5	1.6
Crushers (Gyratory-Jaw-Roll) Mills (Ball-Rod-Tube) Hoists Rubber Calenders-Extruders-Mills		1.3	1.4	1.5	1.5	1.6	1.8
Chokable Equipment		2.0	2.0	2.0	2.0	2.0	2.0

[1] *Courtesy of Goodyear Tire and Rubber Company*

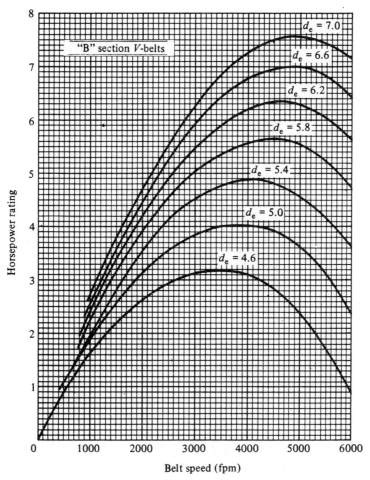

FIGURE 4-14 *Horsepower ratings for "B" belts.*

These ratings apply to 180-degree contact angles and normal belt length, and values must be adjusted for other than normal conditions using Tables 4-5, 4-6, and 4-7. Table 4-8 is a partial list of standard sheaves.

The use of these tables for selecting a suitable belt drive is best illustrated by an example. We will analyze the following application.

A 20-HP squirrel-cage motor operating at 1725 rpm drives a ventilating fan at 800 rpm under normal service conditions. Center distance between sheaves may be a minimum of 46 in. to a maximum of 50 in. Standard pitch diameters will be used for the pulleys. Design the V-belt drive, including sheave sizes, belt length, number of belts, anbd belt size.

First find the service factor from Table 4-4. This factor is 1.2, making the design horsepower 20 × 1.2 or 24 HP.

The speed ratio is $^{1725}\!/_{800}$ or 2.16.

From Fig. 4-12 a B-belt is selected. From Table 4-8 a combination of sheave sizes of 12.4 and 5.6 in. give an approximation to a speed ratio of 2.16. Fan rpm will actually be 780 rpm. Other sheave combinations might be selected.

Belt speed calculated from the small pulley is 3.14 × 5.6 × $^{1725}\!/_{12}$ = 2520 fpm.

To find the belt length we must first decide the center distance between

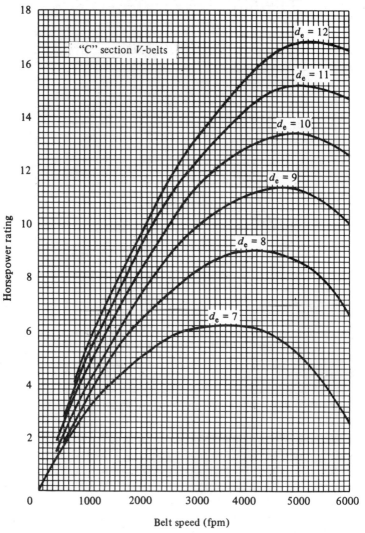

FIGURE 4-15 *Horsepower ratings for "C" belts.*

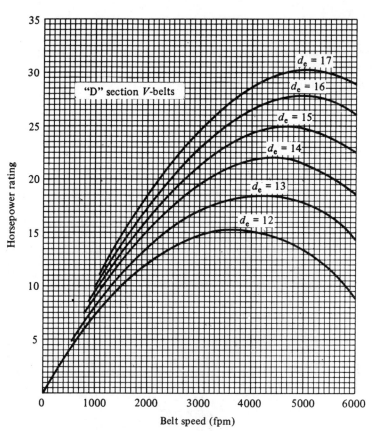

FIGURE 4-16 *Horsepower ratings for "D" belts.*

TABLE 4-5

*Small diameter correction factors
for multiple V-belts.*

Speed Ratio Range	Small-diameter Factor
1.000–1.019	1.00
1.020–1.032	1.01
1.033–1.055	1.02
1.056–1.081	1.03
1.082–1.109	1.04
1.110–1.142	1.05
1.143–1.178	1.06
1.179–1.222	1.07
1.223–1.274	1.08
1.275–1.340	1.09
1.341–1.429	1.10
1.430–1.562	1.11
1.563–1.814	1.12
1.815–2.948	1.13
2.949 and over	1.14

pulleys. A longer center distance will give a larger arc of contact for the small pulley. Suppose we arbitrarily select a center distance of 48 in. The belt length can now be determined.

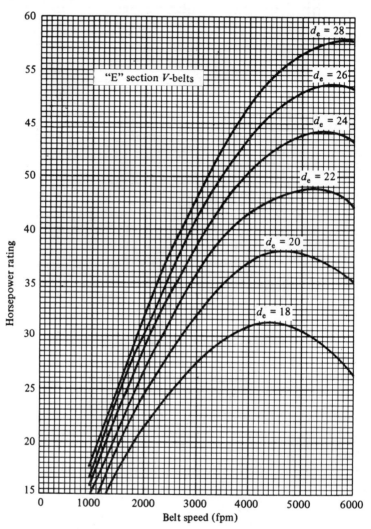

FIGURE 4-17 *Horsepower ratings for "E" belts.*

$$L = 2C + 1.57 (D' + d') + \frac{(D' - d')^2}{4C}$$

$$= (2 \times 48) + 1.57 (12.4 + 5.6) + \frac{(12.4 - 5.6)^2}{4 \times 48}$$

$$= 124.4 \text{ in.}$$

TABLE 4-6

Belt length correction factors.

A-BELT		B-BELT		C-BELT		D-BELT		E-BELT	
Belt Pitch Length	Correc-Tion Factor	Belt Pitch Length	Correc-tion Factor	Belt Pitch Length	Correc-tion Factor	Belt Pitch Length	Correc-tion Factor	Belt Pitch Length	Correc-tion Factor
27.3	0.81	36.8	0.81	53.9	0.80	123.3	0.86	184.5	0.91
32.3	0.84	39.8	0.83	62.9	0.82	131.3	0.87	199.5	0.92
36.3	0.87	43.8	0.85	70.9	0.85	147.3	0.90	214.5	0.94
39.3	0.88	47.8	0.87	77.9	0.87	161.3	0.92	241.0	0.96
43.3	0.90	52.8	0.89	83.9	0.89	176.3	0.93	271.0	0.99
47.3	0.92	56.8	0.90	87.9	0.90	183.3	0.94	301.0	1.01
42.3	0.94	61.8	0.92	92.9	0.91	198.3	0.96	331.0	1.03
56.3	0.96	69.8	0.95	98.9	0.92	213.3	0.96	361.0	1.05
61.3	0.98	76.8	0.97	107.9	0.94	240.8	1.00	391.0	1.07
69.3	1.00	82.8	0.98	114.9	0.95	270.8	1.03	421.0	1.09
76.3	1.02	86.8	0.99	122.9	0.97	300.8	105	481.0	1.12
81.3	1.04	91.8	1.00	130.9	0.98	330.8	1.07	541.0	1.14
86.3	1.05	98.8	1.02	146.9	1.00	360.8	1.09	601.0	1.17
91.3	1.06	106.8	1.04	160.9	1.02	390.8	1.11		
97.3	1.08	113.8	1.05	175.9	1.04	420.8	1.12		
106.3	1.10	121.8	1.07	182.9	1.05	480.8	1.16		
113.3	1.11	129.8	1.08	197.9	1.07	540.8	1.18		
121.3	1.13	145.8	1.11	212.9	1.08	600.8	1.20		
129.3	1.14	159.8	1.13	240.9	1.11				
		174.8	1.15	270.9	1.14				
		181.8	1.16	300.9	1.16				
		196.8	1.18	330.9	1.19				
		211.8	1.19	360.9	1.21				
		240.3	1.22	390.9	1.23				
		270.3	1.25	420.9	1.24				
		300.3	1.27						

The center distance will have to be adjusted to suit the closest available belt length.

To find the maximum horsepower that can be transmitted by a single belt, first find the small diameter correction factor from Table 4-5. Since the speed ratio is 2.14, the factor taken from this table is 1.13. Multiply the pitch diameter of the small pulley by this factor to obtain the equivalent diameter, d_e:

$$1.13 \times 5.6 \text{ in.} = 6.3 \text{ in.} = d_e.$$

Go into Fig. 4-14 for B-belts with this equivalent diameter and belt speed 2500 fpm. The figure shows a maximum horsepower rating per belt of 5 HP. This horsepower figure, however, must be corrected for length and arc of contact. For the length correction factor consult Table 4-6. The nearest belt pitch length in the table is 121.8 in., for which the length cor-

TABLE 4-7

Contact angle correction factors.

Arc of Contact on Small Shave (degrees)	Correction Factor
180°	1.00
174	0.99
169	0.97
163	0.96
157	0.94
151	0.93
145	0.91
139	0.89
133	0.87
127	0.85
120	0.82
113	0.80
106	0.77
99	0.73
91	0.70
83	0.65

rection factor is 1.07. Also since the arc of contact for the small sheave will be less than 180 degrees, a correction factor must be made for the smaller angle from Table 4-7; less horsepower can be transmitted with smaller angles. The contact angle for the small pulley is determined from the following formula:

$$\text{Contact angle for the small sheave} = \beta = 180° - 2 \sin^{-1}\frac{D' - d'}{2C}$$

Substituting the proper values,

$$\beta = 180° - 2 \sin^{-1}\frac{2.4 - 5.6}{2 \times 48}$$
$$= 172°$$

From Table 4-7 the correction factor for an arc of contact of 172° is 0.98.

The maximum horsepower rating before applying these two correction factors is 5 HP. The final calculated horsepower per belt is:

$$5\text{ HP} \times 1.07 \times 0.98 = 5.25\text{ HP per belt}$$

Since 20 HP must be transmitted, 4 belts are required of B size.

Horsepower ratings of L-belts are given in Table 4-9.

TABLE 4-8

Stock sheave pitch diameters.

A	B	C	D	E
3.0	3.4	7.0	12.0	Special
3.2	3.6	7.5	13.0	order
3.4	3.8	8.0	13.5	
3.6	4.0	8.5	14.0	
3.8	4.2	9.0	14.5	
4.0	4.4	9.5	15.0	
4.2	4.6	10.0	15.5	
4.6	5.0	10.5	16.0	
4.8	5.2	11.0	18.0	
5.0	5.4	12.0	20.0	
5.2	5.6	13.0	22.0	
5.6	6.0	14.0	27.0	
6.0	6.4	16.0	33.0	
6.4	6.8	18.0	40.0	
7.0	7.4	20.0	48.0	
8.2	8.6	24.0	50.0	
9.0	9.4	30.0	—	
10.6	11.0	36.0	—	
12.0	12.4	44.0	—	
15.0	15.4	50.0	—	
18.0	18.4	—	—	
—	20.0	—	—	
—	25.0	—	—	
—	30.0	—	—	
—	38.0	—	—	

TABLE 4-9

Horsepower ratings of L-belts.

3L-SECTION V-BELT HORSEPOWER RATINGS

Belt Speed (ft/min)	Effective O.D. of Small Sheave (in.)			
	1½	2	2½	3 and up
200	0.05	0.08	0.10	0.11
1000	0.13	0.28	0.37	0.43
2000	0.13	0.43	0.60	0.72
3000	0.01	0.45	0.72	0.89
4000	. . .	0.31	0.67	0.91
5000	. . .	. . .	0.42	0.72
6000	. . .	. . .	. . .	0.29

TABLE 4-9 *(cont'd).*

4L-SECTION V-BELT HORSEPOWER RATINGS

Belt Speed (ft/min)	Effective O.D. of Small Sheave (in.)				
	2	2½	3	3½	4 and up
200	0.07	0.13	0.16	0.18	0.21
1000	0.18	0.46	0.65	0.78	0.88
2000	0.08	0.64	1.02	1.28	1.47
3000	. . .	0.63	1.19	1.58	1.87
4000	. . .	0.35	1.09	1.61	2.00
5000	. . .	. . .	0.65	1.30	1.78
6000	. . .	. . .	. . .	0.54	1.11

5L-SECTION V-BELT HORSEPOWER-RATINGS

Belt Speed (ft/min)	Effective O.D. of Small Sheave (in.)				
	3	3½	4	4½	5 and up
200	0.13	0.19	0.24	0.27	0.30
1000	0.40	0.72	0.95	1.14	1.28
2000	0.36	1.00	1.47	1.84	2.13
3000	0.08	0.93	1.64	2.19	2.63
1000	. . .	0.43	1.37	2.11	2.69
5000	. . .	. . .	0.58	1.49	2.22
6000	. . .	. . .	. . .	0.23	1.11

4-9 TIMER BELTS (TOOTHED BELTS)

Some machines, and especially business machines, require either accurate speed control or synchronization between shafts. Ordinary belt drives will slip or creep and therefore cannot provide,an accurate drive for these functions. For these applications a timing belt or toothed belt must be used. This is a molded rubber endless flat belt with teeth molded into it (Fig. 4-18). This belt has for its tension member a layer of steel or fiberglass cables which is almost inextensible, so that the tooth pitch is constant as in a gear. Normally a belt take-up is not needed. Among the advantages of this type of belt are the following:

1. No belt slip, creep, or speed variation.
2. Little slack-side tension required.
3. Smaller pulleys may be used.
4. Low noise level.

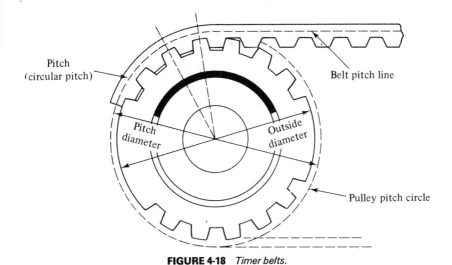

FIGURE 4-18 *Timer belts.*

The timer belt does not depend on friction, but on positive engagement between the teeth and the grooves in the pulley. This characteristic however gives the belt a disadvantage in some applications: it will not slip if overloaded. Overload protection must be provided by a slip clutch or a shear pin.

One pulley in the tooth drive must be flanged because the belt develops some side thrust. It is usual to flange the smaller pulley.

There are five pitches of teeth available, coded as follows:

Pitch (in.)	Code	Designation
⅕	XL	extra light
⅜	L	light
½	H	heavy
⅞	XH	extra heavy
1¼	XXH	double extra heavy

Belts are designated by pitch length, pitch, and width. Thus a 630 XH 150 belt is 63 inches in pitch length, extra heavy, width 2.00 inches. Similarly pulleys are designated by number of grooves, pitch, and width: a belt designation 60 XH 200 indicates a pulley with 60 grooves of extra heavy pitch with a width of 2.00 inches.

4-10 CHAIN DRIVES

A chain drive consists of an endless chain of links meshing with the driving and driven sprocket. This type of drive gives a positive speed ratio between

103

driving and driven sprockets, so that tension on the slack side is unnecessary. Because the links of the chain engage with the sprocket teeth and drive them, chain drives can operate with small arcs of contact and short center distances.

Power chain must articulate over the sprockets and this movement results in wear within the chain. As a result, the chain elongates with use. Chain elongation can be continued until the chain pitch no longer is compatible with the sprocket pitch. The sprockets are designed to accept from 3 to 6 percent chain elongation. See Fig. 4-19. This elongation will be influenced by chain tension and by sprocket size. Larger sprockets reduce wear because the chain flexes through a smaller angle on a large sprocket.

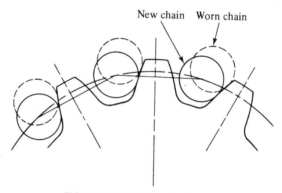

FIGURE 4-19   *Effect of chain wear.*

Chain drives have a special characteristic called *chordal action.* This is a radial motion of the chain on the sprocket that results when the straight segment of chain attempts to follow the circular pitch line of the sprocket. In Fig. 4-20 the roller chain link with roller A entering the sprocket is not tangent to the pitch circle of the sprocket, but below it. As this link moves to the next position B, it will be lifted to the pitch line and then dropped below it again. The rise and fall due to chordal action is equal to $PR-R$ as shown in the figure. If the sprocket is a driven sprocket, the chain will drive it with a fluctuating speed, faster when the roller is elevated and slightly more slowly in the dropped position. These speed variations will be large for fewer than 10 teeth in the sprocket, but decrease as the number of teeth increase. For a 15-tooth sprocket the speed variation is only 2%. Chordal action and the resulting wear are less for small pitches than for large pitches.

4-11 STANDARD ROLLER CHAIN

Standard roller chain consists of alternating roller links and pin links, shown in Fig. 4-21. The roller link consists of two rollers and two bushings, the

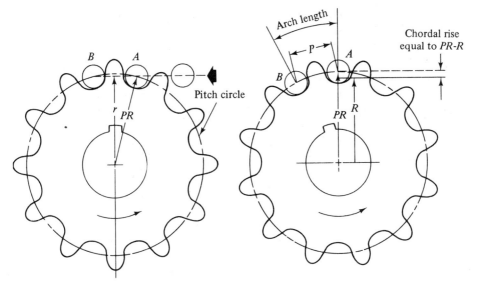

FIGURE 4-20 *Successive positions of roller "A" showing chordal action.*

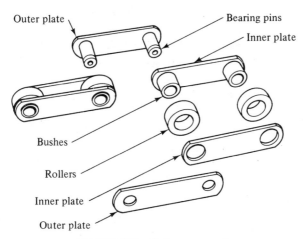

FIGURE 4-21 *Chain components.*

bushings being press-fitted into the link plates (side members). The bushings cannot turn in the link plates as the chain articulates. Special connecting links join the two ends of the chain to make it endless.

Standard roller chain has three principal dimensions: pitch, chain width, and roller diameter. Chain width is the minimum distance between link plates, that is, inside width, and is approximately ⅝ of the pitch of the chain. Roller diameter is outside diameter, also approximately ⅝ of the pitch. The pitch is the distance between centers of adjacent bushings.

Chain is available in single strand or multiple strand (Fig. 4-22). Link plates may be flat or offset (Fig. 4-23).

For reasons of minimum wear, offset sidebar chain must be mounted in a particular orientation. The rule is this: the narrow end of the link on the tight side of the chain should face the smaller sprocket, regardless of whether the smaller sprocket drives or is driven. This orientation gives least wear between the pin and the bore of the bushing. See Fig. 4-24.

Dimensions, strength, and weight of standard roller chain are given in Table 4-10. Note that the ANSI (American National Standards Institute) Chain Numbers indicate the chain pitch in eighths of an inch. In designating multistrand chain, the numbers of strands is indicated by a dash number; thus #80-3 is a triple strand #80 chain.

The weight of the larger pitches is noteworthy. Because of centrifugal effects, the large pitches are unsuited to high chain speeds. As for the rate of wear and of chain elongation, this depends on several factors:

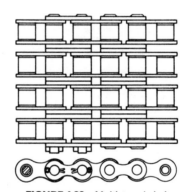

FIGURE 4-22 *Multistrand chain.*

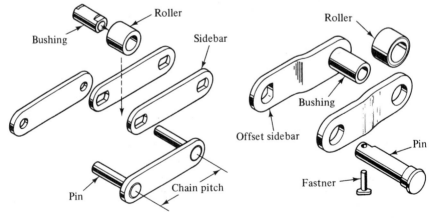

FIGURE 4-23 *Straight sidebar and offset sidebar chain.*

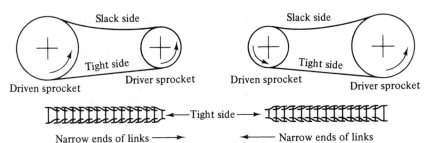

FIGURE 4-24 *Orientation of offset sidebar chain for least wear.*

1. Tension force in the chain.
2. Hardness and smoothness of contacting surfaces.
3. Presence or absence of lubrication.
4. Chain speed and the degree of articulation in chain joints.
5. Area of contact between pin and bushing (pin diameter times bushing length).

4-12 SPROCKETS

Sprocket terminology is given in Fig. 4-25. The pitch diameter is the diameter of the circle that passes through the centers of the link pins as the chain engages the sprocket. The pitch of the chain is measured on a straight line between centers of adjacent pins, and the chain pitch lines form a series of chords on the pitch circle. The pitch diameter depends on the chain pitch and the number of teeth in the sprocket:

$$D = \frac{P}{\sin\left(\frac{180°}{n}\right)}$$

where D = pitch diameter (in.)
P = chain pitch (in.)
n = number of teeth in the sprocket

For example, the pitch diameter of a 20-tooth sprocket for No. 80 chain (pitch 1 in.) is:

$$D = \frac{1}{\sin\left(\frac{180°}{20}\right)} = 6.394 \text{ in.}$$

The bottom diameter is the diameter measured to the bottom of the tooth gap. It is the difference between the pitch diameter and the roller diameter.

The maximum hub and groove diameter, MHD, is the maximum hub diameter that will allow clearance for standard link plates.

$$MHD = P \left[\cot \left(\frac{180°}{n} \right) - 1 \right] - 0.030$$

The caliper diameter is the same as the bottom diameter for any sprocket with an even number of teeth. If the sprocket has an odd number of teeth, the bottom diameter is the distance from the bottom of one tooth gap to that of the nearest opposite tooth gap.

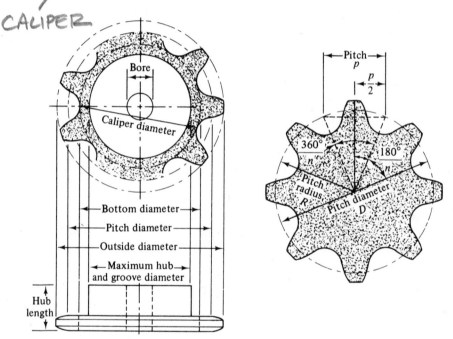

FIGURE 4-25 *Sprocket terminology.*

Four types of sprockets are standard; they are designated A, B, C, and D types. Type A is a splain sprocket without a hub; type B has the hub on one side only; type C has the hub on both sides; and type D has a detachable hub which is bolted to the sprocket.

4-13 DESIGN OF CHAIN DRIVES

The service factors that apply to chain drives are given in Table 4-11. The use of these service factors will be explained in an example below. Typical

TABLE 4-10

Dimensions of power chain.

ASA Chain No.	Pitch	Roller Width E	Roller Diam. H	DIMENSIONS—INCHES Over-All Riveted A	From Pin End to C.L. B	From Pin Head to C.L. C	Side Plate Thickness EE	Side Plate Height F	Pin Diam. G	Average Ultimate Strength Lbs.	Average Weight per Foot Lbs.
25[1]	$\frac{1}{4}$	$\frac{1}{8}$	0.130	0.31	0.19	0.15	0.030	0.23	0.0905	925	0.085
35[1]	$\frac{3}{8}$	$\frac{3}{16}$	.200	.47	.34	.23	.050	.36	.141	2,100	.22
41	$\frac{1}{2}$	$\frac{1}{4}$	.306	.51	.37	.26	.050	.39	.141	2,000	.28
40	$\frac{1}{2}$	$\frac{5}{16}$	$\frac{5}{16}$	.65	.42	.32	.060	.46	.156	3,700	.41
50	$\frac{5}{8}$	$\frac{3}{8}$	.400	.79	.56	.40	.080	.59	.200	6,100	.68
60	$\frac{3}{4}$	$\frac{1}{2}$	$\frac{15}{32}$	.98	.64	.49	.094	.68	.234	8,500	.96
80	1	$\frac{5}{8}$	$\frac{5}{8}$	1.28	.74	.64	.125	$\frac{7}{8}$	.312	14,500	1.7
100	$1\frac{1}{4}$	$\frac{3}{4}$	$\frac{3}{4}$	1.54	.91	.77	.156	$1\frac{5}{32}$	.375	24,000	2.7
120	$1\frac{1}{2}$	1	$\frac{7}{8}$	1.94	1.14	.97	.187	$1\frac{3}{8}$	.437	34,000	4.0
140	$1\frac{3}{4}$	1	1	2.08	1.22	1.04	.218	$1\frac{5}{8}$	.500	46,000	5.2
160	2	$1\frac{1}{4}$	$1\frac{1}{8}$	2.48	1.46	1.24	.250	$1\frac{7}{8}$	.562	58,000	6.8
180	$2\frac{1}{4}$	$1\frac{13}{32}$	$1\frac{13}{32}$	2.81	1.74	1.40	.281	$2\frac{1}{8}$	.687	76,000	9.1
200	$2\frac{1}{2}$	$1\frac{1}{2}$	$1\frac{9}{16}$	3.02	1.86	1.51	.312	$2\frac{5}{16}$	.781	95,000	10.8

[1] *Non-roller*

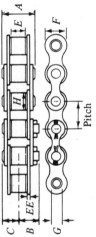

TABLE 4-11

Service factors for power chain.

	TYPE OF INPUT		
Type of Driven Load	*Internal Combustion Engine with Hydraulic Drive*	*Electric Motor or Turbine*	*Internal Combustion Engine with Mechanical Drive*
Smooth	1.0	1.0	1.2
Moderate Shock	1.2	1.3	1.4
Heavy Shock	1.4	1.5	1.7

Atmospheric conditions	Relatively clean and moderate temperature	1.0
	Moderately dirty and moderate temperature	1.2
	Exposed to weather, very dirty, abrasive, mildly corrosive and reasonably high temperatures	1.4

Daily operating range	8–10 Hours	1.0
	10–24 Hours	1.4

smooth loads are the following: liquid agitators, fans (except large fans), rotary screens, driven machines with uniform loads that do not reverse. Examples of machinery with moderate shock loads are conveyors, cranes, and hoists, grinders, machine tools. Heavy shock loads are characteristic of punch presses, hammer mills, shears, ball and rod mills. In determining the design horsepower for a chain drive the following multiple strand factors must also be used:

Number of Strands	*Multiple Strand Factor*
2	1.7
3	2.5
4	3.3

Thus for example, a four-strand roller chain has a horsepower capacity 3.3 times that of a single-strand chain.

The use of these factors can be explained by the following example. A three-strand chain is to be driven by an electric motor. The load provides moderate shock conditions. Conditions are moderately dirty with some temperature rise, and the hours of daily operation are limited to a maximum of eight. Assume a single-strand horsepower rating of 27.

The design factors are 1.3 (electric motor, moderate shock), 1.2 (moderately dirty), and 1.0 for hours of operation. The multiple-strand factor is 2.5. Therefore the design HP is:

$$\frac{27 \times 2.5}{1.3 \times 1.2 \times 1} = 45 \text{ HP}$$

To design a chain drive, first make a tentative selection of chain pitch from Fig. 4-26. Go into this chart with the design horsepower (calculated from design factors as in the example above) and connect with the vertical line for the rpm of the small sprocket. The area in which the two lines intersect gives the probable chain number for the required speed and horsepower.

If a single-strand chain is to be used, the horsepower rating tables of Table 4-12 may be used directly. Follow down the column which is headed by the speed of the small sprocket and find the nearest value to the design horsepower. Then go horizontally to the left to find the required number of teeth for the small sprocket. If a multiple-strand chain is to be used, then the required design horsepower rating per strand is calculated from:

$$\frac{\text{Design HP}}{\text{Multiple strand factor}}$$

As before for a single strand, go down the column giving the speed of the small sprocket and find the nearest value to the required horsepower rating, then the required number of teeth for the small sprocket.

Check the maximum bore of the selected sprocket in Table 4-13. If the sprocket selected will not accommodate the shaft, use a larger sprocket or make a second chain selection using the next larger chain number.

The number of teeth in the large sprocket is determined from the speed ratio and the number of teeth in the small sprocket. It may not be possible to obtain the exact rpm required in the large sprocket, but is an unusual drive that must be given an exact speed in rpm.

The required length of chain must consist of a whole number of links. Therefore it is convenient to specify chain length and center distance in number of pitches. An even number of pitches is to be preferred, since an odd number requires the use of an offset link. Use the following formulas for chain length if center distance is known, or center distance if chain length is known.

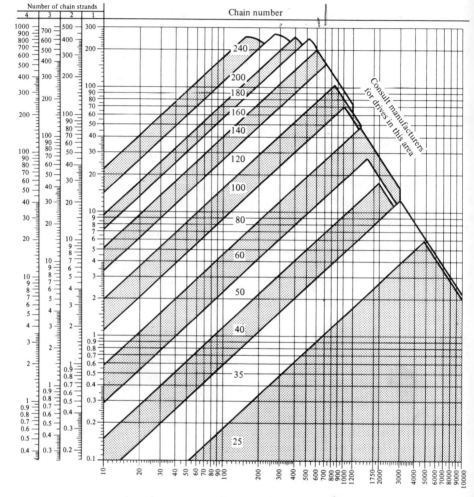

FIGURE 4-26 *Selection chart for drive chain.*

TABLE 4-12.
HORSEPOWER RATINGS STANDARD SINGLE STRAND ROLLER CHAIN — NO. 25 — ¼" PITCH

No. of Teeth Small Spkt.	REVOLUTIONS PER MINUTE—SMALL SPROCKET																								
	50	100	300	500	700	900	1200	1500	1800	2100	2500	3000	3500	4000	4500	5000	5500	6000	6500	7000	7500	8000	8500	9000	10000
9	0.02	0.04	0.12	0.18	0.25	0.31	0.41	0.50	0.58	0.67	0.79	0.93	1.06	1.02	0.86	0.73	0.63	0.56	0.49	0.44	0.40	0.36	0.33	0.30	0.26
10	0.03	0.05	0.13	0.21	0.28	0.35	0.45	0.56	0.65	0.75	0.88	1.04	1.19	1.20	1.00	0.86	0.74	0.65	0.58	0.52	0.47	0.42	0.39	0.35	0.30
11	0.03	0.05	0.14	0.23	0.31	0.39	0.50	0.62	0.73	0.83	0.98	1.15	1.32	1.38	1.16	0.99	0.86	0.75	0.67	0.60	0.54	0.49	0.45	0.41	0.35
12	0.03	0.06	0.16	0.25	0.34	0.43	0.55	0.68	0.80	0.92	1.07	1.26	1.45	1.57	1.32	1.12	0.97	0.86	0.76	0.68	0.61	0.56	0.51	0.47	0.40
13	0.04	0.06	0.17	0.27	0.37	0.47	0.60	0.74	0.87	1.00	1.17	1.38	1.58	1.77	1.49	1.27	1.10	0.96	0.86	0.77	0.69	0.63	0.57	0.53	0.45
14	0.04	0.07	0.19	0.30	0.40	0.50	0.65	0.80	0.94	1.08	1.27	1.49	1.71	1.93	1.66	1.42	1.23	1.08	0.96	0.86	0.77	0.70	0.64	0.59	0.50
15	0.04	0.07	0.20	0.32	0.43	0.54	0.70	0.86	1.01	1.17	1.36	1.61	1.85	2.08	1.84	1.57	1.36	1.20	1.06	0.95	0.86	0.78	0.71	0.65	0.56
16	0.04	0.08	0.22	0.34	0.47	0.58	0.76	0.92	1.09	1.25	1.46	1.72	1.98	2.23	2.03	1.73	1.50	1.32	1.17	1.05	0.94	0.86	0.78	0.72	0.61
17	0.05	0.08	0.23	0.37	0.50	0.62	0.81	0.99	1.16	1.33	1.56	1.84	2.11	2.38	2.22	1.90	1.64	1.44	1.28	1.14	1.03	0.94	0.86	0.79	0.67
18	0.05	0.09	0.25	0.39	0.53	0.66	0.86	1.05	1.24	1.42	1.66	1.96	2.25	2.53	2.42	2.07	1.79	1.57	1.39	1.25	1.12	1.02	0.93	0.86	0.73
19	0.05	0.09	0.26	0.41	0.56	0.70	0.91	1.11	1.31	1.50	1.76	2.07	2.38	2.69	2.62	2.24	1.94	1.70	1.51	1.35	1.22	1.11	1.01	0.93	0.79
20	0.06	0.10	0.28	0.44	0.59	0.74	0.96	1.17	1.38	1.59	1.86	2.19	2.52	2.84	2.83	2.42	2.10	1.84	1.63	1.46	1.32	1.20	1.09	1.00	0.86
21	0.06	0.11	0.29	0.46	0.62	0.78	1.01	1.24	1.46	1.68	1.96	2.31	2.66	2.99	3.05	2.60	2.26	1.98	1.76	1.57	1.42	1.29	1.17	1.08	0.92
22	0.06	0.11	0.31	0.48	0.66	0.82	1.07	1.30	1.53	1.76	2.06	2.43	2.79	3.15	3.27	2.79	2.42	2.12	1.88	1.69	1.52	1.38	1.26	1.16	0.99
23	0.06	0.12	0.32	0.51	0.69	0.86	1.12	1.37	1.61	1.85	2.16	2.55	2.93	3.30	3.50	2.98	2.59	2.27	2.01	1.80	1.62	1.47	1.35	1.24	1.06
24	0.07	0.13	0.34	0.53	0.72	0.90	1.17	1.43	1.69	1.94	2.27	2.67	3.07	3.46	3.73	3.18	2.76	2.42	2.15	1.92	1.73	1.57	1.44	1.32	1.12
25	0.07	0.13	0.35	0.56	0.75	0.94	1.22	1.50	1.76	2.02	2.37	2.79	3.21	3.61	3.96	3.38	2.93	2.57	2.28	2.04	1.84	1.67	1.53	1.40	1.20
26	0.07	0.14	0.37	0.58	0.79	0.98	1.28	1.56	1.84	2.11	2.47	2.91	3.34	3.77	4.19	3.59	3.11	2.73	2.42	2.17	1.95	1.77	1.62	1.49	1.27
28	0.08	0.15	0.40	0.63	0.85	1.07	1.38	1.69	1.99	2.29	2.68	3.15	3.62	4.09	4.54	4.01	3.47	3.05	2.70	2.42	2.18	1.98	1.81	1.66	1.42
30	0.08	0.16	0.43	0.68	0.92	1.15	1.49	1.82	2.15	2.46	2.88	3.40	3.90	4.40	4.89	4.45	3.85	3.38	3.00	2.68	2.42	2.20	2.01	1.84	1.57
32	0.09	0.17	0.46	0.73	0.98	1.23	1.60	1.95	2.30	2.64	3.09	3.64	4.18	4.72	5.25	4.90	4.25	3.73	3.30	2.96	2.67	2.42	2.21	2.03	1.73
35	0.10	0.19	0.51	0.80	1.08	1.36	1.76	2.15	2.53	2.91	3.41	4.01	4.61	5.20	5.78	5.60	4.86	4.26	3.78	3.38	3.05	2.77	2.53	2.32	1.98
40	0.12	0.22	0.58	0.92	1.25	1.57	2.03	2.48	2.93	3.36	3.93	4.64	5.32	6.00	6.68	6.85	5.93	5.21	4.62	4.13	3.73	3.38	3.09	2.83	2.42
45	0.13	0.25	0.66	1.05	1.42	1.78	2.31	2.82	3.32	3.82	4.47	5.26	6.05	6.82	7.58	8.17	7.08	6.21	5.51	4.93	4.45	4.04	3.69	3.38	2.89

Type A   Type B   Type C

TABLE 4-12 (Cont'd).

HORSEPOWER RATINGS STANDARD SINGLE STRAND ROLLER CHAIN — NO. 35 — 3/8" PITCH

No. of Teeth Small Spkt.	REVOLUTIONS PER MINUTE—SMALL SPROCKET																								
	50	100	300	500	700	900	1200	1500	1800	2100	2500	3000	3500	4000	4500	5000	5500	6000	6500	7000	7500	8000	8500	9000	10000
9	0.08	0.15	0.39	0.62	0.84	1.06	1.37	1.68	1.98	2.27	2.65	2.17	1.73	1.41	1.18	1.01	0.88	0.77	0.68	0.61	0.55	0.50	0.46	0.42	0.35
10	0.09	0.16	0.44	0.70	0.95	1.19	1.54	1.88	2.21	2.54	2.97	2.55	2.02	1.65	1.39	1.18	1.03	0.90	0.80	0.71	0.64	0.58	0.53	0.49	0.42
11	0.10	0.18	0.49	0.77	1.05	1.31	1.70	2.08	2.45	2.82	3.30	2.94	2.33	1.91	1.60	1.37	1.18	1.04	0.92	0.82	0.74	0.67	0.62	0.57	0.48
12	0.11	0.20	0.54	0.85	1.15	1.44	1.87	2.29	2.70	3.10	3.62	3.35	2.66	2.17	1.82	1.56	1.35	1.18	1.05	0.94	0.85	0.77	0.70	0.64	0.55
13	0.12	0.22	0.59	0.93	1.26	1.57	2.04	2.49	2.94	3.38	3.95	3.77	3.00	2.45	2.05	1.75	1.52	1.33	1.18	1.06	0.95	0.87	0.79	0.73	0.62
14	0.13	0.24	0.63	1.01	1.36	1.71	2.21	2.70	3.18	3.66	4.28	4.22	3.35	2.74	2.30	1.96	1.70	1.49	1.32	1.18	1.07	0.97	0.88	0.81	0.69
15	0.14	0.25	0.68	1.08	1.47	1.84	2.38	2.91	3.43	3.94	4.61	4.68	3.71	3.04	2.55	2.17	1.88	1.65	1.47	1.31	1.18	1.07	0.98	0.90	0.77
16	0.15	0.27	0.73	1.16	1.57	1.97	2.55	3.12	3.68	4.22	4.94	5.15	4.09	3.35	2.81	2.40	2.08	1.82	1.62	1.45	1.30	1.18	1.08	0.99	0.85
17	0.16	0.29	0.78	1.24	1.68	2.10	2.73	3.33	3.93	4.51	5.28	5.64	4.48	3.67	3.07	2.62	2.27	2.00	1.77	1.58	1.43	1.30	1.18	1.09	0.93
18	0.17	0.31	0.83	1.32	1.78	2.24	2.90	3.54	4.18	4.80	5.61	6.15	4.88	3.99	3.35	2.86	2.48	2.17	1.93	1.73	1.56	1.41	1.29	1.18	1.01
19	0.18	0.33	0.88	1.40	1.89	2.37	3.07	3.76	4.43	5.09	5.95	6.67	5.29	4.33	3.63	3.10	2.69	2.36	2.09	1.87	1.69	1.53	1.40	1.28	1.10
20	0.19	0.35	0.93	1.48	2.00	2.51	3.25	3.97	4.68	5.38	6.29	7.20	5.72	4.68	3.92	3.35	2.90	2.55	2.26	2.02	1.82	1.65	1.51	1.39	1.18
21	0.20	0.37	0.98	1.56	2.11	2.64	3.42	4.19	4.93	5.67	6.63	7.75	6.15	5.03	4.22	3.60	3.12	2.74	2.43	2.17	1.96	1.78	1.62	1.49	1.27
22	0.21	0.38	1.03	1.64	2.22	2.78	3.60	4.40	5.19	5.96	6.97	8.21	6.59	5.40	4.52	3.86	3.35	2.94	2.61	2.33	2.10	1.91	1.74	1.60	1.37
23	0.22	0.40	1.08	1.72	2.33	2.92	3.78	4.62	5.44	6.25	7.31	8.62	7.05	5.77	4.83	4.13	3.58	3.14	2.79	2.49	2.25	2.04	1.86	1.71	1.46
24	0.23	0.42	1.14	1.80	2.44	3.05	3.96	4.84	5.70	6.55	7.66	9.02	7.51	6.15	5.15	4.40	3.81	3.35	2.97	2.66	2.40	2.17	1.99	1.82	1.56
25	0.24	0.44	1.19	1.88	2.55	3.19	4.13	5.05	5.95	6.84	8.00	9.43	7.99	6.54	5.48	4.68	4.05	3.56	3.16	2.82	2.55	2.31	2.11	1.94	1.65
26	0.25	0.46	1.24	1.96	2.66	3.33	4.31	5.27	6.21	7.14	8.35	9.84	8.47	6.93	5.81	4.96	4.30	3.77	3.35	3.00	2.70	2.45	2.24	2.05	1.75
28	0.27	0.50	1.34	2.12	2.88	3.61	4.67	5.71	6.73	7.73	9.05	10.7	9.47	7.75	6.49	5.55	4.81	4.22	3.74	3.35	3.02	2.74	2.50	2.30	1.96
30	0.29	0.54	1.45	2.29	3.10	3.89	5.03	6.15	7.25	8.33	9.74	11.5	10.5	8.59	7.20	6.15	5.33	4.68	4.15	3.71	3.35	3.04	2.77	2.55	2.17
32	0.31	0.58	1.55	2.45	3.32	4.17	5.40	6.60	7.77	8.93	10.4	12.3	11.6	9.47	7.93	6.77	5.87	5.15	4.57	4.09	3.69	3.35	3.06	2.81	0
35	0.34	0.64	1.71	2.70	3.66	4.59	5.95	7.27	8.56	9.84	11.5	13.6	13.2	10.8	9.08	7.75	6.72	5.90	5.23	4.68	4.22	3.83	3.50	3.21	0
40	0.39	0.73	1.97	3.12	4.23	5.30	6.87	8.40	9.89	11.4	13.3	15.7	16.2	13.2	11.1	9.47	8.21	7.20	6.39	5.72	5.15	4.68	0	0	
45	0.45	0.83	2.24	3.55	4.80	6.02	7.80	9.53	11.2	12.9	15.1	17.8	19.3	15.8	13.2	11.3	9.79	8.59	7.62	6.82	0				

Type A   Type B   Type C

TYPE A: Manual or Drip Lubrication
TYPE B: Bath or Disc Lubrication
TYPE C: Oil Stream Lubrication

The limiting RPM for each lubrication type is read from the column to the left of the boundary line shown.

TABLE 4-12 *(Cont'd).*

HORSEPOWER RATINGS STANDARD SINGLE STRAND ROLLER CHAIN — NO. 40 — ½" PITCH

REVOLUTIONS PER MINUTE—SMALL SPROCKET

No. of Teeth Small Spkt.	10	25	50	100	200	300	400	500	700	900	1000	1200	1400	1600	1800	2100	2400	2700	3000	3500	4000	5000	6000	7000	8000
9	0.04	0.10	0.19	0.35	0.65	0.93	1.21	1.48	2.00	2.51	2.75	3.25	3.73	4.12	3.45	2.74	2.24	1.88	1.60	1.27	1.04	0.75	0.57	0.45	0.37
10	0.05	0.11	0.21	0.39	0.73	1.04	1.35	1.65	2.24	2.81	3.09	3.64	4.18	4.71	4.04	3.21	2.63	2.20	1.88	1.49	1.22	0.87	0.66	0.53	0.43
11	0.05	0.12	0.23	0.43	0.80	1.16	1.50	1.83	2.48	3.11	3.42	4.03	4.63	5.22	4.66	3.70	3.03	2.54	2.17	1.72	1.41	1.01	0.77	0.61	0.50
12	0.06	0.14	0.25	0.47	0.88	1.27	1.65	2.01	2.73	3.42	3.76	4.43	5.09	5.74	5.31	4.22	3.45	2.89	2.47	1.96	1.60	1.15	0.87	0.69	0.57
13	0.06	0.15	0.28	0.52	0.96	1.39	1.80	2.20	2.97	3.73	4.10	4.83	5.55	6.26	5.99	4.76	3.89	3.26	2.79	2.21	1.81	1.29	0.98	0.78	0.64
14	0.07	0.16	0.30	0.56	1.04	1.50	1.95	2.38	3.22	4.04	4.44	5.23	6.01	6.78	6.70	5.31	4.35	3.65	3.11	2.47	2.02	1.45	1.10	0.87	0.71
15	0.07	0.17	0.32	0.60	1.12	1.62	2.10	2.56	3.47	4.35	4.78	5.64	6.47	7.30	7.43	5.89	4.82	4.04	3.45	2.74	2.24	1.60	1.22	0.97	0.79
16	0.08	0.19	0.35	0.65	1.20	1.74	2.25	2.75	3.72	4.66	5.13	6.04	6.94	7.83	8.18	6.49	5.31	4.45	3.80	3.02	2.47	1.77	1.34	1.07	0.87
17	0.08	0.20	0.37	0.69	1.29	1.85	2.40	2.93	3.97	4.98	5.48	6.45	7.41	8.36	8.96	7.11	5.82	4.88	4.17	3.31	2.71	1.94	1.47	1.17	0.96
18	0.09	0.21	0.39	0.73	1.37	1.97	2.55	3.12	4.22	5.30	5.82	6.86	7.88	8.89	9.76	7.75	6.34	5.31	4.54	3.60	2.95	2.11	1.60	1.27	0
19	0.09	0.22	0.42	0.78	1.45	2.09	2.71	3.31	4.48	5.62	6.17	7.27	8.36	9.42	10.5	8.40	6.88	5.76	4.92	3.91	3.20	2.29	1.74	1.38	0
20	0.10	0.24	0.44	0.82	1.53	2.21	2.86	3.50	4.73	5.94	6.53	7.69	8.83	9.96	11.1	9.07	7.43	6.22	5.31	4.22	3.45	2.47	1.88	1.49	0
21	0.11	0.25	0.46	0.87	1.62	2.33	3.02	3.69	4.99	6.26	6.88	8.11	9.31	10.5	11.7	9.76	7.99	6.70	5.72	4.54	3.71	2.66	2.02	1.60	0
22	0.11	0.26	0.49	0.91	1.70	2.45	3.17	3.88	5.25	6.58	7.23	8.52	9.79	11.0	12.3	10.5	8.57	7.18	6.13	4.87	3.98	2.85	2.17	1.72	0
23	0.12	0.27	0.51	0.96	1.78	2.57	3.33	4.07	5.51	6.90	7.59	8.94	10.3	11.6	12.9	11.2	9.16	7.68	6.55	5.20	4.26	3.05	2.32	1.84	0
24	0.13	0.29	0.54	1.00	1.87	2.69	3.48	4.26	5.76	7.23	7.95	9.36	10.8	12.1	13.5	11.9	9.76	8.18	6.99	5.54	4.54	3.25	2.47	1.96	0
25	0.13	0.30	0.56	1.05	1.95	2.81	3.64	4.45	6.02	7.55	8.30	9.78	11.2	12.7	14.1	12.7	10.4	8.70	7.43	5.89	4.82	3.45	2.63	0	
26	0.14	0.31	0.58	1.09	2.04	2.93	3.80	4.64	6.28	7.88	8.66	10.2	11.7	13.2	14.7	13.5	11.0	9.23	7.88	6.25	5.12	3.66	2.79	0	
28	0.15	0.34	0.63	1.18	2.20	3.18	4.11	5.03	6.81	8.54	9.39	11.1	12.7	14.3	15.9	15.0	12.3	10.3	8.80	6.99	5.72	4.09	3.11	0	
30	0.16	0.37	0.68	1.27	2.38	3.42	4.43	5.42	7.33	9.20	10.1	11.9	13.7	15.4	17.2	16.7	13.6	11.4	9.76	7.75	6.34	4.54	3.45	0	
32	0.17	0.39	0.73	1.36	2.55	3.67	4.75	5.81	7.86	9.86	10.8	12.8	14.7	16.5	18.4	18.4	15.0	12.6	10.8	8.64	6.99	5.00	0		
35	0.19	0.43	0.81	1.50	2.81	4.04	5.24	6.40	8.66	10.9	11.9	14.1	16.2	18.2	20.3	21.0	17.2	14.4	12.3	9.76	7.99	5.72	0		
40	0.22	0.50	0.93	1.74	3.24	4.67	6.05	7.39	10.0	12.5	13.8	16.3	18.7	21.0	23.4	25.7	21.0	17.6	15.0	11.9	9.76	6.99	0		
45	0.25	0.57	1.06	1.97	3.68	5.30	6.87	8.40	11.4	14.2	15.7	18.5	21.2	23.9	26.6	30.5	25.1	21.0	17.9	14.2	11.7	0			

Type A   Type B   Type C

115

TABLE 4-12 (Cont'd).

HORSEPOWER RATINGS STANDARD SINGLE STRAND ROLLER CHAIN — NO. 41
½" PITCH LIGHT WEIGHT MACHINERY CHAIN

No. of Teeth Small Spkt.	REVOLUTIONS PER MINUTE—SMALL SPROCKET																								
	10	25	50	100	200	300	400	500	700	900	1000	1200	1400	1600	1800	2100	2400	2700	3000	3500	4000	5000	6000	7000	8000
9	0.02	0.05	0.10	0.19	0.36	0.51	0.66	0.81	1.10	1.38	1.52	1.27	1.01	0.82	0.69	0.55	0.45	0.38	0.32	0.25	0.21	0.15	0.11	0.09	0.07
10	0.03	0.06	0.11	0.21	0.40	0.57	0.74	0.91	1.23	1.54	1.70	1.49	1.18	0.96	0.81	0.64	0.53	0.44	0.38	0.30	0.24	0.17	0.13	0.11	0.08
11	0.03	0.07	0.13	0.24	0.44	0.64	0.82	1.01	1.37	1.71	1.88	1.71	1.36	1.11	0.93	0.74	0.61	0.51	0.43	0.34	0.28	0.20	0.15	0.12	0.10
12	0.03	0.07	0.14	0.26	0.49	0.70	0.91	1.11	1.50	1.88	2.07	1.95	1.55	1.27	1.06	0.84	0.69	0.58	0.49	0.39	0.32	0.23	0.17	0.14	0.11
13	0.03	0.08	0.15	0.28	0.53	0.76	0.99	1.21	1.63	2.05	2.25	2.20	1.75	1.43	1.20	0.95	0.78	0.65	0.56	0.44	0.36	0.26	0.20	0.16	0.13
14	0.04	0.09	0.16	0.31	0.57	0.83	1.07	1.31	1.77	2.22	2.44	2.46	1.95	1.60	1.34	1.06	0.87	0.73	0.62	0.49	0.40	0.29	0.22	0.17	0.14
15	0.04	0.09	0.18	0.33	0.62	0.89	1.15	1.41	1.91	2.39	2.63	2.73	2.17	1.77	1.49	1.18	0.96	0.81	0.69	0.55	0.45	0.32	0.24	0.19	0.16
16	0.04	0.10	0.19	0.36	0.66	0.95	1.24	1.51	2.05	2.57	2.82	3.01	2.39	1.95	1.64	1.30	1.06	0.89	0.76	0.60	0.49	0.35	0.27	0.21	0.17
17	0.05	0.11	0.20	0.38	0.71	1.02	1.32	1.61	2.18	2.74	3.01	3.29	2.61	2.14	1.79	1.42	1.16	0.98	0.83	0.66	0.54	0.39	0.29	0.23	0.19
18	0.05	0.12	0.22	0.40	0.75	1.08	1.40	1.72	2.32	2.91	3.20	3.59	2.85	2.33	1.95	1.55	1.27	1.06	0.91	0.72	0.59	0.42	0.32	0.25	0
19	0.05	0.12	0.23	0.43	0.80	1.15	1.49	1.82	2.46	3.09	3.40	3.89	3.09	2.53	2.12	1.68	1.38	1.15	0.98	0.78	0.64	0.46	0.35	0.28	0
20	0.06	0.13	0.24	0.45	0.84	1.21	1.57	1.92	2.60	3.26	3.59	4.20	3.33	2.73	2.29	1.81	1.49	1.24	1.06	0.84	0.69	0.49	0.38	0.30	0
21	0.06	0.14	0.26	0.48	0.89	1.28	1.66	2.03	2.74	3.44	3.78	4.46	3.59	2.94	2.46	1.95	1.60	1.34	1.14	0.91	0.74	0.53	0.40	0.32	0
22	0.06	0.14	0.27	0.50	0.93	1.35	1.74	2.13	2.89	3.62	3.98	4.69	3.85	3.15	2.64	2.09	1.71	1.44	1.23	0.97	0.80	0.57	0.43	0.34	0
23	0.06	0.15	0.28	0.53	0.98	1.41	1.83	2.24	3.03	3.80	4.17	4.92	4.11	3.37	2.82	2.24	1.83	1.54	1.31	1.04	0.85	0.61	0.46	0.37	0
24	0.07	0.16	0.29	0.55	1.03	1.48	1.92	2.34	3.17	3.97	4.37	5.15	4.38	3.59	3.01	2.39	1.95	1.64	1.40	1.11	0.91	0.65	0.49	0.39	
25	0.07	0.17	0.31	0.57	1.07	1.55	2.00	2.45	3.31	4.15	4.57	5.38	4.66	3.81	3.20	2.54	2.08	1.74	1.49	1.18	0.96	0.69	0.53	0	
26	0.07	0.17	0.32	0.60	1.12	1.61	2.09	2.55	3.46	4.33	4.76	5.61	4.94	4.05	3.39	2.69	2.20	1.85	1.58	1.25	1.02	0.73	0.56	0	
28	0.08	0.19	0.35	0.65	1.21	1.75	2.26	2.77	3.74	4.69	5.16	6.08	5.52	4.52	3.79	3.01	2.46	2.06	1.76	1.40	1.14	0.82	0.62		
30	0.08	0.20	0.38	0.70	1.31	1.88	2.44	2.98	4.03	5.06	5.56	6.55	6.13	5.01	4.20	3.33	2.73	2.29	1.95	1.55	1.27	0.91	0.69		
32	0.09	0.22	0.40	0.75	1.40	2.02	2.61	3.20	4.33	5.42	5.96	7.03	6.75	5.52	4.63	3.67	3.01	2.52	2.15	1.71	1.40	1.00	0		
35	0.10	0.24	0.44	0.83	1.54	2.22	2.88	3.52	4.76	5.97	6.57	7.74	7.72	6.32	5.29	4.20	3.44	2.88	2.46	1.95	1.60	1.14	0		
40	0.12	0.27	0.51	0.96	1.78	2.57	3.33	4.07	5.50	6.90	7.59	8.94	9.43	7.72	6.47	5.13	4.20	3.52	3.01	2.39	1.95	1.40	0		
45	0.14	0.31	0.58	1.08	2.02	2.92	3.78	4.62	6.25	7.84	8.62	10.2	11.3	9.21	7.72	6.13	5.01	4.20	3.59	2.85	2.33	0			

Type A   Type B   Type C

TYPE A: Manual or Drip Lubrication
TYPE B: Bath or Disc Lubrication
TYPE C: Oil Stream Lubrication

The limiting RPM for each lubrication type is read from the column to the left of the boundary line shown.

TABLE 4-12 (Cont'd).

HORSEPOWER RATINGS STANDARD SINGLE STRAND ROLLER CHAIN — NO. 50 — 5/8" PITCH

REVOLUTIONS PER MINUTE—SMALL SPROCKET

No. of Teeth Small Spkt.	10	25	50	100	200	300	400	500	700	900	1000	1200	1400	1600	1800	2100	2400	2700	3000	3500	4000	4500	5000	5500	6000
9	0.09	0.19	0.36	0.67	1.26	1.81	2.35	2.87	3.89	4.88	5.36	6.32	6.02	4.92	4.13	3.27	2.68	2.25	1.92	1.52	1.25	1.04	0.89	0.77	0.58
10	0.10	0.22	0.41	0.76	1.41	2.03	2.63	3.22	4.36	5.46	6.01	7.08	7.05	5.77	4.83	3.84	3.14	2.63	2.25	1.78	1.46	1.22	1.04	0.90	0.79
11	0.11	0.24	0.45	0.84	1.56	2.25	2.92	3.57	4.83	6.06	6.66	7.85	8.13	6.65	5.58	4.42	3.62	3.04	2.59	2.06	1.68	1.41	1.20	1.04	0.92
12	0.12	0.26	0.49	0.92	1.72	2.47	3.21	3.92	5.31	6.65	7.31	8.62	9.26	7.58	6.35	5.04	4.13	3.46	2.95	2.34	1.92	1.61	1.37	1.19	1.04
13	0.13	0.29	0.54	1.00	1.87	2.70	3.50	4.27	5.78	7.25	7.97	9.40	10.4	8.55	7.16	5.69	4.65	3.90	3.33	2.64	2.16	1.81	1.55	1.34	0
14	0.14	0.31	0.58	1.09	2.03	2.92	3.79	4.63	6.27	7.86	8.64	10.2	11.7	9.55	8.01	6.35	5.20	4.36	3.72	2.95	2.42	2.03	1.73	1.50	0
15	0.15	0.34	0.63	1.17	2.19	3.15	4.08	4.99	6.75	8.47	9.31	11.0	12.6	10.6	8.88	7.05	5.77	4.83	4.13	3.27	2.68	2.25	1.92	1.66	0
16	0.16	0.36	0.67	1.26	2.34	3.38	4.37	5.35	7.24	9.08	9.98	11.8	13.5	11.7	9.78	7.76	6.35	5.32	4.55	3.61	2.95	2.47	2.11	1.83	0
17	0.17	0.39	0.72	1.34	2.50	3.61	4.67	5.71	7.73	9.69	10.7	12.6	14.4	12.8	10.7	8.50	6.96	5.83	4.98	3.95	3.23	2.71	2.31	2.01	0
18	0.18	0.41	0.76	1.43	2.66	3.83	4.97	6.07	8.22	10.3	11.3	13.4	15.3	13.9	11.7	9.26	7.58	6.35	5.42	4.30	3.52	2.95	2.52	0	
19	0.19	0.43	0.81	1.51	2.82	4.07	5.27	6.44	8.72	10.9	12.0	14.2	16.3	15.1	12.7	10.0	8.22	6.89	5.88	4.67	3.82	3.20	2.73	0	
20	0.20	0.46	0.86	1.60	2.98	4.30	5.57	6.80	9.21	11.5	12.7	15.0	17.2	16.3	13.7	10.8	8.88	7.44	6.35	5.04	4.13	3.46	2.95	0	
21	0.21	0.48	0.90	1.69	3.14	4.53	5.87	7.17	9.71	12.2	13.4	15.8	18.1	17.6	14.7	11.7	9.55	8.01	6.84	5.42	4.44	3.72	3.18	0	
22	0.22	0.51	0.95	1.77	3.31	4.76	6.17	7.54	10.2	12.8	14.1	16.6	19.1	18.8	15.8	12.5	10.2	8.59	7.33	5.82	4.76	3.99	3.41	0	
23	0.23	0.53	1.00	1.86	3.47	5.00	6.47	7.91	10.7	13.4	14.8	17.4	20.0	20.1	16.9	13.4	11.0	9.18	7.84	6.22	5.09	4.27			
24	0.25	0.56	1.04	1.95	3.63	5.23	6.78	8.29	11.2	14.1	15.5	18.2	20.9	21.4	18.0	14.3	11.7	9.78	8.35	6.63	5.42	4.55	0		
25	0.26	0.58	1.09	2.03	3.80	5.47	7.08	8.66	11.7	14.7	16.2	19.0	21.9	22.8	19.1	15.2	12.4	10.4	8.88	7.05	5.77	4.83	0		
26	0.27	0.61	1.14	2.12	3.96	5.70	7.39	9.03	12.2	15.3	16.9	19.9	22.8	24.2	20.3	16.1	13.2	11.0	9.42	7.47	6.12	5.13	0		
28	0.29	0.66	1.23	2.30	4.29	6.18	8.01	9.79	13.2	16.6	18.3	21.5	24.7	27.0	22.6	18.0	14.7	12.3	10.5	8.35	6.84	5.73	0		
30	0.31	0.71	1.33	2.49	4.62	6.66	8.63	10.5	14.3	17.9	19.7	23.2	26.6	25.1	25.1	19.9	16.3	13.7	11.7	9.26	7.58	0			
32	0.33	0.76	1.42	2.66	4.96	7.14	9.25	11.3	15.3	19.2	21.1	24.9	28.6	32.2	27.7	22.0	18.0	15.1	12.9	10.2	8.35	0			
35	0.37	0.84	1.57	2.93	5.46	7.86	10.2	12.5	16.9	21.1	23.2	27.4	31.5	35.5	31.6	25.1	20.6	17.2	14.7	11.7	9.55	0			
40	0.43	0.97	1.81	3.38	6.31	9.08	11.8	14.4	19.5	24.4	26.8	31.6	36.3	41.0	38.7	30.7	25.1	21.0	18.0	14.3	0				
45	0.48	1.10	2.06	3.84	7.16	10.3	13.4	16.3	22.1	27.7	30.5	35.9	41.3	46.5	46.1	36.6	30.0	25.1	21.4	0					

Type A   Type B   Type C

117

TABLE 4-12 (Cont'd).

HORSEPOWER RATINGS STANDARD SINGLE STRAND ROLLER CHAIN — NO. 60 — 3/4" PITCH

No. of Teeth Small Spkt.	REVOLUTIONS PER MINUTE—SMALL SPROCKET																								
	10	25	50	100	150	200	300	400	500	600	700	800	900	1000	1100	1200	1400	1600	1800	2000	2500	3000	3500	4000	4500
9	0.15	0.33	0.62	1.16	1.67	2.16	3.12	4.04	4.94	5.82	6.68	7.54	8.38	9.21	9.99	8.77	6.96	5.70	4.77	4.08	2.92	2.22	1.76	1.44	1.21
10	0.16	0.37	0.70	1.30	1.87	2.43	3.49	4.53	5.53	6.52	7.49	8.44	9.39	10.3	11.2	10.3	8.15	6.67	5.59	4.77	3.42	2.60	2.06	1.69	1.41
11	0.18	0.41	0.77	1.44	2.07	2.69	3.87	5.02	6.13	7.23	8.30	9.36	10.4	11.4	12.5	11.9	9.41	7.70	6.45	5.51	3.94	3.00	2.38	1.95	1.63
12	0.20	0.45	0.85	1.58	2.28	2.95	4.25	5.51	6.74	7.94	9.12	10.3	11.4	12.6	13.7	13.5	10.7	8.77	7.35	6.28	4.49	3.42	2.71	2.22	1.86
13	0.22	0.50	0.92	1.73	2.49	3.22	4.64	6.01	7.34	8.65	9.94	11.2	12.5	13.7	14.9	15.2	12.1	9.89	8.29	7.08	5.06	3.85	3.06	2.50	0
14	0.24	0.54	1.00	1.87	2.69	3.49	5.02	6.51	7.96	9.37	10.8	12.1	13.5	14.8	16.2	17.0	13.5	11.1	9.26	7.91	5.66	4.31	3.42	2.80	0
15	0.25	0.58	1.08	2.01	2.90	3.76	5.41	7.01	8.57	10.1	11.6	13.1	14.5	16.0	17.4	18.8	15.0	12.3	10.3	8.77	6.28	4.77	3.79	3.10	0
16	0.27	0.62	1.16	2.16	3.11	4.03	5.80	7.52	9.19	10.8	12.4	14.0	15.6	17.1	18.7	20.2	16.5	13.5	11.3	9.66	6.91	5.26	4.17	3.42	0
17	0.29	0.66	1.24	2.31	3.32	4.30	6.20	8.03	9.81	11.6	13.3	15.0	16.7	18.3	19.9	21.6	18.1	14.8	12.4	10.6	7.57	5.76	4.57	3.74	0
18	0.31	0.70	1.31	2.45	3.53	4.58	6.59	8.54	10.4	12.3	14.1	15.9	17.7	19.5	21.2	22.9	19.7	16.1	13.5	11.5	8.25	6.28	4.98	4.08	0
19	0.33	0.75	1.39	2.60	3.74	4.85	6.99	9.05	11.1	13.0	15.0	16.9	18.8	20.6	22.5	24.3	21.4	17.5	14.6	12.5	8.95	6.81	5.40	4.42	0
20	0.35	0.79	1.47	2.75	3.96	5.13	7.38	9.57	11.7	13.8	15.8	17.9	19.8	21.8	23.8	25.7	23.1	18.9	15.8	13.5	9.66	7.35	5.83	0	
21	0.36	0.83	1.55	2.90	4.17	5.40	7.78	10.1	12.3	14.5	16.7	18.8	20.9	23.0	25.1	27.1	24.8	20.3	17.0	14.5	10.4	7.91	6.28	0	
22	0.38	0.87	1.63	3.05	4.39	5.68	8.19	10.6	13.0	15.3	17.5	19.8	22.0	24.2	26.4	28.5	26.6	21.8	18.2	15.6	11.1	8.48	6.73	0	
23	0.40	0.92	1.71	3.19	4.60	5.96	8.59	11.1	13.6	16.0	18.4	20.8	23.1	25.4	27.7	29.9	28.4	23.3	19.5	16.7	11.9	9.07	7.19	0	
24	0.42	0.96	1.79	3.35	4.82	6.24	8.99	11.6	14.2	16.8	19.3	21.7	24.2	26.6	29.0	31.3	30.3	24.8	20.8	17.8	12.7	9.66	7.67	0	
25	0.44	1.00	1.87	3.50	5.04	6.52	9.40	12.2	14.9	17.5	20.1	22.7	25.3	27.8	30.3	32.7	32.2	26.4	22.1	18.9	13.5	10.3	8.15	0	
26	0.46	1.05	1.95	3.65	5.25	6.81	9.80	12.7	15.5	18.3	21.0	23.7	26.4	29.0	31.6	34.1	34.2	28.0	23.4	20.0	14.3	10.9	8.65	0	
28	0.50	1.13	2.12	3.95	5.69	7.37	10.6	13.8	16.8	19.8	22.8	25.7	28.5	31.4	34.2	37.0	38.2	31.3	26.2	22.4	16.0	12.2	0		
30	0.54	1.22	2.28	4.26	6.13	7.94	11.4	14.8	18.1	21.4	24.5	27.7	30.8	33.8	36.8	39.8	42.4	34.7	29.1	24.8	17.8	13.5	0		
32	0.57	1.31	2.45	4.56	6.57	8.52	12.3	15.9	19.4	22.9	26.3	29.7	33.0	36.3	39.5	42.7	46.7	38.2	32.0	27.3	19.6	14.9	0		
35	0.63	1.44	2.69	5.03	7.24	9.38	13.5	17.5	21.4	25.2	29.0	32.7	36.3	39.9	43.5	47.1	53.4	43.7	36.6	31.3	22.4	17.0	0		
40	0.73	1.67	3.11	5.81	8.37	10.8	15.6	20.2	24.7	29.1	33.5	37.7	42.0	46.1	50.3	54.4	62.5	53.4	44.7	38.2	27.3	0			
45	0.83	1.89	3.53	6.60	9.50	12.3	17.7	23.0	28.1	33.1	38.0	42.0	47.7	52.4	57.1	61.7	70.9	63.7	53.4	45.6	32.6	0			

Type A   Type B   Type C

The limiting RPM for each lubrication type is read from the column to the left of the boundary line shown.

TYPE A: Manual or Drip Lubrication
TYPE B: Bath or Disc Lubrication
TYPE C: Oil Stream Lubrication

118

TABLE 4-12 (Cont'd).

HORSEPOWER RATINGS STANDARD SINGLE STRAND ROLLER CHAIN — NO. 80 — 1" PITCH

No. of Teeth Small Spkt.	10	25	50	100	150	200	300	400	500	600	700	800	900	1000	1100	1200	1400	1600	1800	2000	2200	2400	2700	3000	3400
									REVOLUTIONS PER MINUTE—SMALL SPROCKET																
9	0.34	0.78	1.45	2.71	3.90	5.05	7.28	9.43	11.5	13.6	15.6	17.6	17.0	14.5	12.6	11.0	8.76	7.17	6.01	5.13	4.45	3.90	3.27	2.79	2.32
10	0.38	0.87	1.63	3.03	4.37	5.66	8.16	10.6	12.9	15.2	17.5	19.7	19.9	17.0	14.7	12.9	10.3	8.40	7.04	6.01	5.21	4.57	3.83	3.27	2.71
11	0.42	0.97	1.80	3.36	4.84	6.28	9.04	11.7	14.3	16.9	19.4	21.9	23.0	19.6	17.0	14.9	11.8	9.69	8.12	6.93	6.01	5.27	4.42	3.77	1.70
12	0.47	1.06	1.98	3.69	5.32	6.89	9.93	12.9	15.7	18.5	21.3	24.0	26.2	22.3	19.4	17.0	13.5	11.0	9.25	7.90	6.85	6.01	5.04	4.30	0
13	0.51	1.16	2.16	4.03	5.80	7.52	10.8	14.0	17.1	20.2	23.2	26.2	29.1	25.2	21.8	19.2	15.2	12.5	10.4	8.91	7.72	6.78	5.68	4.85	0
14	0.55	1.25	2.34	4.36	6.29	8.14	11.7	15.2	18.6	21.9	25.1	28.4	31.5	28.2	24.4	21.4	17.0	13.9	11.7	9.96	8.63	7.57	6.35	5.42	0
15	0.59	1.35	2.52	4.70	6.77	8.77	12.6	16.4	20.0	23.6	27.1	30.6	34.0	31.2	27.1	23.8	18.9	15.4	12.9	11.0	9.57	8.40	7.04	6.01	0
16	0.63	1.45	2.70	5.04	7.26	9.41	13.5	17.6	21.5	25.3	29.0	32.8	36.4	34.4	29.8	26.2	20.8	17.0	14.2	12.2	10.5	9.25	7.76	6.62	0
17	0.68	1.55	2.88	5.38	7.75	10.0	14.5	18.7	22.9	27.0	31.0	35.0	38.9	37.7	32.7	28.7	22.7	18.6	15.6	13.3	11.5	10.1	8.49	7.25	0
18	0.72	1.64	3.07	5.72	8.25	10.7	15.4	19.9	24.4	28.7	33.0	37.2	41.4	41.1	35.6	31.2	24.8	20.3	17.0	14.5	12.6	11.0	9.25	7.90	
19	0.76	1.74	3.25	6.07	8.74	11.3	16.3	21.1	25.8	30.4	34.9	39.4	43.8	44.5	38.6	33.9	26.9	22.0	18.4	15.7	13.6	12.0	10.0	8.57	
20	0.81	1.84	3.44	6.41	9.24	12.0	17.2	22.3	27.3	32.2	37.0	41.7	46.3	48.1	41.7	36.6	29.0	23.8	19.9	17.0	14.7	12.9	10.8	0	
21	0.85	1.94	3.62	6.76	9.74	12.6	18.2	23.5	28.8	33.9	39.0	43.9	48.9	51.7	44.8	39.4	31.2	25.6	21.4	18.3	15.9	13.9	11.7	0	
22	0.90	2.04	3.81	7.11	10.2	13.3	19.1	24.8	30.3	35.7	41.0	46.2	51.4	55.5	48.1	42.2	33.5	27.4	23.0	19.6	17.0	14.9	12.5	0	
23	0.94	2.14	4.00	7.46	10.7	13.9	20.1	26.0	31.8	37.4	43.0	48.5	53.9	59.3	51.4	45.1	35.8	29.3	24.6	21.0	18.2	15.9	13.4	0	
24	0.98	2.24	4.19	7.81	11.3	14.6	21.0	27.2	33.2	39.2	45.0	50.8	56.4	62.0	54.8	48.1	38.2	31.2	26.2	22.3	19.4	17.0	14.2	0	
25	1.03	2.34	4.37	8.16	11.8	15.2	21.9	28.4	34.7	40.9	47.0	53.0	59.0	64.8	58.2	51.1	40.6	33.2	27.8	23.8	20.6	18.1	15.1	0	
26	1.07	2.45	4.56	8.52	12.3	15.9	22.8	29.4	36.2	42.7	49.1	55.3	61.5	67.6	61.8	54.2	43.0	35.2	29.5	25.2	21.8	19.2	16.1	0	
28	1.16	2.65	4.94	9.23	13.3	17.2	24.8	32.1	39.3	46.3	53.2	59.9	66.7	73.3	69.0	60.6	48.1	39.4	33.0	28.2	24.4	21.4	0		
30	1.25	2.85	5.33	9.94	14.3	18.5	26.7	34.6	42.3	49.9	57.3	64.6	71.8	78.9	76.6	67.2	53.3	43.6	36.6	31.2	27.1	23.8	0		
32	1.34	3.06	5.71	10.7	15.3	19.9	28.6	37.1	45.4	53.5	61.4	69.2	77.0	84.6	84.3	74.0	58.7	48.1	40.3	34.4	29.8	26.2	0		
35	1.48	3.37	6.29	11.7	16.9	21.9	31.6	40.9	50.0	58.9	67.6	76.3	84.8	93.3	96.5	84.7	67.2	55.0	46.1	39.4	34.1	0			
40	1.71	3.89	7.27	13.6	19.5	25.3	36.4	47.2	57.7	68.0	78.1	88.1	98.0	108	117	103	82.1	67.2	56.3	48.1	20.0	0			
45	1.94	4.42	8.25	15.4	22.2	28.7	41.4	53.6	65.6	77.2	88.7	100	111	122	133	123	98.0	80.2	67.2	54.1	0				

Type A   Type B   Type C

119

TABLE 4-12 (Cont'd).

HORSEPOWER RATINGS STANDARD SINGLE STRAND ROLLER CHAIN — NO. 100 — 1¼" PITCH

No. of Teeth Small Spkt.	REVOLUTIONS PER MINUTE—SMALL SPROCKET																								
	10	25	50	100	150	200	300	400	500	600	700	800	900	1000	1100	1200	1300	1400	1600	1800	2000	2200	2400	2600	2700
9	0.65	1.49	2.78	5.19	7.47	9.68	13.9	18.1	22.1	26.0	29.6	24.2	20.3	17.4	15.0	13.2	11.7	10.5	8.57	7.19	6.13	5.32	4.67	4.14	0
10	0.73	1.67	3.11	5.81	8.37	10.8	15.6	20.2	24.7	29.2	33.5	28.4	23.8	20.3	17.6	15.5	13.7	12.3	10.0	8.42	7.19	6.23	5.47	4.85	0
11	0.81	1.85	3.45	6.44	9.28	12.0	17.3	22.4	27.4	32.3	37.1	32.8	27.4	23.4	20.3	17.8	15.8	14.2	11.6	9.71	8.29	7.19	6.31	1.29	0
12	0.89	2.03	3.79	7.08	10.2	13.2	19.0	24.6	30.1	35.5	40.8	37.3	31.3	26.7	23.2	20.3	18.0	16.1	13.2	11.1	9.45	8.19	7.19	0	
13	0.97	2.22	4.13	7.72	11.1	14.4	20.7	26.9	32.8	38.7	44.5	42.1	35.3	30.1	26.1	22.9	20.3	18.2	14.9	12.5	10.6	9.23	8.10	0	
14	1.05	2.40	4.48	8.36	12.0	15.6	22.5	29.1	35.6	41.9	48.2	47.0	39.4	33.7	29.2	25.6	22.7	20.3	16.6	13.9	11.9	10.3	9.05	0	
15	1.13	2.59	4.83	9.01	13.0	16.8	24.2	31.4	38.3	45.2	51.9	52.2	43.7	37.3	32.4	28.4	25.2	22.5	18.4	15.5	13.2	11.4	10.0	0	
16	1.22	2.77	5.17	9.66	13.9	18.0	26.0	33.6	41.1	48.4	55.6	57.5	48.2	41.1	35.7	31.3	27.7	24.8	20.3	17.0	14.5	12.6	11.1	0	
17	1.30	2.96	5.52	10.3	14.8	19.2	27.7	35.9	43.9	51.7	59.4	63.0	52.8	45.0	39.0	34.3	30.4	27.2	22.3	18.7	15.9	13.8	0.79	0	
18	1.38	3.15	5.88	11.0	15.8	20.5	29.5	38.2	46.7	55.0	63.2	68.6	57.5	49.1	42.5	37.3	33.1	29.6	24.2	20.3	17.4	15.0	0		
19	1.46	3.34	6.23	11.6	16.7	21.7	31.2	40.5	49.5	58.3	67.0	74.4	62.3	53.2	46.1	40.5	35.9	32.1	26.3	22.0	18.8	16.3	0		
20	1.55	3.53	6.58	12.3	17.7	22.9	33.0	42.8	52.3	61.6	70.8	79.8	67.3	57.5	49.8	43.7	38.8	34.7	28.4	23.8	20.3	17.6	0		
21	1.63	3.72	6.94	13.0	18.7	24.2	34.8	45.1	55.1	65.0	74.6	84.2	72.4	61.8	53.6	47.0	41.7	37.3	30.6	25.6	21.9	19.0	0		
22	1.71	3.91	7.30	13.6	19.6	25.4	36.6	47.4	58.0	68.3	78.5	88.5	77.7	66.3	57.5	50.4	44.7	40.0	32.8	27.5	23.4	20.3	0		
23	1.80	4.10	7.66	14.3	20.6	26.7	38.4	49.8	60.8	71.7	82.3	92.8	83.0	70.9	61.4	53.9	47.8	42.8	35.0	29.4	25.1	7.74	0		
24	1.88	4.30	8.02	15.0	21.5	27.9	40.2	52.1	63.7	75.0	86.2	97.2	88.5	75.6	65.5	57.5	51.0	45.6	37.3	31.3	26.7	0			
25	1.97	4.49	8.38	15.6	22.5	29.2	42.0	54.4	66.6	78.4	90.1	102	94.1	80.3	69.6	61.1	54.2	48.5	39.7	33.3	28.4	0			
26	2.05	4.68	8.74	16.3	23.5	30.4	43.8	56.8	69.4	81.8	94.0	106	99.8	85.2	73.8	64.8	57.5	51.4	42.1	35.3	30.1	0			
28	2.22	5.07	9.47	17.7	25.5	33.0	47.5	61.5	75.2	88.6	102	115	112	95.2	82.5	72.4	64.2	57.5	47.0	39.4	33.7	0			
30	2.40	5.47	10.2	19.0	27.4	35.5	51.2	66.3	81.0	95.5	110	124	124	106	91.5	80.3	71.2	63.7	52.2	43.7	10.0	0			
32	2.57	5.86	10.9	20.4	29.4	38.1	54.9	71.1	86.9	102	118	133	136	116	101	88.5	78.5	70.2	57.5	48.2	0				
35	2.83	6.46	12.0	22.5	32.4	42.0	60.4	78.3	95.7	113	130	146	156	133	115	101	89.8	80.3	65.8	55.1	0				
40	3.27	7.46	13.9	26.0	37.4	48.5	69.8	90.4	111	130	150	169	188	163	141	124	110	98.1	80.3	0					
45	3.71	8.47	15.8	29.5	42.5	55.0	79.3	103	126	148	170	192	213	194	168	148	131	117	45.3						

Type A (columns 10–150) Type B (columns 200–300) Type C (columns 400–2700)

TYPE A: Manual or Drip Lubrication
TYPE B: Bath or Disc Lubrication
TYPE C: Oil Stream Lubrication

The limiting RPM for each lubrication type is read from the column to the left of the boundary line shown. For optimum results, it is recommended that the Roller Chain manufacturer be given the opportunity to evaluate the conditions of operation of chains in the shaded (galling range) speed area.

TABLE 4-12 *(Cont'd.)*

HORSEPOWER RATINGS STANDARD SINGLE STRAND ROLLER CHAIN — NO. 120 — 1½" PITCH

REVOLUTIONS PER MINUTE—SMALL SPROCKET

No. of Teeth Small Spkt.	10	25	50	100	150	200	300	400	500	600	700	800	900	1000	1100	1200	1300	1400	1500	1600	1700	1800	1900	2000	2100
9	1.10	2.52	4.69	8.76	12.6	16.3	23.5	30.5	37.3	43.2	34.3	28.1	23.5	20.1	17.4	15.3	13.5	12.1	10.9	9.92	9.06	8.31	7.67	7.10	6.60
10	1.24	2.82	5.26	9.81	14.1	18.3	26.4	34.2	41.8	49.2	40.1	32.9	27.5	23.5	20.4	17.9	15.9	14.2	12.8	11.6	10.6	9.74	8.98	8.31	7.73
11	1.37	3.12	5.83	10.9	15.7	20.3	29.2	37.9	46.3	54.6	46.3	37.9	31.8	27.1	23.5	20.6	18.3	16.4	14.8	13.4	12.2	11.2	10.4	9.59	0
12	1.50	3.43	6.40	11.9	17.2	22.3	32.1	41.6	50.9	59.9	52.8	43.2	36.2	30.9	26.8	23.5	20.9	18.7	16.8	15.3	13.9	12.8	11.8	10.9	
13	1.64	3.74	6.98	13.0	18.8	24.3	35.0	45.4	55.5	65.3	59.5	48.7	40.8	34.9	30.2	26.5	23.5	21.0	19.0	17.2	15.7	14.4	13.3	12.3	
14	1.78	4.05	7.56	14.1	20.3	26.3	37.9	49.1	60.1	70.8	66.5	54.4	45.6	39.0	33.8	29.6	26.3	23.5	21.2	19.2	17.6	16.1	14.9	8.94	
15	1.91	4.37	8.15	15.2	21.9	28.4	40.9	53.0	64.7	76.3	73.8	60.4	50.6	43.2	37.4	32.9	29.1	26.1	23.5	21.3	19.5	17.0	16.5	0	
16	2.05	4.68	8.74	16.3	23.5	30.4	43.8	56.8	69.4	81.8	81.3	66.5	55.7	47.6	41.2	36.2	32.1	28.7	25.9	23.5	21.5	19.7	18.2	0	
17	2.19	5.00	9.33	17.4	25.1	32.5	46.8	60.6	74.1	87.3	89.0	72.8	61.0	52.1	45.2	39.6	35.2	31.5	28.4	25.8	23.5	21.6	19.9	0	
18	2.33	5.32	9.92	18.5	26.7	34.6	49.8	64.5	78.8	92.9	97.0	79.4	66.5	56.8	49.2	43.2	38.3	34.3	30.9	28.1	25.6	23.5	11.3	0	
19	2.47	5.64	10.5	19.6	28.3	36.6	52.8	68.4	83.6	98.5	105	86.1	72.1	61.6	53.4	46.8	41.5	37.2	33.5	30.4	27.8	25.5	0		
20	2.61	5.96	11.1	20.7	29.9	38.7	55.8	72.2	88.3	104	114	92.9	77.9	66.5	57.6	50.6	44.9	40.1	36.2	32.9	30.0	27.5	0		
21	2.75	6.28	11.7	21.9	31.5	40.8	58.8	76.2	93.1	110	122	100	83.8	71.6	62.0	54.4	48.3	43.2	39.0	35.4	32.3	29.6	0		
22	2.90	6.60	12.3	23.0	33.1	42.9	61.8	80.1	97.9	115	131	107	89.9	76.7	66.5	58.4	51.8	46.3	41.8	37.9	34.6	16.6	0		
23	3.04	6.93	12.9	24.1	34.8	45.0	64.9	84.0	103	121	139	115	96.1	82.0	71.1	62.4	55.3	49.5	44.6	40.5	37.0	0			
24	3.18	7.25	13.5	25.3	36.4	47.1	67.9	88.0	108	127	146	122	102	87.4	75.8	66.5	59.0	52.8	47.6	43.2	39.4	0			
25	3.32	7.58	14.1	26.3	38.0	49.3	71.0	91.9	112	132	152	130	109	92.9	80.6	70.7	62.7	56.1	50.6	45.9	41.3	0			
26	3.47	7.91	14.8	27.5	39.7	51.4	74.0	95.9	117	138	159	138	115	98.6	85.4	75.0	66.5	59.5	53.7	48.7	26.6	0			
28	3.76	8.57	16.0	29.8	43.0	55.7	80.2	104	127	150	172	154	129	110	95.5	83.8	74.3	66.5	60.0	54.4	0				
30	4.05	9.23	17.2	32.1	46.3	60.0	86.4	112	137	161	185	171	143	122	106	92.9	82.4	73.8	66.5	42.4	0				
32	4.34	9.90	18.5	34.5	49.6	64.3	92.6	120	147	173	199	188	158	135	117	102	90.8	81.3	73.3	0					
35	4.78	10.9	20.3	38.0	54.7	70.9	102	132	162	190	219	215	180	154	133	117	104	92.9	47.7	0					
40	5.52	12.6	23.5	43.9	63.2	81.8	118	153	187	220	253	263	220	188	163	143	127	59.5	0						
45	6.27	14.3	26.7	49.8	71.7	92.9	134	173	212	250	287	314	263	224	195	171	143	104	80.0	0					

Type A Type B Type C

TABLE 4-12 (Cont'd).

HORSEPOWER RATINGS STANDARD SINGLE STRAND ROLLER CHAIN — NO. 140 — 1¾" PITCH

REVOLUTIONS PER MINUTE—SMALL SPROCKET

NO. OF TEETH SMALL SPKT.	10	25	50	100	150	200	250	300	350	400	450	500	550	600	700	800	900	1000	1100	1200	1300	1400	1500	1600	1700
9	1.71	3.89	7.26	13.6	19.5	25.3	30.9	36.4	41.8	47.2	52.5	57.7	55.7	48.9	38.8	31.7	26.6	22.7	19.7	17.3	15.3	13.7	12.4	11.2	10.2
10	1.91	4.36	8.14	15.2	21.9	28.3	34.6	40.8	46.9	52.9	58.8	64.6	65.2	57.2	45.4	37.2	31.2	26.6	23.1	20.2	17.9	16.1	14.5	13.1	0
11	2.12	4.83	9.02	16.8	24.2	31.4	38.4	45.2	52.0	58.6	65.2	71.6	75.2	66.0	52.4	42.9	35.9	30.7	26.6	23.3	20.7	18.5	16.7	15.2	0
12	2.33	5.31	9.91	18.5	26.6	34.5	42.2	49.7	57.1	64.4	71.6	78.7	85.7	75.2	59.7	48.9	41.0	35.0	30.3	26.6	23.6	21.1	19.0	17.3	0
13	2.54	5.79	10.8	20.2	29.0	37.6	46.0	54.2	62.2	70.2	78.0	85.8	93.5	84.8	67.3	55.1	46.2	39.4	34.2	30.0	26.5	23.8	21.5	19.5	0
14	2.75	6.27	11.7	21.8	31.5	40.8	49.8	58.7	67.4	76.0	84.5	93.0	101	94.8	75.2	61.6	51.6	44.1	38.2	33.5	29.7	26.6	24.0	21.8	0
15	2.96	6.76	12.6	23.5	33.9	43.9	53.7	63.2	72.7	81.9	91.1	100	109	105	83.4	68.3	57.2	48.9	42.4	37.2	33.0	29.5	26.6	0	0
16	3.18	7.24	13.5	25.2	36.3	47.1	57.5	67.8	77.9	87.8	97.7	107	117	116	91.9	75.2	63.1	53.8	46.7	41.0	36.3	32.5	29.3	0	0
17	3.39	7.73	14.4	26.9	38.8	50.3	61.4	72.4	83.2	93.8	104	115	125	127	101	82.4	69.1	59.0	51.1	44.9	39.8	35.6	32.1	0	0
18	3.61	8.23	15.4	28.6	41.3	53.5	65.3	77.0	88.5	99.8	111	122	133	138	110	89.8	75.2	64.2	55.7	48.9	43.3	38.8	35.0	0	0
19	3.82	8.72	16.3	30.4	43.7	56.7	69.3	81.6	93.8	106	118	129	141	150	119	97.4	81.6	69.7	60.4	53.0	47.0	42.1	37.9	0	0
20	4.04	9.22	17.2	32.1	46.2	59.9	73.2	86.3	99.1	112	124	137	149	161	128	105	88.1	75.2	65.2	57.2	50.8	45.4	0	0	0
21	4.26	9.72	18.1	33.8	48.7	63.1	77.2	91.0	104	118	131	144	157	170	138	113	94.8	80.9	70.2	61.6	54.6	48.9	0	0	0
22	4.48	10.2	19.1	35.6	51.3	66.4	81.2	95.6	110	124	138	151	165	178	148	121	102	86.8	75.2	66.0	58.6	52.4	0	0	0
23	4.70	10.7	20.0	37.3	53.8	69.7	85.2	100	115	130	145	159	173	187	158	130	109	92.8	80.4	70.6	62.6	56.0	0	0	0
24	4.92	11.2	20.9	39.1	56.3	72.9	89.2	105	121	136	151	166	181	196	169	138	116	98.9	85.7	75.2	66.7	59.7	0	0	0
25	5.14	11.7	21.9	40.8	58.8	76.2	93.2	110	126	142	158	174	189	205	180	147	123	105	91.1	80.0	70.9	63.5	0	0	0
26	5.37	12.2	22.8	42.6	61.4	79.5	97.2	115	132	148	165	181	198	214	190	156	131	112	96.7	84.8	75.2	0	0	0	0
28	5.81	13.3	24.7	46.2	66.5	86.2	105	124	143	161	179	197	214	232	213	174	146	125	108	94.8	84.1	0	0	0	0
30	6.26	14.3	26.7	49.7	71.6	92.8	113	134	154	173	193	212	231	249	236	193	162	138	120	105	93.2	0	0	0	0
32	6.71	15.3	28.6	53.3	76.8	99.5	122	143	165	186	206	227	247	267	260	213	178	152	132	116	0	0	0	0	0
35	7.40	16.9	31.5	58.7	84.6	110	134	158	181	205	227	250	272	295	297	243	204	174	151	130	0	0	0	0	0
40	8.54	19.5	36.4	67.9	97.7	127	155	182	210	236	263	289	315	340	363	297	249	213	178	0	0	0	0	0	0
45	9.70	22.1	41.3	77.1	111	144	176	207	238	268	298	328	357	387	434	355	297	237	92.7	0	0	0	0	0	0

Type A   Type B   Type C

TYPE A: Manual or Drip Lubrication
TYPE B: Bath or Disc Lubrication
TYPE C: Oil Stream Lubrication

The limiting RPM for each lubrication type is read from the column to the left of the boundary line shown. For optimum results, it is recommended that the Roller Chain manufacturer be given the opportunity to evaluate the conditions of operation of chains in the shaded (galling range) speed area.

TABLE 4-12 (Cont'd).

HORSEPOWER RATINGS STANDARD SINGLE STRAND ROLLER CHAIN — NO. 160 — 2" PITCH

NO. OF TEETH SMALL SPKT.	REVOLUTIONS PER MINUTE—SMALL SPROCKET																								
	10	25	50	100	150	200	250	300	350	400	450	500	550	600	650	700	750	800	850	900	1000	1100	1200	1300	1400
9	2.48	5.65	10.5	19.7	28.3	36.7	44.8	52.8	60.7	68.5	76.1	71.5	62.0	54.4	48.2	43.2	38.9	35.3	32.2	29.6	25.3	21.9	19.2	17.0	0
10	2.77	6.33	11.8	22.0	31.7	41.1	50.3	59.2	68.0	76.7	85.3	83.7	72.6	63.7	56.5	50.5	45.6	41.4	37.8	34.7	29.6	25.7	22.5	20.0	0
11	3.07	7.01	13.1	24.4	35.2	45.6	55.7	65.6	75.4	85.0	94.5	96.6	83.7	73.5	65.2	58.3	52.6	47.7	43.6	40.0	34.1	29.6	26.0	23.0	0
12	3.38	7.70	14.4	26.8	38.6	50.1	61.2	72.1	82.8	93.4	104	110	95.4	83.7	74.2	66.4	59.9	54.4	49.6	45.6	38.9	33.7	29.6	26.3	0
13	3.68	8.40	15.7	29.2	42.1	54.6	66.7	78.6	90.3	102	113	124	108	94.4	83.7	74.9	67.5	61.3	56.0	51.4	43.9	38.0	33.4	29.6	0
14	3.99	9.10	17.0	31.7	45.6	59.1	72.3	85.2	97.8	110	123	135	120	105	93.6	83.7	75.5	68.5	62.6	57.4	49.0	42.5	37.3	33.1	0
15	4.30	9.80	18.3	34.1	49.2	63.7	77.9	91.7	105	119	132	145	133	117	104	92.8	83.7	76.0	69.4	63.7	54.4	47.1	41.4	0	
16	4.61	10.5	19.6	36.6	52.7	68.3	83.5	98.4	113	127	142	156	147	129	114	102	92.2	83.7	76.4	70.2	59.9	51.9	45.6	0	
17	4.92	11.2	20.9	39.1	56.3	72.9	89.1	105	121	136	151	166	161	141	125	112	101	91.7	83.7	75.8	65.6	56.9	49.9	0	
18	5.23	11.9	22.3	41.6	59.9	77.6	94.8	112	128	145	161	177	175	154	136	122	110	99.9	91.2	83.7	71.5	62.0	54.4	0	
19	5.55	12.7	23.6	44.1	63.5	82.2	101	118	136	153	171	188	190	167	148	132	119	108	98.9	90.8	77.5	67.2	59.0	0	
20	5.86	13.4	25.0	46.6	67.1	86.9	106	125	144	162	180	198	205	180	160	143	129	117	107	98.1	83.7	72.6	63.7	0	
21	6.18	14.1	26.3	49.1	70.7	91.6	112	132	152	171	190	209	221	194	172	154	139	126	115	105	90.1	78.1	68.5	0	
22	6.50	14.8	27.7	51.6	74.4	96.3	118	139	159	180	200	220	237	208	184	165	149	135	123	113	96.6	83.7	0		
23	6.82	15.6	29.0	54.2	78.0	101	124	146	167	189	210	231	251	222	197	176	159	144	132	121	103	98.5	0		
24	7.14	16.3	30.4	56.7	81.7	106	129	152	175	197	220	241	263	237	210	188	169	154	140	129	110	95.4	0		
25	7.46	17.0	31.8	59.3	85.4	111	135	159	183	206	229	252	275	252	223	200	180	164	149	137	117	101	0		
26	7.78	17.8	33.1	61.8	89.1	115	141	166	191	215	239	263	287	267	237	212	191	173	158	145	124	108	0		
28	8.43	19.2	35.9	67.0	96.5	125	153	180	207	233	259	285	311	298	265	237	214	194	177	162	139	120	0		
30	9.08	20.7	38.7	72.2	104	135	165	194	223	251	279	307	335	331	293	263	237	215	196	180	154	0			
32	9.74	22.2	41.5	77.4	111	144	176	208	239	269	300	329	359	365	323	289	261	237	216	198	169	0			
35	10.7	24.5	45.7	85.2	123	159	194	229	263	297	330	363	395	417	370	331	298	271	247	227	180	0			
40	12.4	28.3	52.8	98.5	142	184	225	265	304	343	381	419	457	494	452	404	365	331	302	257	0				
45	14.1	32.1	59.9	112	161	209	255	301	345	389	433	476	519	561	538	482	418	348	271	189	0				

Type A   Type B   Type C

123

TABLE 4-12 (Cont'd).

HORSEPOWER RATINGS STANDARD SINGLE STRAND ROLLER CHAIN — NO. 180 — 2¼" PITCH

NO. OF TEETH SMALL SPKT.	— REVOLUTIONS PER MINUTE—SMALL SPROCKET

No. of Teeth Small Spkt.	10	25	50	100	150	200	250	300	350	400	450	500	550	600	650	700	750	800	850	900	950	1000	1050	1100	1150
9	3.42	7.80	14.5	27.1	39.1	50.7	61.9	73.0	83.8	94.5	92.0	78.5	68.1	59.7	53.0	47.4	42.8	38.8	35.4	32.5	30.0	27.8	25.8	24.1	0
10	3.83	8.74	16.3	30.4	43.8	56.8	69.4	81.8	93.9	106	108	92.0	79.7	70.0	62.1	55.5	50.1	45.5	41.5	38.1	35.1	32.5	30.2	28.2	0
11	4.24	9.68	18.1	33.7	48.6	62.9	76.9	90.6	104	117	124	106	92.0	80.7	71.6	64.1	57.8	52.4	47.9	43.9	40.5	37.5	34.9	32.5	0
12	4.66	10.6	19.8	37.0	53.4	69.1	84.5	99.6	114	129	142	121	105	92.0	81.6	73.0	65.8	59.7	54.6	50.1	46.2	42.8	39.7	37.1	0
13	5.08	11.6	21.6	40.4	58.2	75.4	92.1	109	125	141	156	136	118	104	92.0	82.3	74.2	67.4	61.5	55.5	52.1	48.2	44.8	0	
14	5.51	12.6	23.4	43.7	63.0	81.6	99.8	118	135	152	169	152	132	116	103	92.0	82.9	75.3	68.7	63.1	58.2	53.9	50.1	0	
15	5.93	13.5	25.3	47.1	67.9	88.0	108	127	146	164	182	169	146	129	114	102	92.0	83.5	76.2	70.0	64.5	59.7	55.5	0	
16	6.36	14.5	27.1	50.5	72.8	94.3	115	136	156	176	196	186	161	142	126	112	101	92.0	84.0	77.1	71.1	65.8	61.2	0	
17	6.79	15.5	28.9	54.0	77.7	101	123	145	167	188	209	204	177	155	138	123	111	101	92.0	84.4	77.9	72.1	0		
18	7.22	16.5	30.8	57.4	82.7	107	131	154	177	200	222	222	193	169	150	134	121	110	100	92.0	84.8	78.5	0		
19	7.66	17.5	32.6	60.8	87.6	114	139	164	188	212	236	241	209	183	163	145	131	119	109	99.8	92.0	85.2	0		
20	8.10	18.5	34.5	64.3	92.6	120	147	173	199	224	249	260	226	198	175	157	142	129	117	108	99.3	92.0	0		
21	8.53	19.5	36.3	67.8	97.6	126	155	182	209	236	262	280	243	213	189	169	152	138	126	116	107	99.0	0		
22	8.97	20.5	38.2	71.3	103	133	163	192	220	248	276	300	260	228	203	181	163	148	135	124	115	0			
23	9.41	21.5	40.1	74.8	108	140	171	201	231	260	290	318	278	244	216	194	175	159	145	133	123	0			
24	9.86	22.5	42.0	78.3	113	146	179	210	242	273	303	333	296	260	231	206	186	169	154	142	131	0			
25	10.3	23.5	43.9	81.8	118	153	187	220	253	285	317	348	315	277	245	220	198	180	164	151	139	0			
26	10.7	24.5	45.7	85.4	123	159	195	229	264	297	331	363	334	293	260	233	210	191	174	160	0				
28	11.6	26.6	49.6	92.5	133	173	211	249	286	322	358	394	374	328	291	260	235	213	194	178	0				
30	12.5	28.6	53.4	99.6	144	186	227	268	308	347	386	424	414	364	322	289	260	236	216	198	0				
32	13.4	30.7	57.2	107	154	199	244	287	330	372	414	455	456	401	355	318	287	260	238	0					
35	14.8	33.8	63.1	118	170	220	268	316	363	410	456	501	522	458	406	364	328	291	220	0					
40	17.1	39.0	72.9	136	196	254	310	365	420	473	526	579	575	524	465	398	324	244	0						
45	19.4	44.3	82.7	154	222	288	352	415	477	538	598	631	578	514	441	360	271	0							

Type A   Type B   Type C

TYPE A: Manual or Drip Lubrication
TYPE B: Bath or Disc Lubrication
TYPE C: Oil Stream Lubrication

The limiting RPM for each lubrication type is read from the column to the left of the boundary line shown. For optimum results, it is recommended that the Roller Chain manufacturer be given the opportunity to evaluate the conditions of operation of chains in the shaded (galling range) speed area.

TABLE 4-12 (Cont'd).

HORSEPOWER RATINGS STANDARD SINGLE STRAND ROLLER CHAIN — NO. 200 — 2½″ PITCH

No. of Teeth Small Spkt.	10	15	20	30	40	50	70	100	150	200	250	300	350	400	450	500	550	600	650	700
9	4.54	6.54	8.47	12.2	15.8	19.3	26.1	36.0	51.9	67.3	82.2	96.9	111	119	100	85.4	74.1	65.0	57.6	0
10	5.08	7.32	9.49	13.7	17.7	21.6	29.3	40.4	58.2	75.4	92.1	109	125	140	117	100	86.7	76.1	67.5	0
11	5.64	8.12	10.5	15.1	19.6	24.0	32.5	44.8	64.5	83.5	102	120	138	156	135	115	100	87.8	77.9	0
12	6.19	8.92	11.6	16.6	21.6	26.4	35.7	49.2	70.8	91.8	112	132	152	171	154	132	114	100	0	
13	6.75	9.72	12.6	18.1	23.5	28.7	38.9	53.6	77.2	100	122	144	166	187	174	148	129	113	0	
14	7.31	10.5	13.6	19.7	25.5	31.1	42.1	58.1	83.7	108	132	156	179	202	194	166	144	126	0	
15	7.88	11.3	14.7	21.2	27.4	33.5	45.4	62.6	90.1	117	143	168	193	218	215	184	159	140	0	
16	8.45	12.2	15.8	22.7	29.4	36.0	48.7	67.1	96.6	125	153	180	207	234	237	203	176	154	0	
17	9.02	13.0	16.8	24.2	31.4	38.4	52.0	71.6	103	134	163	193	221	249	260	222	192	169	0	
18	9.59	13.8	17.9	25.8	33.4	40.8	55.3	76.2	110	142	174	205	235	265	283	242	209	184	0	
19	10.2	14.6	19.0	27.3	35.4	43.3	58.6	80.8	116	151	184	217	249	281	307	262	227	199	0	
20	10.7	15.5	20.1	28.9	37.4	45.8	61.9	85.4	123	159	195	229	264	297	331	283	245	0		
21	11.3	16.3	21.1	30.5	39.5	48.2	65.3	90.0	130	168	205	242	278	313	348	305	264	0		
22	11.9	17.2	22.2	32.0	41.5	50.7	68.7	94.6	136	177	216	254	292	330	366	327	283	0		
23	12.5	18.0	23.3	33.6	43.5	53.2	72.0	99.3	143	185	226	267	307	346	384	349	303	0		
24	13.1	18.9	24.4	35.2	45.6	55.7	75.4	104	150	194	237	279	321	362	402	372	323	0		
25	13.7	19.7	25.5	36.8	47.6	58.2	78.8	109	156	203	248	292	335	378	421	396	343	0		
26	14.3	20.6	26.6	38.4	49.7	60.7	82.2	113	163	212	259	305	350	395	439	420	364	0		

REVOLUTIONS PER MINUTE—SMALL SPROCKET

Type A   Type B   Type C

125

TABLE 4-12 /(Cont'd).

HORSEPOWER RATINGS STANDARD SINGLE STRAND ROLLER CHAIN — NO. 240 — 3" PITCH

REVOLUTIONS PER MINUTE—SMALL SPROCKET

No. of Teeth Small Spkt.	5	10	15	20	25	30	40	50	60	80	100	125	150	175	200	250	300	350	400	450	500
9	3.92	7.31	10.5	13.6	16.7	19.6	25.4	31.1	36.7	47.5	58.1	71.0	83.6	96.1	108	132	156	169	138	116	0
10	4.39	8.19	11.8	15.3	18.7	22.0	28.5	34.9	41.1	53.2	65.0	79.5	93.7	108	121	148	175	198	162	136	0
11	4.86	9.08	13.1	16.9	20.7	24.4	31.6	38.6	45.5	59.0	72.1	88.1	104	119	135	164	194	223	187	156	0
12	5.34	9.97	14.4	18.6	22.7	26.8	34.7	42.4	50.0	64.8	79.2	96.8	114	131	148	181	213	245	218	0	
13	5.83	10.9	15.7	20.3	24.8	29.2	37.9	46.3	54.5	70.6	86.4	106	124	143	161	197	232	267	240	0	
14	6.31	11.8	17.0	22.0	26.9	31.7	41.0	50.1	59.1	76.5	93.6	114	135	155	175	213	251	289	268	0	
15	6.80	12.7	18.3	23.7	28.9	34.1	44.2	54.0	63.6	82.4	101	123	145	167	188	230	271	311	297	0	
16	7.29	13.6	19.6	25.4	31.0	36.6	47.4	57.9	68.2	88.4	108	132	156	179	202	247	290	334	328	0	
17	7.78	14.5	20.9	27.1	33.1	39.0	50.6	61.8	72.9	94.4	115	141	166	191	215	263	310	356	359	0	
18	8.28	15.4	22.3	28.8	35.2	41.5	53.8	65.8	77.5	100	123	150	177	203	229	280	330	379	377	0	
19	8.78	16.4	23.6	30.6	37.4	44.0	57.0	69.7	82.2	106	130	159	187	215	243	297	350	402	393	0	
20	9.28	17.3	24.9	32.3	39.5	46.5	60.3	73.7	86.8	112	138	168	198	228	257	314	370	423	407	0	
21	9.78	18.2	26.3	34.1	41.6	49.0	63.5	77.7	91.5	119	145	177	209	240	270	331	390	439	421	0	
22	10.3	19.2	27.6	35.8	43.8	51.6	66.8	81.7	96.2	125	152	186	220	252	284	348	410	454	435	0	
23	10.8	20.1	29.0	37.6	45.9	54.1	70.1	85.7	101	131	160	195	230	265	298	365	430	469	448	0	
24	11.3	21.1	30.4	39.3	48.1	56.7	73.4	89.7	106	137	167	205	241	277	312	382	450	483	0		
25	11.8	22.0	31.7	41.1	50.3	59.2	76.7	93.8	110	143	175	214	252	290	327	399	470	496	0		
26	12.3	23.0	33.1	42.9	52.4	61.8	80.0	97.8	115	149	183	223	263	302	341	416	491	509	0		

Type A   Type B   Type C

The limiting RPM for each lubrication type is read from the column to the left of the boundary line shown.

TYPE A: Manual or Drip Lubrication
TYPE B: Bath or Disc Lubrication
TYPE C: Oil Stream Lubrication

$$L = 2C + \frac{N + n}{2} + \frac{(N - n)^2}{4 \pi^2 C}$$

$$C = \frac{L - \frac{N + n}{2} + \sqrt{\left(L - \frac{N + n}{2}\right)^2 - 8 \frac{(N - n)^2}{4 \pi^2}}}{4}$$

where L = length of chain in pitches
           C = center distance in pitches
           N = number of teeth in large sprocket
           n = number of teeth in small sprocket

EXAMPLE 4-4:   An electric gear motor with an output shaft rotating at 460 rpm drives a conveyor shaft at 160 rpm through a chain drive, transmitting 65 HP. Shaft center distance for the chain drive must be 48 in. ± 1 inch. Service conditions include moderate shock, with exposure to dirt, and continuous operation.

SOLUTION:

Service Factors

For electric drive and shock load	1.5
Atmospheric conditions	1.3
Continuous operation	1.4

Design HP $= 65 \times 1.5 \times 1.3 \times 1.4 = 177.5$ HP

This is a large design horsepower, therefore assume a four-strand chain to keep chain pitch as small as possible. Then

$$\frac{HP}{strand} = \frac{177.5}{3.3} = 54 \text{ HP}$$

since 4 strands can sustain 3.3 times the horsepower of a single strand.

Figure 4-26 indicates a No. 100 or 120 chain. From the tables for No. 100 chain, 54 HP at 460 rpm lies between 52.1 HP at 400 rpm and 63.7 HP at 500 rpm, using a small sprocket of 24 teeth. The large sprocket then requires $\frac{460}{160} \times 24$ or 69 teeth. Assuming that 69-teeth are not available, but that a 70-tooth sprocket is, the conveyor shaft will rotate at $\frac{24}{70} \times 460$ or 158 rpm.

A center distance of 30 to 50 pitches is preferred for chain drives. For No. 100 chain, pitch is 1¼ in.; a center distance of 48 in. would be 38 pitches. Too long a center distance could cause the slack side of the chain to whip; too small a center distance reduces the wrap on the small pulley.

For chain length

$$L = 2C + \frac{N + n}{2} + \frac{(N - n)^2}{4\pi^2 C}$$

$$= 2 \times 48 + \frac{70 + 24}{2} + \frac{(70 - 24)^2}{4 \times 9.86 \times 48} = 144.12$$

Use 144 pitches, adjusting the center distance if necessary. The theoretical center distance can be calculated from the center distance formula using $L = 144$ pitches.

4-14 DESIGN AND OPERATIONAL DETAILS

The service factors are ratings applied to the actual horsepower to ensure an adequate chain life for various circumstances of operation. These service factors are intended to provide a life of 15,000 operating hours. Use of smaller service factors than those given above, called "underchaining," is justified for equipment that will have a reduced life expectancy. The opposite case, "overchaining," is justified if unusually long life is desired.

High-speed operation requires the selection of the smallest suitable chain pitch. Smaller pitch also reduces noise level. Such requirements normally dictate the use of multiple-strand chain.

In selecting sprockets, the designer must frequently fit the sprocket to a given shaft size, as on an electric motor. Table 4-13 gives maximum hub and bore diameters for a range of small numbers of sprocket teeth. For example, using ½ in. pitch, if the shaft size is ⅞ in., it is not possible to use 11 teeth; the minimum number of teeth for this shaft size is 12.

Speed reductions in excess of 10:1 are generally avoided in a single reduction; use two or more drives in series. If center distances are very great, such as 80 pitches or more, the slack side of the chain must be supported by an idler or flat guides, or two drives in series may be used, thus dividing the center distance into two shorter distances. Very long center distances require excessive tension in the slack side.

Maximum bore and hub diameters. (with Standard Keyways) All dimensions are in inches

Chain drives must be carefully aligned. Shafts must be parallel and sprockets must be aligned opposite each other. If the shafts are not rigidly supported they will flex and misalign the drive. Misalignment of a multiple-strand drive will overload one side of the chain and give the effect of a single-strand drive. Sprockets may be aligned by laying a straightedge along the sides of the two sprockets.

TABLE 4-13

Maximum bore and hub diameters (with standard keyways)—all dimensions are in inches.

No. of Teeth	3/8" Pitch		1/2"		5/8"		3/4"		1"	
	Max. Bore	Maximum Hub Dia.	Max. Bore	Maximum Hub Dia.	Max. Bore	Maximum Hub Dia.	Max. Bore	Maximum Hub Dia.	Max. Bore	Maximum Hub Dia.
11	19/32	55/64	25/32	1 11/64	31/32	1 15/32	1 1/4	1 49/64	1 5/8	2 3/8
12	5/8	63/64	7/8	1 21/64	1 5/32	1 43/64	1 9/32	2 1/64	1 25/32	2 45/64
13	3/4	1 7/64	1	1 1/2	1 9/32	1 7/8	1 1/2	2 1/4	2	3 1/64
14	27/32	1 15/64	1 5/32	1 21/32	1 5/16	2 5/64	1 3/4	2 1/2	2 9/32	3 11/32
15	7/8	1 23/64	1 1/4	1 13/16	1 17/32	2 9/32	1 25/32	2 3/4	2 13/32	3 43/64
16	31/32	1 15/32	1 9/32	1 63/64	1 11/16	2 31/64	1 31/32	2 63/64	2 23/32	3 63/64
17	1 3/32	1 19/32	1 3/8	2 9/64	1 25/32	2 11/16	2 7/32	3 7/32	2 13/16	4 5/16
18	1 7/32	1 23/32	1 17/32	2 19/64	1 7/8	2 57/64	2 9/32	3 15/32	3 1/8	4 41/64
19	1 1/4	1 27/32	1 11/16	2 29/64	2 1/16	3 5/64	2 7/16	3 45/64	3 5/16	4 61/64
20	1 9/32	1 61/64	1 25/32	2 5/8	2 1/4	3 9/32	2 11/16	3 61/64	3 1/2	5 9/32
21	1 5/16	2 5/64	1 25/32	2 25/32	2 9/32	3 33/64	2 13/16	4 3/16	3 3/4	5 19/32
22	1 7/16	2 13/64	1 15/16	2 15/16	2 7/16	3 11/16	2 15/16	4 7/16	3 7/8	5 59/64
23	1 9/16	2 5/16	2 3/32	3 3/32	2 5/8	3 57/64	3 1/8	4 43/64	4 5/16	6 15/64
24	1 11/16	2 7/16	2 1/4	3 17/64	2 13/16	4 5/64	3 1/4	4 29/32	4 9/16	6 9/16
25	1 3/4	2 9/16	2 9/32	3 27/64	2 27/32	4 9/32	3 3/8	5 5/32	4 11/16	6 7/8

TABLE 4-13 (Cont'd).

NO. OF TEETH	1¼" MAX. BORE	1¼" MAXIMUM HUB DIA.	1½" MAX. BORE	1½" MAXIMUM HUB DIA.	1¾" MAX. BORE	1¾" MAXIMUM HUB DIA.	2" MAX. BORE	2" MAXIMUM HUB DIA.	2½" MAX. BORE	2½" MAXIMUM HUB DIA.
11	$1\frac{31}{32}$	$2\frac{31}{32}$	$2\frac{5}{16}$	$3\frac{37}{64}$	$2\frac{13}{16}$	$4\frac{11}{64}$	$3\frac{9}{32}$	$4\frac{25}{32}$	$3\frac{15}{16}$	$5\frac{63}{64}$
12	$2\frac{9}{32}$	$3\frac{3}{8}$	$2\frac{3}{4}$	$4\frac{1}{16}$	$3\frac{1}{4}$	$4\frac{3}{4}$	$3\frac{5}{8}$	$5\frac{27}{64}$	$4\frac{23}{32}$	$6\frac{51}{64}$
13	$2\frac{17}{32}$	$3\frac{25}{32}$	$3\frac{1}{16}$	$4\frac{33}{64}$	$3\frac{9}{16}$	$5\frac{5}{16}$	$4\frac{1}{16}$	$6\frac{5}{64}$	$5\frac{3}{32}$	$7\frac{39}{64}$
14	$2\frac{11}{16}$	$4\frac{3}{16}$	$3\frac{5}{16}$	$5\frac{1}{32}$	$3\frac{7}{8}$	$5\frac{7}{8}$	$4\frac{11}{16}$	$6\frac{23}{32}$	$5\frac{23}{32}$	$8\frac{27}{64}$
15	$3\frac{3}{32}$	$4\frac{19}{32}$	$3\frac{3}{4}$	$5\frac{33}{64}$	$4\frac{7}{16}$	$6\frac{29}{64}$	$4\frac{7}{8}$	$7\frac{3}{8}$	$6\frac{1}{4}$	$9\frac{7}{32}$
16	$3\frac{9}{32}$	5	4	6	$4\frac{11}{16}$	$7\frac{1}{64}$	$5\frac{1}{2}$	$8\frac{1}{64}$	7	$10\frac{1}{32}$
17	$3\frac{21}{32}$	$5\frac{13}{32}$	$4\frac{15}{32}$	$6\frac{31}{64}$	$5\frac{1}{16}$	$7\frac{37}{64}$	$5\frac{11}{16}$	$8\frac{21}{32}$	$7\frac{7}{16}$	$10\frac{27}{32}$
18	$3\frac{25}{32}$	$5\frac{51}{64}$	$4\frac{21}{32}$	$6\frac{31}{32}$	$5\frac{5}{8}$	$8\frac{9}{64}$	$6\frac{1}{4}$	$9\frac{5}{16}$	$8\frac{1}{8}$	$11\frac{41}{64}$
19	$4\frac{3}{16}$	$6\frac{13}{64}$	$4\frac{15}{16}$	$7\frac{29}{64}$	$5\frac{11}{16}$	$8\frac{45}{64}$	$6\frac{7}{8}$	$9\frac{61}{64}$	9	$12\frac{7}{16}$
20	$4\frac{19}{32}$	$6\frac{39}{64}$	$5\frac{7}{16}$	$7\frac{15}{16}$	$6\frac{1}{4}$	$9\frac{17}{64}$	7	$10\frac{19}{32}$	$9\frac{3}{4}$	$13\frac{1}{4}$
21	$4\frac{11}{16}$	7	$5\frac{11}{16}$	$8\frac{27}{64}$	$6\frac{13}{16}$	$9\frac{53}{64}$	$7\frac{3}{4}$	$11\frac{15}{64}$	10	$14\frac{3}{64}$
22	$4\frac{7}{8}$	$7\frac{13}{32}$	$5\frac{7}{8}$	$8\frac{57}{64}$	$7\frac{1}{4}$	$10\frac{25}{64}$	$8\frac{3}{8}$	$11\frac{7}{8}$	$10\frac{7}{8}$	$14\frac{27}{32}$
23	$5\frac{5}{16}$	$7\frac{13}{16}$	$6\frac{3}{8}$	$9\frac{1}{8}$	$7\frac{7}{16}$	$10\frac{15}{16}$	9	$12\frac{33}{64}$	$11\frac{5}{8}$	$15\frac{21}{32}$
24	$5\frac{11}{16}$	$8\frac{13}{64}$	$6\frac{13}{16}$	$9\frac{55}{64}$	8	$11\frac{1}{2}$	$9\frac{5}{8}$	$13\frac{5}{32}$	13	$16\frac{29}{64}$
25	$5\frac{23}{32}$	$8\frac{39}{64}$	$7\frac{1}{4}$	$10\frac{11}{32}$	$8\frac{9}{16}$	$12\frac{1}{16}$	$10\frac{1}{4}$	$13\frac{51}{64}$	$13\frac{1}{2}$	$17\frac{1}{4}$

To adjust chain tension, turn one sprocket to tighten the lower strand of the chain, then measure the sag of the upper strand. This sag should be in the range of 2–3% of the center distance of the sprockets. The slack-side sag may be calculated from the formula:

$$\text{Sag in inches} = S = \sqrt{0.375CE}$$

where C = center distance between sprockets (in.)
         E = excess chain = return strand length—C
Slack-side tension can be calculated from the sag thus:

$$\text{Slack-side tension} = \frac{C^2 W_c}{96S}$$

where W_c = weight of chain in pounds per foot, and C and S are as defined above. See Fig. 4-27.

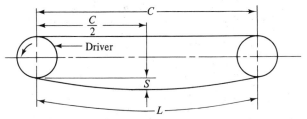

FIGURE 4-27 *Slack-side sag.*

Low-viscosity oils are employed for chain lubrication. Generally the lube oil suitable for automobile engine lubrication is acceptable for chain:

Temp. °F	Lube Oil
− 20 to + 20°	SAE #10
20 to 40°	SAE #20
20 to 40°	SAE #20
40 to 100°	SAE #30
100 to 120°	SAE #40
120 to 140°	SAE #50

4-15 SILENT CHAIN

Silent chain operates with less noise and can be used in high-speed applications. The silent chain is a series of toothed steel link plates (Fig. 4-28) with these teeth engaging mating teeth in the sprocket. The pitch of silent chain is designated by one or two digits giving the number of eighth-inches of the pitch. The width of the chain is indicated with two or three digits that give the number of quarter-inches in the chain width. For example SC404 is a silent chain of ½ in. pitch (4/8) and 4/4 or 1 in. width.

Silent chain pitches and standard chain widths are given in Table 4-14.

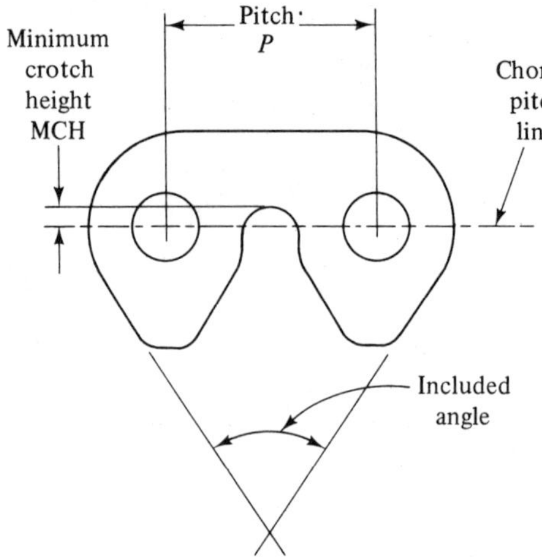

FIGURE 4-28 *Dimensions of silent chain link.*

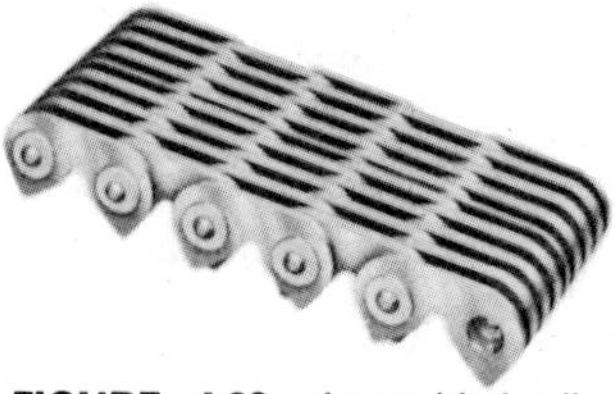

FIGURE 4-29 *Assembled silent chain.*

TABLE 4-14

Standard silent chain widths.

Chain Pitch	*Standard Widths*																								
⅜	½	¾	1	1¼	1½	1¾	2	2¼	2½		3		4	5	6										
½	½	¾	1	1¼	1½	1¾	2	2¼	2½	2¾	3	3½	4	5	6		8								
⅝			1	1¼	1½	1¾	2		2½		3		4	5	6	7	8		10						
¾			1	1¼	1½		2		2½		3	3½	4	5	6	7	8	9	10	12					
1							2		2½		3		4	5	6	7	8	9	10	12	14	16			
1¼									2½		3		4	5	6	7	8	9	10	12	14	16	18	20	
1½											3		4	5	6	7	8	9	10	12	14	167	18	20	2
2													4	5	6	7	8		10	12	14	16	18	20	22

It is recommended that the small sprocket for silent chain have not less than 21 teeth.

QUESTIONS

4-1. Why does a leather belt require periodic belt dressing?

4-2. A flat belt with 180° of wrap on the driving pulley is on the verge of slipping when transmitting 20 HP to the driven shaft. The diameter of the drive pulley is 12 in. and coefficient of friction between belt and pulley is 0.32. Belt speed is 1200 fpm. What is the force on the tight side of the belt?

4-3. Determine the length of belt required for the following open belt drives:

    (a) large pulley 30 in. diameter, small pulley 10 in. diameter, center distance 60 in.

    (b) large pulley 24 in. diameter, small pulley 8 in. diameter, center distance 48 in.

4-4. Determine the horsepower rating required for a flat-belt drive on a two-cylinder refrigerator compressor requiring 10 HP. The motor is a squirrel-cage type with across-the-line starting, and operation is continuous.

4-5. Determine the horsepower rating required for a flat-belt drive for an engine lathe requiring 5 HP from a squirrel-cage motor of the high-torque type.

4-6. Determine the required length of a V-belt for a drive between pulleys 12.4 in. and 4.6 in. pitch diameter, with center distance 16 in.

4-7. What are the advantages and disadvantages of timer belts?

4-8. Select a V-belt section size for the following applications:

    (a) design HP 20, small sheave rpm 500

    (b) design HP 25, small sheave rpm 2500

    (c) design HP 100, small sheave rpm 2400

4-9. Determine the horsepower ratings for the following V-belt drives:

    (a) B size, belt speed 4000 fpm, equivalent diameter of small sheave 5.8 in.

    (b) D size, belt speed 3000 fpm, equivalent diameter of small sheave 16.0 in.

    (c) C size, belt speed 4200 fpm, equivalent diameter of small sheave 10.5 in.

4-10. Determine the design horsepower for the following flat belt drives:

	Rated HP	Driving Machine	Driven Machine	Conditions
(a)	20	high torque	flight conveyor	continuous
(b)	50	normal torque synchronous motor	positive blower	continuous
(c)	100	diesel engine	jaw crusher	continuous

4-11. A 20-HP 1725-rpm squirrel-cage motor drives a fan at 800 rpm under normal service conditions. Sheave centers for a V-belt drive must be between 48 and 50 in. apart. Select standard sheave diameters, belt size and length, and number of belts required.

4-12. A 50-HP 1200-rpm diesel engine drives a piston compressor at 300 rpm through a V-belt drive under normal service conditions. Center distance between sheaves is 72 in. The driven sheave has a pitch diameter of 30 in. Select belt size, number of belts, and belt length.

4-13. Find the chain length in pitches for a drive chain with a center distance of 36 in. approximately, with sprockets of 12 and 32 teeth using ½ in. chain. Determine the exact center distance.

4-14. For an electric motor frame size 145T, give the minimum number of sprocket teeth possible for ⅜ in. pitch and ½ in. pitch chain.

4-15. Calculate the slack side tension in a #50 drive chain with a sprocket center distance of 36 in. and a sag of 1 in.

4-16. Find the required design horsepower for the following chain drives:

(a) 50 HP to be transmitted with double-strand chain. Moderate shock, continuous operation, electric motor.

(b) 80 HP to be transmitted with triple strand chain. Heavy shock, 12-hour operation, high temperatures, internal combustion engine.

4-17. A centrifugal fan with a speed of 2800 rpm is to be driven from a 10-HP a.c. motor with a power chain. The motor speed is 1725 rpm and its shaft is 1⅜ in. in diameter. The fan shaft is 1¼ in. in diameter. Center distance must be 20 in. approximately, and sprocket diameters 5 in and 3 in. approximately. Design the drive, including chain size and length, sprocket sizes, number of strands, and center distance.

4-18. A double reduction chain drive (see figure) must be designed for an air compressor operated at 140 rpm intermittently using a 25-HP 900-rpm motor. The lightest possible chain must be selected and center distance must be as short as possible. Provide the information required for the drive.

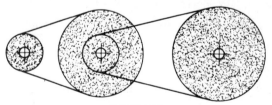

QUES. 4-18.

4-19. A triple strand #80 power chain is driven by a diesel engine in continuous operation under conditions of heavy shock and extreme temperature conditions. The driving sprocket has 18 teeth and rotates at 700 rpm. The driven sprocket has 30 teeth. Center distance is 30 pitches. Decide the pitch diameter of both sprockets, the chain length and the transmitted horsepower.

5

TORQUE CONNECTIONS, COUPLINGS, AND CLUTCHES

5-1 SHAFTS

Power transmission shafting is subject to both torque and bending loads. A gear or chain drive supplies torque, while the tension in the chain or the contact force between mating gear teeth exerts a bending load on the shaft. Pronounced bending deflections are not acceptable in shafts and therefore bending stresses are normally quite low. Gears for example cannot tolerate misalignment due to shaft deflection. Torsion stresses may be high however; failures of shafts due to overloading or shock loading are almost always torsion failures. The only other common mode of failure is a fatigue failure of a shaft, usually at a stress concentration such as a keyway or a shoulder. In a torque failure the shaft breaks at an angle of about 45 degrees due to twisting; in a fatigue failure the break is usually at 90 degrees to the axis of the shaft.

Loads on a shaft and its bearings are produced by the following:

1. Weight of the shaft and its gears, sprockets, rotors, clutches, or other attached parts.

2. The centrifugal force of revolving parts, especially if they are unbalanced.

3. Belt and chain tension.

4. Torque of gears and sprockets.

If horsepower and speed in rpm are known, then torque is calculated from:

$$\text{Torque} = \frac{63{,}025 \text{ HP}}{\text{rpm}} \text{ (torque in pound-inches)}$$

Loads on a shaft may be applied gradually, but often there may be sudden shock loads such as occur at the startup of a long conveyor. Shock loads may increase the effective shaft loading by 1.5 to 3 times.

Shafting must have a smooth surface of close tolerances, both to improve fatigue strength and also for the seating of bearings. Smooth finishes are obtained either by cold-rolling or by grinding. Low-carbon cold-finished steel is used for shafting in applications that are not highly stressed, while medium-carbon steels of about 0.4% carbon, either heat-treated or not, are used where loads and fatigue conditions are more stringent. For severe service conditions low-alloy steels are used, and for corrosive conditions, as in water pumps, stainless steels or bronzes may be used.

Bearing Loads

The determination of bearing loads is necessary in order to select suitable bearings for a shaft. As an example, consider the overhung shaft of Fig. 5-1. This shaft is to transmit 10 HP at 1800 rpm at the overhung pulley, which is 6 in. in diameter.

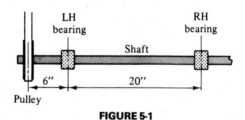

FIGURE 5-1

$$\text{Torque} = \text{belt force} \times \text{pulley pitch radius}$$

$$\text{Belt force} = \frac{63{,}025 \text{ HP}}{\text{rpm} \times \text{radius}} = \frac{63{,}025 \times 10}{1800 \times 3}$$

$$= 116 \text{ lb}$$

$$\text{Force on right-hand bearing} = \frac{116 \times 6}{20} = 35 \text{ lb}$$

$$\text{Force on left-hand bearing} = \frac{116 \times 26}{20} = 151 \text{ lb}$$

The various forces on the shaft may not all be in the same direction, as shown in Fig. 5-2. For this case, the following are the calculations for bearing loads.

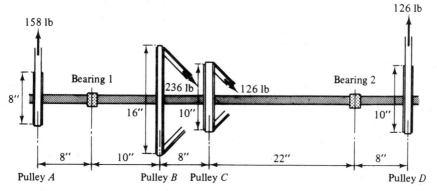

FIGURE 5-2 *Power transmission shaft. The belt forces on pulleys A and D are vertical on B and C horizontal.*

The forces at each power transmission location:

$$\text{Force at } A = \frac{63,000 \times 10}{4 \times 1000} = 158 \text{ lb}$$

$$\text{at } B = \frac{63,000 \times 30}{8 \times 1000} = 236 \text{ lb}$$

$$\text{at } C = \frac{63,000 \times 10}{5 \times 1000} = 126 \text{ lb}$$

$$\text{at } D = \frac{63,000 \times 10}{5 \times 1000} = 126 \text{ lb}$$

Bearing loads:

Part	Load at Bearing 1	Load at Bearing 2
A	$\frac{158 \times 48}{40} = 190$ ↓	$190 - 158 = 32$ ↑
B	$\frac{236 \times 30}{40} = 177$ ↓	$236 - 177 = 59$ ↓
C	$\frac{126 \times 22}{40} = 69$ ↓	$126 - 69 = 57$ ↓
D	$\frac{126 \times 8}{40} = 25$ ↑	$126 + 25 = 141$ ↓

Total radial loads:

Bearing 1 $\sqrt{(190 - 25)^2 + (177 + 69)^2} = 295\,\text{lb}$

Bearing 2 $\sqrt{(141 - 32)^2 + (59 + 57)^2} = 159\,\text{lb}$

Before bearings for the shafts can be selected, the bearing loads must be known.

5-2   CRITICAL SPEEDS OF SHAFTS

If the center of gravity of a shaft lies on its axis of rotation and the shaft does not deflect under load, then the shaft will not vibrate. These two conditions almost never hold, however. Manufacturing tolerances often indicate that the center of gravity of a shaft will not lie on its axis of rotation. Shafts for much agricultural equipment and machines as an example are allowed a total indicator runout (TIR) of 0.005 in. maximum. The method of measuring TIR with a dial indicator is shown in Fig. 5-3, the runout being the total movement on the dial indicator as the shaft is rotated 360 degrees. The actual deformation is of course only one-half of this amount.

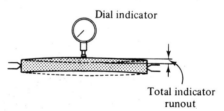

FIGURE 5-3 *Measurement of total indicator runout.*

Because of such imperfections and deflections under loads, centrifugal forces are set up in shafts that tend to increase the shaft deflection, and as the rotational speed increases, a speed is reached at which vibration (whip) is strong enough to be noticed. This speed is the critical speed of the shaft. If the speed is increased beyond the critical speed, the vibration is reduced, increasing again at multiples of the critical speed. As a general rule, shafts should not operate at speeds exceeding 80% of their critical speed.

If the shaft is of solid steel and cylindrical, then the critical speed in rpm can be calculated from the following formula:

$$\text{Critical speed} = 387 \times 10^3 \frac{D^2}{ab}\sqrt{\frac{L}{P}}$$

where D = shaft diameter (in.)

a, b = distances from the load (gear, sprocket, clutch, etc.) to the bearings (in.)

L = center-to-center distance between bearings (in.)

$= a + b$

P = concentrated load on the shaft (lb)

EXAMPLE 5-1:   A solid steel shaft 1.5 in. in diameter and 30 in. long between bearing centers carries a load of 150 lb due to power chain pull. The sprocket is centered between bearings. Determine the approximate critical speed using the above formula.

SOLUTION: Here $a = b = 15$.

$$\text{Critical speed} = 387 \times 10^3 \, \frac{(1.5)^2}{15 \times 15} \sqrt{\frac{30}{150}}$$

$$= 1720 \text{ rpm}$$

If operated above 80% of this critical speed, this shaft should whip.

5-3   PINS FOR TORQUE TRANSMISSION

Gears, sprockets, pulleys, brakes, couplings and other power transmission devices must be attached to shafts in some manner that prevents relative motion between them and the shaft but which allows them to be removed from the shaft for maintenance. Setscrews and pins are some of the smaller hardware used for these purposes; they are generally limited to low torque applications.

The *setscrew* is limited to fractional horsepower requirements and low torques. It is a headless screw with a hexagon socket head and a conical tip that bears on the shaft or a shallow hole drilled into the shaft. The setscrew is threaded into the hub of the pulley or gear and should be short enough in length that it does not project above the hub to act as a possible hazard when rotating.

If two setscrews are used in one hub, they must be placed at 90 degrees to one another. If installed opposite one another, the shaft will be supported on the two setscrews and will not lie against the hub. With the right-angle arrangement of two screws the shaft must lie against the hub, giving an improved frictional resistance to prevent relative movement between shaft and hub.

Taper pins (Fig. 5-5) have a standard taper of ½ inch per foot. The seating hole for the pin is finished with a taper reamer and the pin is driven into place.

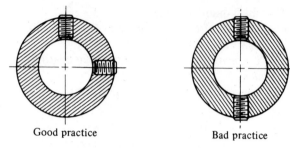

Good practice   Bad practice

FIGURE 5-4 *Use of setscrews.*

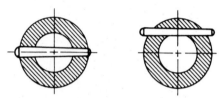

FIGURE 5-5 *Concentric and eccentric installation of taper pins.*

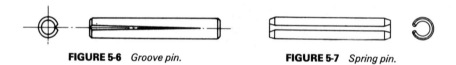

FIGURE 5-6 *Groove pin.*   **FIGURE 5-7** *Spring pin.*

The *groove pin* of Fig. 5-6 has one or more longitudinal grooves over a part of the length, so that the farther it is driven into the hole the tighter it locks.

The *spring pin* or *rolled pin* is a hollow tube with a longitudinal slot down the whole length and tapered ends to facilitate driving the pin. The slot allows the diameter to reduce slightly when the pin is driven into its hole. The torque resistance can be improved by driving a spring pin of the next smaller size into the first pin. This is an economical pin to install because a drilled hole is sufficient, without reaming.

The *spiral pin* is similar in use to the spring pin. It is made of sheet metal wrapped twice around itself (Fig. 5-8).

A *shear pin* is used as a weak torque-transmitting element stressed in shear. It is designed to fail at a predetermined torque or stress which is

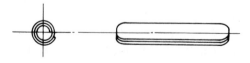

FIGURE 5-8 *Spiral pin.*

less than the torque required to damage more costly transmission elements in the power train such as a gear or a sprocket. The shear pin thus protects a power transmission drive against damage from overloads. If the pin shears, the hub in which it is located will idle or stop until the drive is shut down and the pin replaced.

5-4   SHAFT KEYS

Keys are perhaps the most familiar torque-transmitting fasteners.

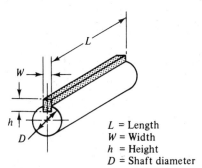

L = Length
W = Width
h = Height
D = Shaft diameter

FIGURE 5-9   *Key dimensions: L = length; W = width; h = height; D = shaft diameter.*

Square   Round end   Woodruff   Taper key

FIGURE 5-10   *Types of keys: square, round end, woodruff, and taper key.*

The simplest key shape is the square key. Half the height of the key lies in the shaft and the other half in the hub of the machine element. In addition to the square key, the round-end key, the taper key, and the Woodruff key of Fig. 5-10 are also used.

The rules for sizing plain and round-end keys are these:

1. Key width should be one-quarter of shaft diameter.

2. Skeyway depth should be one-sixth of shaft diameter.

3. Minimum key length should be 1½ shaft diameters.

4. The depth of a square keyway in the shaft or hub should be half the width of the key.

Key thickness is measured radially, key width tangentially. See Fig. 5-9.

The semicircular side of the Woodruff key is seated in the shaft, the keyway being cut with a milling cutter of the diameter and width of the key. The size of a Woodruff key is given by a system of digits. The last two digits of the key number indicate the key diameter in eighths of an inch and the digit or digits preceding the last two give the width of the key in 32nds of an inch. For example, the 1012 size has a diameter of $1\frac{2}{8}$ or $1\frac{1}{2}$ inch and a width of $\frac{10}{32}$ or $\frac{5}{16}$ inch.

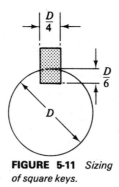

FIGURE 5-11 *Sizing of square keys.*

5-5 SPLIT-TAPER BUSHINGS

A flanged type of split-taper bushing used with a square key is shown in Fig. 5-12. Flangeless types are also used. These bushings are used to fasten any shaft-mounting part that is equipped with a hub. The split-taper bushing is flexible and is drawn into the mating internal taper of the hub by three pull-up screws. It seats with very high friction and requires removal screws for dismounting.

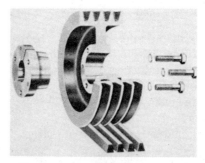

FIGURE 5-12 *Flanged split taper bushing attaching a pulley to a shaft.*

5-6 SPLINES

Splines are a series of teeth cut into the surface of a shaft in the axial direction which mate with a series of keyways cut into the hub of the mounted part. Splines are used instead of keys when a sliding connection is required and when heavy torque loads, especially reversing loads, are present, as in power takeoffs. To ensure sliding under load, the bearing stress against the sides of the splines is usually limited to 100 psi.

Spline contours are shown in Fig. 5-13. The more common are the parallel-side spline and the involute spline. The involute spline resembles the shape of a gear tooth but is modified from the standard gear tooth profile. This spline shape gives greater strength and ease of manufacture.

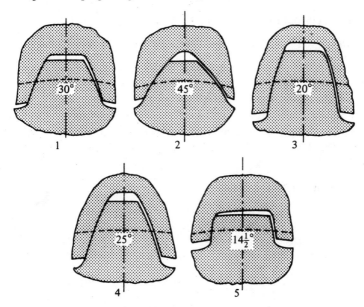

FIGURE 5-13 *Spline contours.*

5-7 SHAFT COUPLINGS

A common requirement in designing machinery is the connecting of two shafts in line. A familiar case is the electric motor which must be direct-connected to a pump. The pump manufacturer will buy a standard electric motor and join the motor and pump shafts with some type of rigid or flexible coupling.

Shaft couplings are grouped into two broad classes: rigid and flexible. A rigid coupling makes no provision for misalignment of the two shafts joined, nor will it reduce shock or vibration transmitted across it from one shaft to the other.

Shafts are subject to the types of misalignment shown in Fig. 5-14.

FIGURE 5-14   *Types of shaft misalignment: radial, angular, and float.*

Where such misalignments occur, a flexible coupling must be used. The misalignment may be

radial, such that the axes of the two shafts are parallel but offset;

angular, such that the two shafts make a slight angle with each other;

float, such that there may be a small axial movement of one or both shafts.

Some misalignment may be due to deflection from loads on the shafts. Severe misalignment must be corrected; slight misalignments can be accommodated by flexible couplings to prevent damage to bearings and fatigue failure in the shafts.

5-8 FLANGED COUPLINGS

The usual rigid coupling is the flanged shaft coupling of Fig. 5-15. The flange at the outside diameter prevents the rotating bolt heads from catching in clothing. Torque is transmitted from one shaft to the other by shear

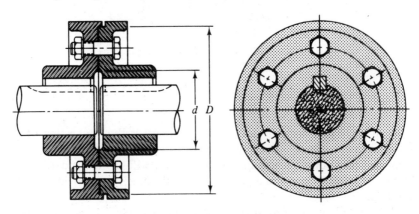

FIGURE 5-15   *Flanged coupling.*

stress in the bolts of the two-piece coupling. The torque load is assumed to be divided equally among the coupling bolts provided the bolt holes are reamed after drilling.

The diameter of the hub of the coupling is usually sized to be 1.75 times shaft diameter plus 0.25 in.

5-9 FLEXIBLE COUPLINGS

A flexible coupling can be produced by substituting a more flexible medium for the bolts of the flanged coupling. One such flexible coupling is the *chain coupling* of Fig. 5-16. This consists of two identical sprockets coupled by two-strand roller chain. Disconnection is easy, requiring the removal of only one pin in the chain. Misalignment of as much as 5 degrees can be accommodated by this coupling. However it transmits shock loads and generates some noise. The gear type of flexible coupling is similar in principle. It substitutes gears of special tooth profile for sprockets mating with internal splines in a housing sleeve.

Instead of bolts, the *Falk Steelflex coupling* uses a continuous steel strip which weaves through serrations in the two flanges of the coupling. This coupling is illustrated in Fig. 5-17.

The spider type of coupling uses a spider inside the jaws of the two coupling hubs, as shown in Fig. 5-18.

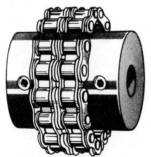

FIGURE 5-16 *Chain coupling. A double-strand chain mates with sprockets on both shafts.*

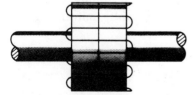

FIGURE 5-17 *Falk steelflex coupling.*

Spider

FIGURE 5-18 *Coupling with spider. In some designs a rubber spider is used.*

One class of flexible coupling contains a nonmetallic flexing insert. A flat rubber membrane or cushion may be included in the coupling to compensate for angular and axial misalignment. But since rubbers generate heat when flexed, this type of coupling is limited to low-speed applications and therefore low horsepower.

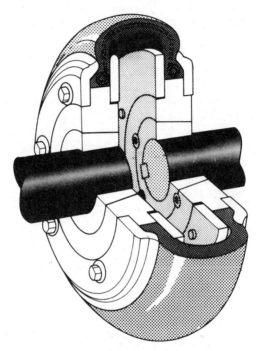

FIGURE 5-19 *Shear type of flexible coupling using a rubber element.*

5-10 UNIVERSAL JOINTS

For very large angular or offset misalignment between two shafts, a universal joint must be employed. Figure 5-20 shows the simplest type of universal joint, consisting of a yoke on each shaft connected by a central bar. Almost always universal joints are used in pairs as in the figure, with equal angles in the two joints. The use of equal angles provides uniform angular velocity in the driven shaft.

5-11 CLUTCHES

A clutch is a mechanism used for repeated connection and disconnection of a torsion load from the driving power. A clutch is designed to transmit a certain maximum torque, hence its horsepower rating depends on rpm.

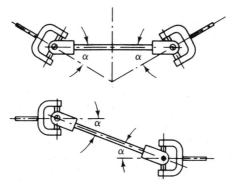

FIGURE 5-20 *Universal joint.*

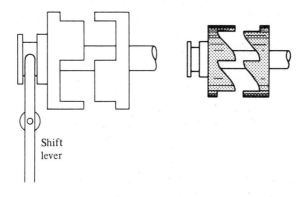

Shift
lever

FIGURE 5-21 *Square-jaw clutch*   **FIGURE   5-22** *Spiral-
jaw clutch.*

5-12 POSITIVE ENGAGEMENT CLUTCHES

In a positive engagement clutch, the engaging clutch surfaces interlock to produce a rigid joint. Most positive clutches are of the jaw type (Fig. 5-21). One of the jaws must be splined or keyed so that it can move axially to engage. The jaws may be square or spiral (Fig. 5-22). The spiral clutch is an overrunning clutch, that is, it transmits power in one direction only.

Positive clutches are inexpensive and generate no heat. But their applications are limited to small torques and low speeds. Engagement of the jaws produces considerable shock. The design of a jaw clutch is a relatively simple matter: there must be sufficient bearing area and shear area. The clutch surfaces must be wear-resistant.

The slip clutch of Fig. 5-23 is a positive engagement clutch provided that the torque is below a value set by the force of the spring. The triangular teeth on the clutch faces give a component of the transmitted torque in the axial direction which cannot exceed the spring force.

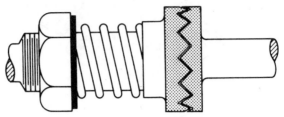

FIGURE 5-23 *Spring-loaded slip clutch.*

5-13 FRICTION CLUTCHES

Friction clutches are adapted to the smooth engagement of shafts with a large difference in relative speeds. Two mating friction surfaces are forced into contact and torque is transmitted by means of friction. The driven shaft can be accelerated up to the speed of the driver shaft because the clutch can slip. This type of clutch can be used as an overload protective clutch by designing for slip when a certain torque is reached, and by slipping whenever a shock application occurs. Most of the friction clutches are either of the *disk* or *rim* type.

The friction element of the disk type consists of one or more friction disks which engage axially. The single disk is usually run dry, while multiple disk clutches usually run in oil for smoother engagement and heat dissipation.

The basic disk or plate clutch is shown in Fig. 5-24. The inner diameter of the friction surface is designated d and the outer diameter D. Since the friction torque that can be transmitted is proportional to diameter, d is usually at least one-half of D. For these clutches it is assumed either that clutch pressure is uniformly distributed or that surface wear is uniform, though neither assumption is strictly true. A reasonably useful design equation based on uniform wear is the following:

$$T = \frac{\mu P(D + d)}{4}$$

where T = transmitted torque in lb-inches
  P = axial force
  μ = coefficient of friction

The coefficient of friction depends on the facing materials and their condition and temperature. A worn facing has a reduced coefficient; for design purposes it is assumed that a worn condition exists. For gray cast iron against gray cast iron, both dry, the friction coefficient is 0.20 and the allowable pressure is 150 psi maximum. For gray cast iron against steel, both

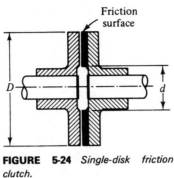

FIGURE 5-24 *Single-disk friction clutch.*

dry, the corresponding values are 0.30 and 150 psi maximum. To allow for slipping and inertia of the mass to be rotated the nominal required torque is increased by a factor of 1.5 to 2.0. A shock factor is also included. If the clutch will be subjected to frequently repeated operation, the pressure is reduced to increase the life of the friction facing.

The capacity of this clutch may be increased by increasing the number of friction plates; two plates of the same design supply double the torque capacity. The equation above for transmitted torque applies to each of the several plates. The number of plates cannot be indefinitely increased because of increasing heat generation and increasing difficulty of complete disengagement. One kind of multiple-disk clutch is shown in Fig. 5-25. When air is forced into the air tube this tube forces the two floating plates with their friction faces against the backplate. Thus four friction disks transmit torque. The torque is directly proportional to air pressure. To disengage, the air pressure is removed and springs re-center the plates.

The *cone clutch* of Fig. 5-26 is another friction clutch. In this design a

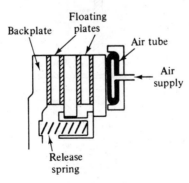

FIGURE 5-25 *Air-operated multiple-disk clutch.*

small axial force results in a large force between the friction surfaces. The clutch angle is in the range of 8° to 15°, smaller angles giving greater contact forces. The transmitted torque may be found from the following equation, which is that for a plate clutch modified to allow for the conical angle:

$$T = \frac{\mu P(D + d)}{4 \sin \alpha}$$

The cone clutch is less commonly used in the U.S. than it formerly was. Its disadvantages are a tendency to grab and some reluctance in disengagement.

The *radial clutch,* also called a rim, shoe, band, or ring clutch, has a cylindrical friction surface (Fig. 5-27). This type can be built into pulleys and flywheels. One widely used type is the Fawick Airflex Clutch, with two concentric friction rims which are engaged by air pressure in an annular tube fastened to the outer rim in the same manner as described above for a multiple-disk clutch. Disengagement occurs by exhausting the air in the

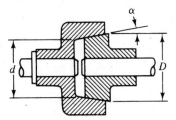

FIGURE 5-26   *Cone clutch.*

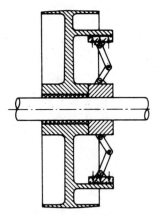

FIGURE 5-27 *Radial friction clutch built into a belt pulley.*

tube and is assisted by centrifugal force on the tube. The air tube compensates automatically for wear.

5-14 CENTRIFUGAL CLUTCHES

The centrifugal clutch engages by centrifugal force after a certain driven rpm is reached. This clutch is recommended for connecting equipment of high inertia to the commonly used alternating-current induction motor, since this motor can then pick up its load at a speed giving a higher torque than it can safely deliver at a standstill. The electric motor then can be of smaller capacity than would be required by direct connection to the load. Another advantage is automatic disengagement at overload, when the electric motor decelerates. This type of clutch is also used with internal combustion engines, which cannot be started under load. Other applications include fans, chain saws, compressors, presses and conveyor belts.

The centrifugal clutch consists of a driving hub, a driven drum, and a set of shoes with a brake lining material connected to the hub. The driving shaft carries the hub, and the driven shaft the drum. When the hub rotates, centrifugal force carries the shoes outward against the inside surface of the drum, transmitting power to the load. Because of slippage, smooth starting is assured.

Centrifugal force is proportional to the square of the speed. Torque is directly proportional to centrifugal force and also varies as the square of the speed. Power, being the product of speed and torque, varies as the cube of the speed in this clutch.

The centrifugal clutch is not suited to variable-speed drives because its horsepower rating varies with the cube of the rpm. Nor is it suited to low speeds, which would require a large clutch diameter to obtain sufficient centrifugal effect.

The *dry fluid coupling,* though not termed a centrifugal clutch, uses centrifugal force. This clutch has a housing keyed to the motor shaft and a rotor connected to the load. The housing contains a charge of steel shot. As the motor accelerates, centrifugal force throws the steel shot to the periphery of the housing where it packs around the rotor (Fig. 5-28). There is some slippage before the housing and rotor are locked together at the same speed, thus giving smooth acceleration. Other proprietary designs substitute mercury or other materials for steel shot.

The "over-running" or "one-way" coupling uses rollers which roll outward to wedge or jam between an inner hub member and an outer housing. With this type of clutch the motor cannot drive the load in reverse (Fig. 5-29).

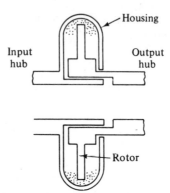

FIGURE 5-28 *Dry fluid clutch, a type of centrifugal clutch. Centrifugal force casues fine steel shot to wedge between rotor and housing.*

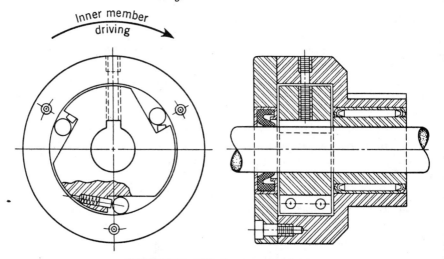

FIGURE 5-29 *Hilliard overrunning clutch.*

5-15 ELECTRIC AND MAGNETIC CLUTCHES

A *rotating field clutch* is illustrated in Fig. 5-30. This type of clutch is a single-disk friction clutch that is electrically operated. The rotating electromagnet on the driving shaft pulls in the armature on the driven shaft. The friction surfaces on electromagnet and armature transmit the torque. Since the electromagnet is heavier than the armature, it is usual to mount the electromagnet on the driver shaft so that its greater weight does not have to be accelerated when the clutch is operated.

The *stationary field clutch* is a modification of this principle. This is

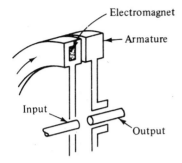

FIGURE 5-30 *Rotating field clutch. the clutch engages when the armature on the output shaft is pulled to the input electromagnet.*

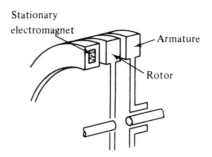

FIGURE 5-31 *Stationary field clutch.*

illustrated in Fig. 5-31. Here the magnetic coil is fixed. It pulls the output armature in to the input rotor.

The *magnetic fluid clutch* of Fig. 5-32 uses two parallel magnetic plates. One of these contains an electromagnet, the other is an input housing containing a driving disk. The magnetic particles are suspended in an oil. By varying the excitation of the magnetic coil with a direct current, the shear strength of the magnetic fluid suspension can be controlled, so that any speed of the driven shaft is possible from idling to full speed. A disadvantage of this clutch is the generation of heat during slip of the driven shaft.

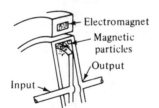

FIGURE 5-32 *Magnetic fluid clutch*

The *magnetic particle clutch* is similar but uses a dry magnetic powder.

The *eddy current* or *hysteresis clutch* transmits torque by magnetic drag from eddy current induced in a driven member by a rotating magnetic field (Fig. 5-33). Magnetic flux links the input drum and the output rotor. The eddy currents in the input drum interact with the magnetic field induced in the output rotor to produce a coupling torque which is proportional to the exciting field coil current. Torque is adjusted by adjusting this current.

The driven shaft in an eddy current clutch always slips, that is, rotates at a somewhat slower speed, behind the speed of the driven shaft. At zero slip, both shafts at the same speed, there is no torque transmission. However

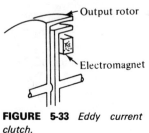

FIGURE 5-33 *Eddy current clutch.*

the energy lost in slip is converted into heat. Small units are air-cooled, but larger clutches require water cooling to remove the large quantity of heat generated.

Because of its high slip the eddy current clutch is best employed as an adjustable speed drive. Service life is long because there is no wear in this clutch.

5-16 THE HYDRAULIC COUPLING

The hydraulic or fluid coupling uses a hydraulic fluid for transmitting torque. The input member of the coupling, the impeller, has radial vanes to produce kinetic energy in the fluid, this energy being absorbed by the output

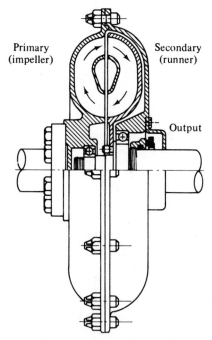

FIGURE 5-34 *Fluid coupling.*

member of the coupling, the runner, except for losses due to fluid friction. These losses as usual appear as heat, which is dissipated to the surrounding air by cooling ribs on the housing.

Coupling of the two shafts can occur only when the driver shaft is rotating. There is some slip of the driven shaft behind the driving shaft, this slip being about 3 to 6%. Heat generation increases with slip. Maximum torque occurs when the driven shaft stalls.

The transmission of power through a fluid coupling can be understood by reference to Fig. 5-34. In the primary member or impeller, fluid moves radially outward, then axially to the more slowly rotating runner or secondary member. In the runner the fluid must decelerate because the secondary is moving more slowly and also because the fluid moves toward the center of rotation. There is no transfer of energy unless the secondary rotates at a slower speed than the primary. This difference of speeds is called *slip,* usually expressed as a percent:

$$\text{Slip} = \frac{\text{primary speed} - \text{secondary speed}}{\text{primary speed}} \times 100\%$$

Output torque is always equal to input torque, and power output is less than power input by the percent slip:

$$\text{Efficiency} = \frac{\text{power output}}{\text{power input}} \times 100\%$$

$$= 100\% - \text{slip}$$

If the fluid coupling connects a torque load to an electric motor, it picks up the load gradually and smoothly, greatly reducing peak current demand of the motor. Since the coupling will stall, it provides overload protection, although a prolonged stall may overheat the hydraulic oil. The hydraulic coupling will absorb both shock and vibration but cannot compensate for shaft misalignment. Power output varies with the cube of the speed. If a stator is included between the two halves of the coupling, then the coupling becomes a torque converter, which may be used as a variable-speed drive.

5-17   SELECTION OF CLUTCHES

A clutch must be able to deliver the required torque and horsepower and at the same time be able to dissipate the heat generated during clutch engagements. Most catalogue ratings for clutches are based on only a few engagements of the clutch per hour, but should engagements be more frequent, then the heat-dissipating capacity of the clutch becomes a governing consideration. Heat is generated only during clutch slip: heat (in horsepower)

= delivered horsepower × percent slip. If there is no slip (difference in speed between driver and driven shaft) then no heat is generated.

Since higher speeds result in lower torques, the clutch is usually located in the power train at a position where the rotational speed is high.

The selection of a clutch with the wrong capacity has serious consequences. If the clutch capacity is too small for the load, it will not pick up the load but instead will overheat (if it is a type of clutch that can slip) and could destroy itself. But too large a clutch may exceed the overload capacity of the prime mover or may hold engine or motor speeds to low levels. If the prime mover is an electric motor, the clutch should have a torque capacity slightly below the motor breakdown torque.

Brakes are in principle similar to clutches. Obviously a clutch becomes a brake if it can decelerate the driven member. The kinetic energy of rotation must be dissipated either in braking or in slip in a clutch, and this energy is transformed by friction into heat. The heat dissipation problem is an even more serious problem in a brake.

A brake is a type of clutch that imposes an artificial load for the purpose of deceleration.

5-18 BRAKES

Many types of brakes, though not all, use friction surfaces to stall the load. The energy of rotation or of movement is wholly converted into heat. Therefore brake capacity is limited by temperature rise.

Braking torque increases with the coefficient of friction of the brake lining material. Coefficients of friction are tabulated in handbooks, but it must be remembered that brake linings will absorb moisture which may reduce the coefficient of friction by as much as 30%. The heat of braking will evaporate this moisture and restore the coefficient of friction. Variations in the surface condition of the lining and wheel, and in the brake lining material may give variations of plus or minus 10% in braking torque.

The external shoe brake has a brake shoe, or more usually two opposite shoes, which press against a rotating brake drum, as in Fig. 5-35. The shoes are usually pivoted. Heavy industrial shoe brakes may be operated by coil springs and opened by a hydraulic cylinder supplied by a small electric-driven pump. This gives a fail-safe arrangement, since if electric power is lost the brakes close on the drum.

The internal shoes brake of Fig. 5-36 is familiar in automobiles. Two long pivoted shoes are used, the pivot points of the shoes being usually adjustable to compensate for brake wear.

The band brake of Fig. 5-37 uses a steel band lined on the inside surface with a friction material and wrapped against the rotating drum. The difference in the tensions F_1 and F_2 at the ends of the belt is the friction force

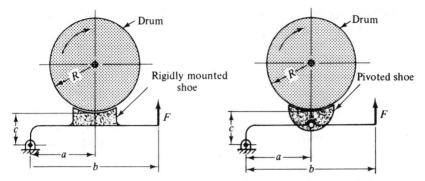

FIGURE 5-35 *Shoe brakes, rigid and pivoted, with important dimensions indicated.*

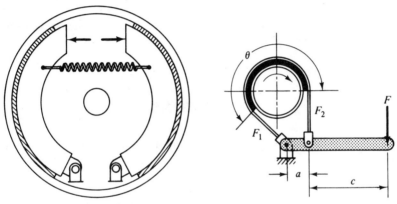

FIGURE 5-36 *Internal shoe brake.*   **FIGURE 5-37** *Band brake.*

(similarly for a power belt the difference in tension is the driving force. See Chapter 4). The braking torque

$$T = R(F_1 - F_2)$$

where R = brake drum radius.

The tension forces are determined from the following relationships:

$$\frac{F_1}{F_2} = e^{\mu\beta} \quad \text{(as in Chapter 4)}$$

$$F_1 = Rbp$$

where p = maximum allowable pressure (psi)
         b = width of the brake band

A disk brake operates like a disk clutch. This type of brake has the advantage of a large braking surface and good heat dissipation. Grabbing, chatter, squeal, and brake fade (loss of braking capacity with increasing temperature) are minimized.

The eddy-current brake is unusual in that it does not employ friction for the braking operation, but is electrically operated. This brake has a smooth cylindrical drum keyed to the shaft which requires braking. This drum rotates in a magnetic field produced by a stationary field coil. Eddy currents generated in the surface of the drum react with the magnetic poles of the stationary coil to produce a braking torque. The braking action can be precisely adjusted by the electrical control system.

The eddy-current brake is a precision brake, but it has its limitations. There is no braking action when the drum has stopped rotating, and therefore it cannot hold a load from rotating. It cannot of course be operated during a power failure, and against this eventuality must be backed up by some type of mechanical brake.

QUESTIONS

5-1. Calculate the loads on each of the bearings shown in the figure.

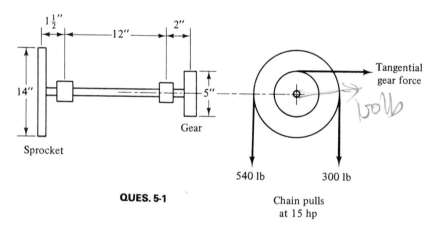

QUES. 5-1

5-2. Supply dimensions for a square key in a 3.0 in. diameter shaft.

5-3. What advantages do splines offer over keys?

5-4. Why is a centrifugal clutch suitable for connecting a load to an internal combustion engine?

5-5. Why is it usual to locate a clutch at the high-speed end of a power train?

5-6. Select shaft couplings that can compensate for radial misalignment, for angular misalignment, for float, and for shock loadings.

5-7. Which of the clutches discussed can be adjusted for variable torque transmission?

5-8. Determine the torque capacity of a single-plate clutch with friction surfaces having an inside radius of 5 cm. and outside radius of 10 cm. The axial force is 2200 newtons and the coefficient of friction is 0.25.

5-9. How much heat in Btu must be dissipated to bring a 4500-lb vehicle to a stop from 60 mph (88 fps)?

6

BEARINGS

6-1 SLEEVE AND ROLLING BEARINGS

All bearings are grouped into two broad classes: those in which the mating parts slide, called *plain bearings* or *sleeves bearings,* and those in which the moving parts roll on one another, called *rolling bearings* or *antifriction bearings.* The second group includes the many types of ball and rolling bearings.

Bearings may be required to resist either radial loads or thrust loads or both. A radial load is a force at right angles to the shaft axis such as a pull from a belt or a power chain. Thrust loads are loads applied parallel to the axis of the shaft, such as the load imposed by a turntable on a shaft or the load on the crane hook of Fig. 6-1.

Often either a sleeve bearing or a rolling bearing will serve equally well, but certain circumstances may dictate the selection of one type rather than the other:

1. Space limitations: if the bearing must have the smallest possible diameter, then a sleeve bearing with its thin cylindrical shape must be the choice. But if the bearing must be as short as possible, then an antifriction bearing is to be selected. Antifriction bearings have length-to-diameter ratios of much less than 1, whereas this ratio is always close to 1 for sleeve bearings.

2. If starting torque is high, the rolling bearing has the advantage because it rolls.

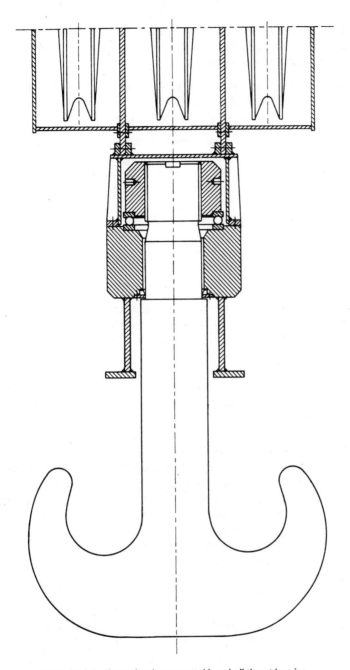

FIGURE 6-1 *Crane hook supported by a ball thrust bearing.*

3. If the bearing must resist thrust loads, then the usual types of sleeve bearings cannot be used. While special types of sleeve bearings are available for thrust loadings, rolling bearings are preferred.

4. If shafts and machine elements such as gears or grinding wheels must be accurately located radially and axially, then the antifriction bearing is the choice, because clearances are much smaller.

5. In the case of fractional horsepower drives power losses must be closely controlled, and the antifriction bearing develops less frictional horsepower. The friction torque of this type of bearing can be approximated by the following formula:

$$0.0015 \times \text{bearing load} \times \text{shaft radius}$$

6. If electric currents must not be allowed to flow across the bearing, as in the case of electric motors and welding turntables, then a sleeve bearing with its insulating oil film must be selected.

7. The sleeve bearing is preferred for high speeds, heavy loadings, and long life. Some types of antifriction bearings are not suited to high-speed applications. All antifriction bearings tend to produce more noise at high speeds.

6-2 BEARING LUBRICATION

Friction may be either sliding friction or rolling friction. Sliding friction occurs between surfaces, either with or without lubrication. Rolling friction, as in a ball or rolling bearing, may reduce friction losses to perhaps one-tenth those of sliding friction (though the friction loss in a rolling bearing will not be one-tenth that in a sleeve bearing). Sliding friction is a more complex effect, since it is very high when movement begins but is greatly reduced at high velocities. High break-away friction is apparent in the piston of a hydraulic or peneumatic cylinder, though the piston slides readily once in motion. Similarly it is more difficult to start an automobile rolling than to keep it rolling.

If there is no lubrication, the relationship between two surfaces sliding on each other is as shown in Fig. 6-2. Because of some degree of surface roughness the two surfaces are in contact only over extremely small areas. If sliding occurs there will be a tendency for the irregularities of the two surfaces to interlock. If a considerable force pushes the two surfaces together, the small contact areas will weld together or *seize*. The force required to break these small welds results in a high friction effect as the surfaces move one on another. A sleeve bearing is made of a different material

FIGURE 6-2 *Miscroscopic surface roughness of two apparently smooth surfaces in contact.*

from that of the shaft (and a worm is made of a different material from its gear) because dissimilar materials are less likely to seize if the lubricant fails to separate them.

A lubricant is a substance, solid, liquid, or gas, that will produce a friction-reducing film between two sliding surfaces by preventing their intimate contact. Lubricants serve three principal functions in bearings:

1. Reduction of friction.

2. Reduction in wear, thus increasing the life of the bearing.

3. Removal of frictional heat from the bearing by lubricant flow.

The lubricating system may also be so designed as to serve a fourth function, the prevention of foreign particles from entry into the bearing.

Most, though not all, sleeve bearing failures result from some failure in these lubricating functions.

The most important property of a lubricant is its viscosity, which is the resistance of a liquid to flow. A liquid with a high viscosity such as a heavy oil or grease, flows reluctantly; a liquid with a low viscosity such as water flows or pours readily. Viscosity changes markedly with temperature, being greatly reduced at elevated temperatures. Higher viscosity oils must be used to lubricate surfaces operated at higher temperatures because the elevated temperature of operation reduces the viscosity to a desirable level. High-viscosity oils mut also be used in bearings supporting heavy loads. Lower viscosities are required for low-temperature operation. The viscosity of the lubricant must be carefully selected to suit the temperature and the pressure of the bearing. The variation of viscosity with temperature is shown in Fig. 7-1.

The viscosity of a lubricant is given as the number of seconds required for 60 milliliters of the lubricant to flow through a standard orifice at a standard temperature. Temperatures of 100° and 210°F are the standard temperatures used.

Viscosity index is a measure of how viscosity varies with temperature, a high viscosity index indicating a lesser variation. *Pour point* of an oil is the lowest temperature at which an oil will flow or can be poured. Pour point can be lowered with the addition of pour point depressants.

Petroleum lube oils are of two types: naphthenic or paraffinic. Naphthene oils contain little wax and as a result have low pour points. Paraffin oils contain wax and find their chief application in hydraulic equipment. Naphthene lubricants are preferred for bearing lubrication. Either broad type may include additives to improve the characteristics and performance of the lubricant. Oxidation inhibitors reduce the formation of gums and varnishes in the oil by delaying oxidation. Rust inhibitors plate out on ferrous surfaces to protect against rusting. Pour point depressants prevent wax crystals from developing at low temperatures. EP (extreme pressure) additives react with metals to form antiseize compounds and thus reduce wear.

Greases are also commonly used as lubricants. A grease is a lubricating oil in some soap compound that keeps the oil in suspension. The properties of the grease depend on the metal base of the soap and the chemical composition of the fatty acids used in the grease. The soaps employed for greases may use calcium, sodium, lithium, aluminum or barium as their metal base. Greases using calcium soaps (lime soaps) are the most generally used because of low cost and good resistance to water, but their extreme temperature range is limited to a maximum of 200 °F. Sodium greases may be used up to 250 °F. Because sodium soaps are soluble in water, this type of grease is not suitable for such applications as water pumps or tractor treads, calcium greases being used instead. Aluminum soap greases are often used in low-speed rolling bearings but are not suited to elevated temperatures. Lithium soap greases are more expensive, but function well at very low or very high temperatures and are waterproof. Aluminum and barium bases are the choice for an all-purpose soap grease.

The stiffness of a grease is designated by NLGI number (National Lubricating Grease Institute), the numbers ranging from 000 to 6. Usually a grade 2 or 3 grease is used for lubrication.

A few solid lubricants are in frequent use. A solid lubricant must fill the surface roughness of the part lubricated and must shear readily. Molybdenum disulfide and graphite have these characteristics. Molybdenum disulfide is applied either as a paste, a grease, or an oil dispersion. Both it and graphite are excellent lubricants at either extreme pressures or high temperatures, though MoS_2 decomposes above 800 °F. Below this temperature it has a lower coefficient of friction than graphite.

Aircraft bearings and some other special types of bearings may use synthetic lubricants such as polyglycols, silicones, or diesters. Less common still are gas-lubricated bearings.

Plastic bearings such as nylon and Delrin (trade name) are able to operate without lubrication under light loads and slow speeds.

6-3 SLEEVE BEARING OPERATION

For sleeve bearings the most important operating conditions are the bearing pressure in pounds per square inch and the surface velocity of the rotating shaft in feet per minute. The product of these two values, called the PV value, is a measure of the frictional heat generated on a unit area of the bearing surface. The severity of bearing service increases with PV, that is, with an increase in load, shaft diameter, or rpm. Greater loads must be supported by larger shafts and bearings of larger diameter. A heavier load cannot be supported by making a sleeve bearing very long, because the ends of an excessively long bearing would be crushed by shaft deflection. Sleeve bearings therefore are approximately as long as the bearing bore. Maximum values of P, V, and PV are given in Table 6-1; units of P are psi, of V are fpm.

TABLE 6-1

Maximum pressure and velocity for some bearing materials.

Material	P	V	PV
Sintered leaded bronze	800	1500	60,000
Cast bronze	3000	750	75,000
Tin babbitt	1500	1200	30,000
Lead babbitt	1300	1400	18,000
Nylon	2000	600	3000
Acetal (Delrin)	2000	600	3000
Teflon	500	50	1000

EXAMPLE 6-1: Consider the case of a ¾-inch shaft rotating at 500 rpm, with a load on each of its bearings of 400 lb. Assume a bearing length of the same dimension as the bore, ¾ in.

SOLUTION:

Bearing area $= 0.75 \times 0.75 = 0.56 \text{ in}^2$

Bearing pressure $P = {}^{400}\%_{.56} = 700 \text{ psi}$

Surface velocity $V = \frac{3}{4} \pi \times 500 = 1185 \text{ ipm} = 100 \text{ fpm}$

$PV = 700 \times 100 = 70,000$

This is a high value. Of the materials tabulated above, only cast bronze is rated for a PV of 70,000.

The three bearing variables viscosity, pressure, and speed are sometimes combined as ZN/P, where $Z = $ viscosity, $P = $ pressure, and $N = $ rpm. To understand the operation of a bearing, consider the graph of coefficient of friction versus ZN/P in Fig. 6-3. If we assume this graph to apply to a

165

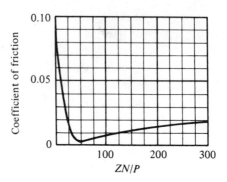

FIGURE 6-3 *Variation of coefficient of friction with $\dfrac{ZN}{P}$*

specific bearing, then P and Z cannot be altered, and only the rpm can be varied. When the shaft is stopped, N and ZN/P are zero. Assuming that oil is not pumped into the bearing, when the shaft is at rest it is lying against the bearing and is virtually unlubricated. At startup the friction is very high. As the shaft gains speed, lubricant begins to smear the mating surfaces and friction falls. As the shaft draws oil around its surface at higher speeds, the bearing becomes self-lubricating. Finally when the shaft reaches high rotational speeds there is a slight increase in friction resulting from the power required to shear or churn the lubricant in the bearing.

Since at operating speed a shaft draws lubricant around itself to float in the bearing bore, in theory a shaft that is never stopped should have an infinite bearing life so long as it is supplied with oil. This of course does not happen, for reasons of corrosion, contamination, and shaft deflection. Nevertheless the effect of continuous operation upon bearing life may be seen in comparing engine life of a family car with that of a Greyhound bus. The life of the bus engine is expected to be 2,000,000 miles.

When the shaft is rotating at operating speed, the fully lubricated condition on the right-hand side of the graph of Fig. 6-3 prevails. Friction is low because the rotating shaft serves as its own oil pump. Forced lubrication from an oil pump is not necessary. Figure 6-4 shows the relationship of shaft and bearing for this condition. The shaft rolls up one side of the bearing to a slightly eccentric position, thus producing a wedge-shaped channel of oil. If the rotation is clockwise, more oil is pulled under the right-hand side of the shaft than escapes from under the left-hand side. This self-lubricating condition characteristic of higher speeds is called *hydrodynamic* lubrication. For hydrodynamic lubrication, the oil hole introducing the oil must be located in the area of minimum hydrodynamic pressure.

Hydrodynamic lubrication is possible only at speeds high enough to pull the wedge of film under the rotating shaft. At low speeds and under heavy

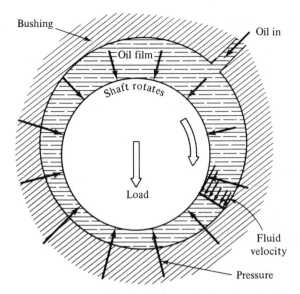

Bushing

Oil in

Oil film

Shaft rotates

Load

Fluid velocity

Pressure

FIGURE 6-4 *Hydraudynamic lubrication in a sleeve bearing.*

shaft loads *hydrostatic* lubrication may be used. Here oil is supplied under positive pressure by an oil pump.

Toward the left-hand side of the graph of Fig. 6-3 the friction increases. This is the region of *boundary lubrication,* where hydrodynamic action cannot be maintained because speeds are too slow. There is some metal-to-metal contact, and the bearing and its journal are supported partly on a film of oil and partly by rubbing contact. If rotation is slow and infrequent, boundary lubrication may however be satisfactory, as for example in the hinge bearings of aircraft landing gear.

6-4 SLEEVE BEARING MATERIALS

Several characteristics are required of the materials used in bearings, and selection is based on these characteristics.

1. **Hardness:** Greater hardness is accompanied by greater strength, provides resistance to fatigue failure and also the capacity to carry heavy loads. A harder bearing may also wear more slowly. However, a harder bearing requires a harder shaft material. Soft bearing materials generally show a greater readiness to seize to the shaft than harder materials. The harder bearing however lacks conformability and embeddability, to be discussed.

2. **Compatibility:** An ideal bearing material should not weld or seize to its shaft when metal-to-metal contact occurs. Compatibility is a ~~is a~~ measure of the antiseizing characteristics of the bearing material when operated against a given shaft material. A hard steel shaft does not tend to weld to a gray iron bearing, but an aluminum shaft in an aluminum bearing material would be prone to seize. *Also Stainless steel in Stainless steel,*

3. **Conformability:** This is the ability to deform and compensate for slight shaft misalignment, shaft deflection, and geometric errors in the shaft.

4. **Embeddability:** This characteristic permits abrasive particles to embed ~~or sink~~ into the bearing material so that they do not abrade the journal area of the shaft. A bearing material sufficiently soft for embedment will also provide comformability.

5. **Corrosion resistance:** The bearing material must not be corroded by additives or other agents in the lubricant, by oxidation products developed as the oil ages, by water, or by corrodents in the atmosphere.

The babbitts, both tin-base and lead-base, are soft bearing materials with excellent embeddability and conformability. Compatibility with steel shafting is excellent. But the load-carrying capacity of a babbitt bearing is not high, nor is fatigue strength. Other limitations of babbitt bearings are a loss in strength at elevated temperatures, and somewhat higher cost than most bearing materials. Tin babbitts are more expensive than lead babbitts, because tin is considerably more expensive than lead. These limitations of babbitt alloys are partially overcome by using babbitt coatings over steel strip.

Lead babbitts have compositions of 10 to 15% antimony with as much as 10% tin, the balance of the alloy being lead. They have a microscopic structure of hard antimony–tin crystals in soft lead. Lead babbitt alloy SAE 15 contains arsenic. This alloy has higher strength and resistance to fatigue and can carry heavier loads, especially at elevated temperatures.

Because of higher cost, tin babbitts are less commonly selected than lead babbitts. Tin babbitts contain 80 to 90% tin, with copper and antimoney for hardness. An increase in the copper or antimony content gives increased hardness and load capacity. Despite the higher cost, tin babbitt may be preferred for its better corrosion resistance and good performance under conditions of poor lubrication.

Copper alloys, including the brasses and bronzes, provide higher load capacities than the babbitts and better wear resistance, but are scored more readily. The leaded copper alloys contain microscopic globules of lead which supply a continuous lead film on the surface of the bearing. The hardest of the copper-bearing alloys are the aluminum bronzes; these are preferred for heavy bearing loads at low speeds. Harder shafts are required with aluminum bronze, and compatibility, conformability, and embeddability are limited.

The aluminum-bearing alloys also have high load capacity with rather poor compatibility, embeddability, and conformability. These characteristics are improved by using a thin lead babbitt overlay. Aluminum alloys are selected for bearings in internal combustion engines, gear pumps, and reciprocating compressors.

Silver is used in quality bearings. A thin plating of silver may prevent seizing when metal-to-metal contact is severe.

Gray cast iron is used in inexpensive bearings for moderate loads and speeds. This material contains graphite flakes which act as a solid lubricant to prevent seizing. Conformability is poor.

Sintered metal, also called powder metal or PM bearings, are self-lubricating and inexpensive. They are usually bronze alloys, though aluminum is also employed. The interconnecting pores in the bearing comprise 10 to 35% of the volume and retain a supply of lubricant sufficient for as much as two years' supply. They are useful in locations where regular lubrication is difficult because of inaccessibility.

For metal sleeve bearings, but not for plastic bearings, the bearing clearance is of the order of 0.001 in. per inch of shaft diameter. If the bearing is press-fitted into its housing, allowance for the reduced diameter due to pressing must be made. This reduction will approximate the interference of the press fit.

The usual plastics employed for self-lubricated bearings are nylon, acetal (trade name Delrin), and polytetrafluoroethylene (trade name Teflon). These have applications at low loads, low speeds, and low temperatures (except that Teflon can sustain elevated temperatures). All three plastic materials show an improvement in bearing characteristics if modified with additive materials such as glass fiber, graphite, or molybdenum disulfide. To use these materials as bearings, bearing clearances must be much larger than those employed with metals.

The radial wear of plastic, rubber, graphite, and wood bearings is closely proportional to the bearing load times the distance traveled in operation:

$$R = K(PV)T$$

where
R = radial wear in the sleeve bearing (in.)
P = radial bearing load (psi)
V = surface velocity of shaft (fpm, not ipm)
T = time (hours)
K = wear factor

The values of K tabulated here can be influenced by a number of factors. Harder shafts and smoother shafts will reduce K. K-values will be very small if plastic bearings are lubricated. Finally, the K-factors apply to pure and unfilled materials: additives greatly reduce these factors.

K-factors for nonmetallic bearings.

Material	K-factor
Nylon	200×10^{-10}
MoS$_2$-filled nylon	35×10^{-10}
Acetal	50×10^{-10}
Teflon-filled acetal	17×10^{-10}
Teflon-filled nylon	13×10^{-10}

6-5 BALL AND ROLLER BEARINGS

Those bearings in which rolling elements are included are referred to as rolling or antifriction bearings. The rolling elements are either balls or rollers, and the rollers may be cylindrical or tapered. In most types of antifriction bearings, the rolling elements may also slide as well as roll; this sliding action will be discussed below. The parts of an antifriction bearing are named in Fig. 6-5.

The load-carrying capacity of a ball or roller increases with the square of the diameter. Thus a ⅛-in ball can support only one-quarter the load of a ¼ in. ball.

The load capacity of a rolling bearing depends on whether the load is static (nonrotating) or dynamic (rotating). The basic static load is defined as the static radial load that will produce a permanent deformation of the rolling element and raceway of 0.0001 of the diameter of the rolling element at the most heavily stressed contact. The static load rating must govern such installations as the crane hook of Fig. 6-1 which experiences little rotation. Static load ratings are given in manufacturers' catalogues.

An antifriction bearing properly sized and selected for a dynamic application and suitably maintained will fail as a result of fatigue in compression. Once each revolution each ball or roller receives a contact stress of hundreds of thousands of pounds per square inch on a minute bearing area. The fatigue failure appears as a spalling or separation of flakes of metal from the rolling elements or from the race. When this fatigue failure occurs the bearing must be replaced, even though it will still rotate and carry the load. Harder materials have longer lives under fatigue, hence the necessity for a very hard rolling element. The life of a rotating antifriction bearing therefore is a certain number of revolutions at a specified load. The calculation of this probable life is explained in a later section.

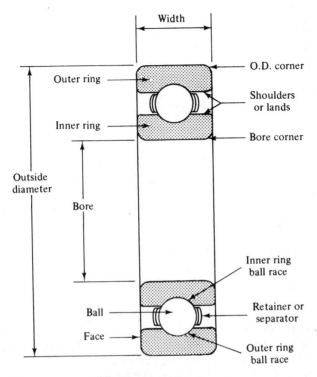

FIGURE 6-5 *Ball bearing parts.*

The required hardness in the rolling elements is obtained from high-carbon steel alloys. The most common ball and roller alloy is 52100, containing about 1% carbon and 1.3–1.6% chromium. Rolling elements that must resist corrosive attack are usually made of stainless steel alloy 440C, which contains about 1% carbon and 16–18% chromium. This alloy is also used in very high-temperature applications. Carbon provides the required hardness and chromium the resistance to corrosion.

6-6 LUBRICATION OF ROLLING BEARINGS

Lubrication principles for a rolling bearing are quite different from those that apply to sleeve bearings because the load is carried on rolling elements and not by a film of oil. Nevertheless a lubricant is required, and serves the same three functions in both types of bearings:

1. Reduction of sliding wear.

2. Removal of heat from the bearing.

3. Protection of the bearing from dirt, water, and other contaminants.

171

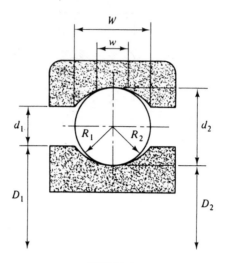

FIGURE 6-6.

Since an antifriction bearing rolls, it might be supposed that lubrication is unnecessary for the first of these functions, the reduction of sliding wear. Actually most ball and roller bearings involve some sliding. This action is explained for a ball bearing by Fig. 6-6. The surface speed of a point near the outside diameter of the inner race is $\pi D_1 \times$ rpm. The speed at the bottom of the groove in this race is less, because the diameter D_2 is less. In the case of the ball, the maximum surface speed is the ball rpm $\times \pi d_2$, but at a point at d_1 the diameter is less and the surface speed is lower. Thus a slower part of the ball is in contact with the fastest moving part of the race and therefore there must be sliding. The manufacturer makes the groove in the race with a radius about 4% larger than the ball radius; this partially prevents slippage between them. Hence the roll path is a narrow path of width w instead of the full groove width W. Sliding friction and wear are slight if the bearing is lightly loaded, but wearing effects become more severe under heavy loads. If there is end thrust on the bearing, there is a displacement of races and ball as shown in Fig. 6-7, because the grooves have a larger curvature than the balls. Under this condition of end thrust, sliding wear is more severe.

Usually antifriction bearings are lubricated with grease, which in addition to lubrication prevents the entry of foreign particles. High-speed or high-temperature bearings, however, are lubricated with oil for removal of heat. The life of a grease is considerably reduced by hot temperatures. A sealed bearing should be packed one-third full of grease.

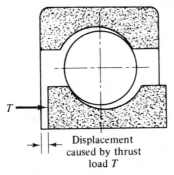

T

Displacement
caused by thrust
load *T*

FIGURE 6-7 *Displacement in a rolling bearing due to thrust.*

6-7 BEARING SEALS AND SHIELDS

Dirt must be excluded from any kind of bearing because it will act as a grinding abrasive within the bearing. Seals and shields are required to prevent such contamination and also to retain oil or grease applied to the bearing. Felt, rubber, leather, or other materials are used as seals in a variety of configurations to seal lubricants in and contaminants out.

Felt seals should be soaked in oil of about SAE #20 before installation. This soaking reduces the coefficient of rubbing friction by about one-third. Other sealing materials are oiled after mounting in place. Since the seal rubs on the shaft, a smooth shaft surface is required to reduce abrasion of the seal.

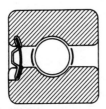

FIGURE 6-8 *Ball bearing with seal.*

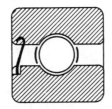

FIGURE 6-9 *Ball bearing with shield.*

Shields (Fig. 6-9) are made of strip steel fastened to the outer race of the bearing. Shields do not rub on the shaft or inner race as a seal does. There is just enough clearance between the shield and the inner race to allow excess lubricant to leak but still prevent entrance of foreign matter.

6-8 TYPES OF ANTIFRICTION BEARINGS

The common types of antifriction bearings are illustrated in Figs. 6-10 to 6-20. The following remarks concern their characteristics and functions.

1. **Self-aligning ball bearing:** of this bearing has two rows of balls which roll on the spherical surface of the outer race (Fig. 6-10). This spherical surface allows for angular misalignment in the shaft arising from errors in shaft mounting, deflection of the shaft, or frame distortion in the machine. This type of bearing is suited to the carrying of radial loads or moderate thrust loads.

FIGURE 6-10 *Self-alignment ball bearing.*

2. **Single-row deep-groove ball bearings:** Also called Conrad bearings, these are the most widely used of the antifriction type bearings (Fig. 6-11). Both radial and thrust loads can be carried by this bearing.

FIGURE 6-11 *Single row deep groove ball bearing.*

3. **Angular contact ball bearings:** These have deep grooves in the races and one shoulder of the outer race partially removed to allow assembly (Fig. 6-12). The design allows the bearing to carry a heavier thrust load or a combined thrust and radial load because of the deeper groove and the larger number of balls used. The thrust can be taken in one direction only. To carry a radial load only, such a bearing must be mounted in pairs as in (a) or (b) of Fig. 6-13. The figure shows a double-row angular contact bearing in a single unit. Figure 6-13(a) shows an internally converging type while 6-13(b) illustrates an externally converging (angles converge inside the bearing) variety.

FIGURE 6-12 *Angular contact ball bearing.*

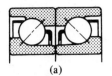

(a)

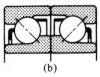

(b)

FIGURE 6-13 *Duplex mounting, angular contact bearings: (a) internally converging; (b) externally converging.*

4. **Double-row deep-groove ball bearing:** As shown in Fig. 6-14, this bearing resembles the single-row deep-groove bearing in its design. The load lines through the balls may be outwardly or inwardly converging. This type of bearing can sustain high radial and thrust loads.

FIGURE 6-14 *Double row deep groove ball bearing.*

5. **Spherical roller bearing:** The bearing in Fig. 6-15 has a spherical surface on the outer race and thus is self-aligning. It too can carry either radial or thrust loads or a combination of both.

FIGURE 6-15 *Sperical roller bearing.*

6. **Cylindrical roller bearing:** The bearing in Fig. 6-16 is designed for very high radial load capacity but not for thrust. There is little sliding in this bearing so that friction is unusually low and high speeds are possible.

FIGURE 6-16 *Cylindrical roller bearing.*

175

3. **Ball thrust bearing:** This bearing, shown in Fig. 6-17, can carry only thrust loads.

FIGURE 6-17 *Ball thrust bearing.*

8. **Tapered roller bearings:** This type (Fig. 6-18) can carry heavy radial and axial loads. These bearings are mounted with another tapered roller bearing elsewhere on the shaft, the two bearings opposing each other's thrust. The steeper the cone angle, the greater the thrust load than can be carried, but at a reduction in radial load capacity. These bearings are not used at high speeds.

FIGURE 6-18 *Tapered roller bearing.*

9. **Spherical roller thrust bearing:** This bearing (Fig. 6-19), carries large thrust loads but has limited radial capacity. It is self-aligning.

FIGURE 6-19 *Sperical roller thrust bearing.*

10. **Precision bearings:** Many of the above bearing types are available as either standard or precision bearings. The use of the phrase "precision bearing" seems to imply that the standard antifriction bearing is not made to precise tolerances. Actually all antifriction bearings are precision bearings, being produced to tolerances of a few ten-thousandths of an inch. A precision bearing is actually a standard bearing for which the tolerances on dimensions are about one-half those allowed in standard bearings. Thus, if the bore tolerance allowed in a standard bearing is 0.0000 in. oversize and

0.0005 in. undersize, for a precision bearing the same tolerances might be 0.0000 in. oversize and 0.0002 in. undersize.

Precision bearings are required for high-speed applications and for precision machinery such as engine lathes, automatic lathes, and grinding machines.

11. **Bearings with larger clearances:** Sometimes operating conditions require bearings with clearances larger than normal. A hot inner race could expand and cause binding in the bearing. Bearings with special clearances are available for such equipment as fans handling hot gases.

12. **Needle bearings:** These are bearings with rollers of very small diameter and no inner race (Fig. 6-20). The needles roll on the shaft itself. The shaft must have sufficient hardness for this purpose. This type of bearing is used when the smallest possible diameter is required.

Bearings are also available in premounted form in pillow blocks (Fig. 6-21), as flanged bearings for bolting in place (Fig. 6-22) and also mounted in a housing or cartridge.

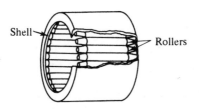

FIGURE 6-20 *Needle roller bearing.*

FIGURE 6-21 *Pillow block.*

FIGURE 6-22 *Ball bearing in a flanged cartridge.*

6-9 MOUNTING ARRANGEMENTS

If bearing loads are too heavy for ball bearings, an arrangement such as that shown in Fig. 6-23 may be used. The roller bearings in the figure support the radial loads, while the ball bearing carries any thrust load and also fixes the shaft axially.

The arrangement of two angular contact bearings as in Fig. 6-24 is used where axial adjustment is required to remove slackness. This is done by controlled clamping pressure on the outer ring of one of the bearings.

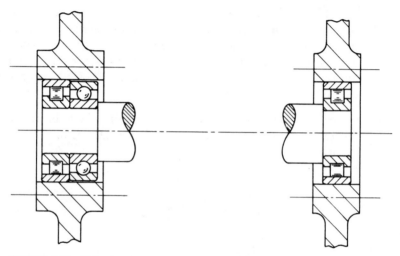

FIGURE 6-23 *Roller bearings for the radial loading; ball location bearing for the axial "fix" and the thrust load.*

FIGURE 6-24 *Two angular contact bearings. Axial adjustment is effected by a sliding fit of the outer ring of the left-hand bearing in the housing, with controlled pressure against this ring.*

A bearing design suited to grease lubrication is shown in Fig. 6-25. Grease is charged through the grease nipple at the top of the housing, while the existing grease discharges through the grease vent at the bottom of the housing after removal of the grease vent plug. The grease space on each side of the bearing should not be unnecessarily wide; about one-third of the bearing width is sufficient. Note that the grease vent is on the opposite side of the housing to the grease nipple.

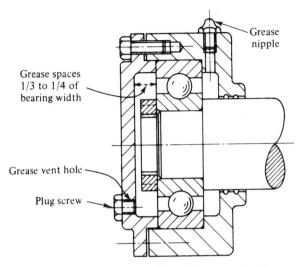

Grease nipple

Grease spaces 1/3 to 1/4 of bearing width

Grease vent hole

Plug screw

FIGURE 6-25 *Bearing mounting for grease lubrication.*

Other details of the design should be noted. Two grease grooves are machined in the housing where it bears against the shaft. These serve as a sufficient grease seal at the shaft. The clearance between housing and shaft at this seal should be about 0.010 in. on radius (0.020 in. on diameter). The shaft is reduced in diameter where it enters the bearing. The shaft shoulder must have a fillet with a radius slightly smaller than the corner radius of the bearing. A minimum of three bolts is required in the cover plate on the left-hand side of the mounting.

For oil lubrication a design such as that of Fig. 6-26 is used, with a sealing ring to seal the oil at the shaft. An oil vent at the proper oil level prevents charging too much oil to the bearing.

A mounting design for a fixed and an axially floating bearing is shown in Fig. 6-27. The right-hand bearing can be adjusted axially. As temperature of the shaft changes, the shaft can expand at the left-hand bearing.

If the bearing is held to the shaft by a clamping nut as in Fig. 6-28, the nut will be wider than the inner race which it must clamp, and this is undesirable. Therefore the nut is chamfered to reduce the width of the nut against the bearing. An alternate clamping arrangement is given in Fig. 6-29, using a minimum of three bolts. Clamping of the outer race is shown in Fig. 6-30.

Temperature variations will cause a shaft to expand, resulting in small variations in the distance between bearings. One of the bearings on a shaft should be fixed in place axially in the housing. All the other bearings should have sufficient axial clearance to move with expansion and contraction. The held or fixed bearing is usually the one at the drive end of the shaft.

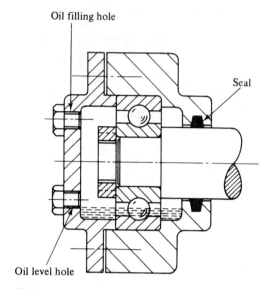

Oil filling hole

Seal

Oil level hole

FIGURE 6-26 *A bearing mounting with oil lubrication.*

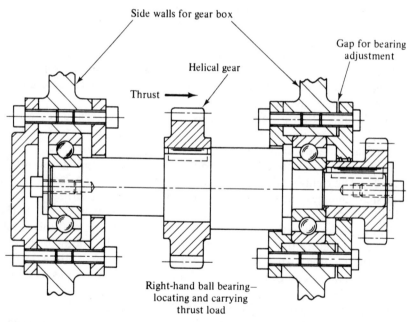

Side walls for gear box

Gap for bearing adjustment

Helical gear

Thrust →

Right-hand ball bearing—
locating and carrying
thrust load

FIGURE 6-27 *Fixed and floating bearing to accommodate temperature change in a gearbox.*

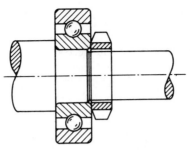

FIGURE 6-28 *Clamping nut chamfered to avoid outer race.*

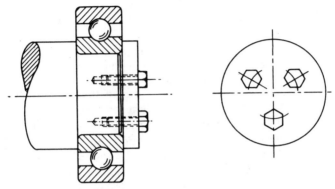

FIGURE 6-29 *A clamping plate.*

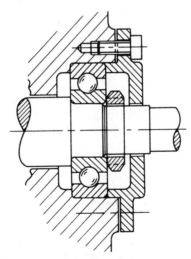

FIGURE 6-30 *Clamping of the outer race.*

181

6-10 BEARING LIFE

Antifriction bearing capacity is influenced by both load and speed, both of which control the fatigue life of the bearing. If the load is doubled, the life of the bearing is reduced to one-eighth. The following are the relationships between life and load:

$$L_n = \left(\frac{C}{P}\right)^3 \qquad \text{for ball bearings}$$

$$L_n = \left(\frac{C}{P}\right)^{10/3} \qquad \text{for roller bearings}$$

where L_n = life in millions of revolutions
       P = radial or equivalent load in pounds
       C = specific dynamic capacity in pounds (see below)

The specific dynamic capacity C is the load that 90% of a group of identical bearings can carry for one million revolutions of the inner race before evidence of fatigue appears. The factor C is obtainable from manufacturers' catalogues. The life L_n is the minimum or "B-10" life of the bearing, defined as the number of revolutions that will be reached or exceeded before fatigue failure by 90% of a group of identical bearings operated under identical conditions. Some manufacturers use the average life, which is that of 50% of a group of bearings rather than 90%.

The following relationships may also be used for bearing life under a difference load:

$$\text{for ball bearings:} \quad \frac{L_A}{L_B} = \left(\frac{P_B}{P_A}\right)^3$$

$$\text{for rolling bearings:} \quad \frac{L_A}{L_B} = \left(\frac{P_B}{P_A}\right)^{10/3}$$

If the life in hours is required,

$$L = \frac{16,667}{\text{rpm}} \left(\frac{C}{P}\right)^3 \quad \text{or} \quad \frac{16,667}{\text{rpm}} \left(\frac{C}{P}\right)^{10/3}$$

EXAMPLE 6-2:   A ball bearing with a specific dynamic capacity C of 23,200 lb. must support a load of 3500 lb. What is the expected life in millions of revolutions and in hours at a rotational speed of 800 rpm?

182

SOLUTION:

$$L_n = \left(\frac{C}{P}\right)^3 = \left(\frac{23,200}{3500}\right)^3 = 292$$

The expected life is 292,000,000 revolutions. At a speed of 800 rpm or 48,000 rev/hour, the expected life is 6080 hours.

Alternately, the life in hours may be calculated thus:

$$\frac{C}{P} = \frac{23,200}{3300} = 6.67$$

$$L = \frac{16,667}{\text{rpm}}\left(\frac{C}{P}\right)^3 = \frac{16,667}{\text{rpm}}(6.67)^3 = 6080 \text{ hours}$$

In the bearing life equation, P represented the radial load or an equivalent radial load in pounds. An equivalent load means some calculated combination of radial and thrust load. The equivalent load is determined in different ways by different manufacturers, but may be approximately and conservatively determined for single-row bearings by the formula:

$$P_e = 0.5R + 1.7T$$

where P_e = equivalent radial load in pounds
          R = radial load, pounds
          T = thrust load, pounds.

But if this equivalent load should be less than the radial load, the radial load should be used in the life equation.

EXAMPLE 6-3: A ball bearing must support a radial load of 2600 lb and a thrust load of 500 lb, with a life of 1000 hours at 800 rpm. What should be the specific dynamic capacity of this bearing?

SOLUTION: The total number of revolutions required of the bearing is 48×10^6.

The equivalent radial load $= 0.5 \times 2600 + 1.7 \times 500 = 2150$ lb. This equivalent load is less than the actual radial load. Therefore the actual load must used to determine C.

$$\sqrt[3]{L_n} = \frac{C}{P}$$

$$\sqrt[3]{48} = \frac{C}{2600}$$

$$3.63 = \frac{C}{2600}$$

$$C = 9450$$

The maximum speed at which an antifriction bearing may be operated is limited by centrifugal force in the bearing and by frictional heat. This limit is expressed by the factor 25.4*DN*, where *D* is the bore diameter in inches and *N* is the rpm. If the bore diameter is given in millimeters, the factor is *DN*. For radial ball bearings, *DN* is about 500,000; for double-row bearings and radial roller bearings, *DN* is 300,000 approximately. Higher speeds are possible with oil lubrication than with grease.

In most antifriction bearing applications, the inner race rotates. If it is the outer race that rotates, the circumstances are quite different. The inner race has a sharper curvature than the outer race and this curvature is opposite to the curvature of the ball or roller. Hence there is a smaller contact area between the rolling element and the inner race than between the rolling element and the outer race and therefore a higher contact stress. When the inner race rotates the same point in the outer race sustains the radial load, but because of the lower stress in the outer race, this is not critical. But if the outer race rotates, the radial load is carried on the same point on the inner race, at a higher stress level than for the outer race. To allow for this difference in stress levels, if the outer race rotates, then the radial load is multiplied by 1.2.

While the above methods of selecting bearings are generally applicable, each manufacturer has a different method of design, selection, and rating of bearings. Since the ratings are taken from the manufacturer's catalogue, it is necessary to use the manufacturer's design and selection methods.

6-11 BEARING CLEARANCE AND PRELOADING

The bearing clearance at the time of manufacturing may be different from the operating clearance, due to such factors as increased temperature during operation, the pressing of the inner race on to the shaft, and the pressing of the outer race in the bearing housing. All these factors reduce the clearance. At the operating temperature, a mounted ball bearing should have a radial clearance ranging from zero to 0.0001 in., or for a roller bearing, slightly more than this range.

Normally antifriction bearings, like journal bearings, will "float" axially and radially to the limit of clearance in both directions. This float, however, is not acceptable in some types of precision equipment such as rotating radar antennas, machine tool spindles, precision gearing, and precision instruments. To eliminate the float, the bearings are preloaded, that is, an initial load is applied to remove end play or radial clearance.

To understand the method of preloading, see Fig. 6-7, where a thrust load is applied to the bearing, thus displacing one race with respect to the other. A typical graph of load against axial displacement is given in Fig. 6-31. Notice that the first increments of load remove most of the clearance;

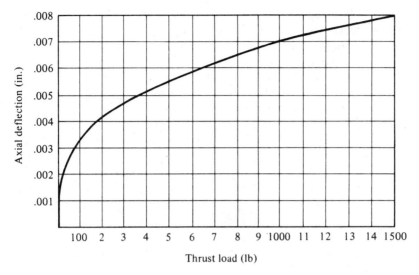

FIGURE 6-31 *Typical deflection curve for thrust leading on a single-row ball bearing.*

a 100-lb thrust removes 0.0035 in. of clearance, while the next 100 lb reduces the clearance only by another 0.001 in.

Suppose this bearing to be preloaded with a 650-lb load during installation, and that the working load on the bearing is an additional 300 lb. The working load produces an additional deflection of only 0.001 in. beyond the preload deflection of 0.006 in. A higher preload would reduce the deflection of the working load still further but might possibly reduce the life of the bearing. Note that without preload, a working load of 300 lb would deflect the bearing 0.005 in.

6-12 HANDLING OF ANTIFRICTION BEARINGS

All antifriction bearings are manufactured to tolerances of a few ten-thousandths of an inch. This degree of precision can be justified by noting that a bearing with an outside diameter of 1 inch will expand in diameter by one ten-thousandth of an inch if heated only 16°F—approximately the temperature rise occasioned by holding the bearing in your hand. If such a precision part is mishandled, struck too hard, or struck in the wrong place, then this precision is easily lost.

Bearings should be removed from their packages only when conditions are ready for installation. Clean working areas and clean hands and gloves will prevent dirt from entering the bearing. When pressing a bearing on a shaft, no force must be used on the outer race; similarly, when pressing a bearing into a housing, no force must be used on the inner race. When the bearing is in place, check to see that it has a slight degree of radial play. This is checked by grasping the outer ring and rocking it gently. Some slight movement should be felt, and the bearing should turn freely. See the installation diagrams of Fig. 6-32.

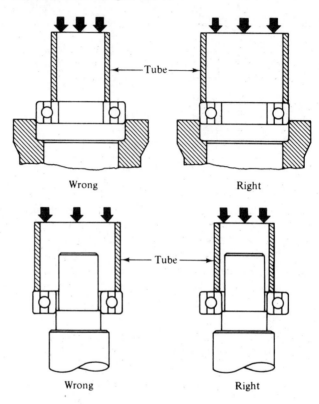

FIGURE 6-32 *Installation of rolling bearings.*

QUESTIONS

6-1. What type of rolling bearing would you select for the following conditions:

    (a)   radial load only, no thrust load

    (b)   shaft must be held by the bearings against axial movement

    (c)   very high radial load on one bearing, small radial load on the other bearing

    (d)   absolute minimum bearing diameter required

    (e)   very high speed, small radial load

6-2. List the four functions of a bearing lubricant.

6-3. A gear pump shaft rotating at 1500 rpm is carried symmetrically in two sleeve bearings each ¾ × ¾ long. The force of the shaft against the bearings due to oil pressure is 3370 lb (each bearing). Determine the bearing pressure in psi and the bearing velocity V in fpm. Calculate PV and select a suitable material for the bearings.

6-4. In Fig. 6-3 why does friction loss in a bearing increase with higher speeds?

6-5. Why are bearings not made of the same material as the shaft?

6-6. Explain the terms hydrostatic, hydrodynamic, and boundary lubrication.

6-7. What are the advantages and disadvantages of babbitts?

6-8. What advantages do the tin babbitts offer over lead babbitts?

6-9. Estimate the life of a nylon bearing, unlubricated, for a radial wear of 0.003 in. if surface velocity is 100 fpm and bearing load is 25 psi.

6-10. Define the static load rating of a rolling bearing.

6-11. Why are sleeve bearings lubricated with oil and rolling bearings with grease (usually)?

6-12. Under what conditions are precision rolling bearings required?

6-13. What purpose does an axially floating bearing serve?

6-14. Explain why the service conditions are more serious in a rolling bearing if the outer race rotates.

6-15. Calculate the equivalent radial load for a rolling bearing carrying 2200 lb radially and a 600-lb thrust load.

6-16. A deep-groove ball bearing has a specific dynamic capacity of 10,400 lb. At 1500 rpm and a radial load of 1800 lb, what is the expected life of this bearing in revolutions and in hours?

6-17. A bearing has a specific dynamic capacity of 5400 lb. What radial load can the bearing sustain at 1500 rpm for a life of 2000 hours?

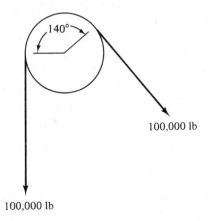

100,000 lb

100,000 lb

QUES. 6-19.

6-18. The specific dynamic capacity of a rolling bearing is 7500 lb. If subject to an equivalent radial load of 1000 lb, what is the expected life of the bearing in millions of revolutions?

6-19. The accompanying figure shows the sheave of a mine hoist, hoisting mine cages weighing 100,000 lb. Ten percent is added to this load to account for acceleration force, since the cage must be accelerated to 65 fps. The main sheave shown has a pitch diameter of 20.65 ft or 248 in. Spherical roller bearings are used on the shaft, and the bearing load is the resultant of the two cable forces shown plus the added 10%.

(a) Determine the load carried by the two bearings.

(b) How many revolutions of the shaft are required to lift a mine cage from a 3000-ft level?

(c) If average hoist speed is 65 fps, what is the rpm of the sheave?

(d) The specific dynamic capacity of the bearings is 590,000 lb. Assuming that the hoist works 20 hours a day lifting and lowering the cage, what is the expected life of the bearings in millions of revolutions and in days?

7

FLUID POWER

7-1 FLUIDS

Fluid power means the transmission of power by pressurized liquids or gases. The word "fluid" means any material that can flow, and includes both liquids and gases. The subject of fluid power divides into two types of systems: pneumatics being the application of fluid power using gases, usually compressed air, and hydraulics, using liquids, normally hydraulic oils. The successful operation of fluid power systems depends above all else on the condition of the fluid in the system and on the seals that prevent leakage. In order to understand fluid power systems and their successful operation it is necessary to understand the characteristics of the fluids that transmit fluid power.

Hydraulic oils are almost incompressible. Actually the volume of an oil will decrease 0.4% for every 1000 psi pressure applied to it. That is, a column of oil 1000 inches or centimeters long would compress to 996 inches or centimeters if pressure is increased by 1000 psi. Oils also expand with temperature rise, about 0.1 percent per degree Fahrenheit, or about half this much per °C. Because oils become heated during power applications, a reservoir or tank is provided in the system to accommodate the increased volume of oil.

In contrast to liquids, gases such as air contract and expand greatly with changes of temperature or pressure. The standard small oxygen bottle used in oxyacetylene welding, 9 inches in diameter and about 4 ft high, actually contains about 200 cubic feet of oxygen at atmospheric pressure. Two hundred cubic feet is a volume approximately 6 × 6 × 6 ft. The compressibility of gases makes them "spongy" in fluid power cylinders, so that the piston of the cylinder may creep after it is stopped in midstroke.

7-2 VISCOSITY

The viscosity of a fluid is its resistance to flow. Water, since it flows and pours readily, has a low viscosity, while a grease, a high-viscosity fluid, does not flow except under pressure, as from a grease gun. The viscosity of a fluid is probably its most important characteristic. If the viscosity of a hydraulic oil is too low, then the leakage past the clearances of valves and pumps and through any other leakage openings will be excessive. But if the viscosity is too high, the oil will not flow fast enough into the inlet side of a hydraulic pump, and the flow resistance through piping and valves will be excessive.

The viscosity of a fluid is reduced at higher temperatures. High-viscosity oils cannot be used at low temperatures, while higher-viscosity oils must be used if operating temperatures are hot enough, say above 120°F, because viscosity increases at low temperatures and decreases at high temperatures.

Many different and confusing units have been used to measure viscosity. Probably under the S.I. metric system a single unit will be adopted in the U.S. in time. To date, the two viscosity units most commonly employed have been the centipoise (cp) or hundredth of a poise, and the Saybolt Second Universal or SSU. Sometimes the viscosity is given in centistokes or hundredths of a stoke, the stoke being the viscosity divided by the density of the fluid. In all these units, a low number means a low viscosity: 20 cp or 20 SSU indicates a "thin" oil, while 1000 cp or a large SSU indicates a "thick" oil. The viscosity of several lubricating oils is given in Fig. 7-1. Generally a viscosity of 150 to 300 SSU at 100°F is preferred for most hydraulic systems, though high-pressure systems sometimes use somewhat higher viscosities. The selection of a hydraulic oil viscosity is however always consistent with the manufacturer's recommendations.

A low-viscosity fluid will flow through an orifice or a pipe more readily than one of high viscosity. The SSU viscosity is determined in a standard laboratory test which measures the time in seconds for 60 milliliters of oil to drain through a Saybolt Universal orifice. The viscosity is measured usually at either of two standard temperatures, 100 or 210°F.

7-3 OTHER HYDRAULIC OIL REQUIREMENTS

1. **Chemical stability:** The oil in a hydraulic system is subject to heating effects in passing through pumps, motors, valves, and piping. At elevated temperatures the oil tends to produce gums, sludges, and

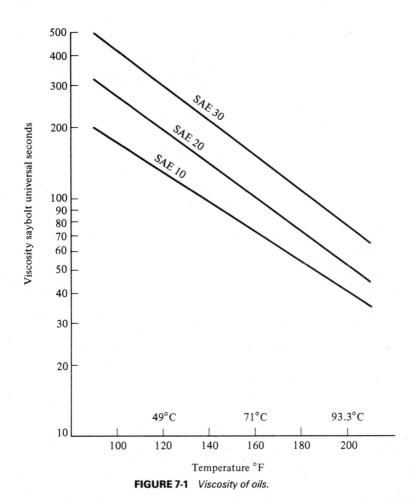

FIGURE 7-1 *Viscosity of oils.*

acid products, all of which are harmful to the parts of the hydraulic system. Some oils are treated with oxidation inhibitors. These delay the onset of oxidation until the additive is depleted, and thus extend the life of the oil under conditions that tend to oxidation.

2. **Demulsibility:** In most hydraulic systems it is not possible to prevent the entry of water into the oil. Water vapor can enter the oil tank through the breather and then condense. Though oil and water do not dissolve in each other, they can combine to form an emulsion. The oil must have the characteristic of demulsibility, which is the ability to separate quickly from water.

The presence of water in the oil will cause rusting of steel components. Antirust additives prevent rust by attaching to steel surfaces to exclude air and moisture.

191

3. **Resistance to foaming:** Air is present in a hydraulic system when it is first started up. After the oil is circulated through the system for a few minutes the air separates from the oil. To prevent foaming, small amounts of antifoaming additives may be included in the oil. The additive produces a weak bubble film so that bubbles will collapse.

4. **Fire resistance:** The fire hazard of mineral oils may be too serious to contemplate in some applications such as hot forging, die-casting, and military applications such as in aircraft carriers. If a nonflammable hydraulic fluid is necessary, then certain synthetic fluids can be used such as phosphate esters and chlorinated hydrocarbons. These however are expensive fluids. Water-base fluids also are sometimes employed. However, these special fluids may attack the usual packings and seals, so that special seals may be required.

5. **Antiwear additives:** Most hydraulic oils now contain an antiwear additive to prevent wear of ferrous metals. If the lubricating oil film should fail and metal-to-metal contact should be made, frictional heat is generated and the additive is activated. The additive reacts chemically with the metal surface to form a lubricating film which prevents further metal-to-metal contact.

6. **Viscosity index improvers.** This type of additive reduces the change in viscosity with temperature. It is used in larger amounts than other oil additives, typically from 3 to 10%, and the larger the quantity used the greater the effect on viscosity.

7-4 THE OIL RESERVOIR

The oil reservoir or tank serves primarily as a supply and storage for the system and its oil. But it has other important functions. Water and air can be separated from oil in the reservoir. The oil heated during circulation through the system can be cooled in the tank. Sludge can be deposited at the bottom of the tank.

The reservoir is usually sized by a simple rule. Its capacity should be 2 to 3 times the delivery of the hydraulic pump in gallons per minute. Thus for a pump delivery of 15 gpm, the reservoir capacity would be within the range of 30 to 45 gallons.

The construction of a typical reservoir is shown in Fig. 7-2. Removable covers at each end allow access for cleaning. The bottom is sloped to a drain plug in the middle. The filler hole is equipped with a fine wire screen to keep foreign material out of the reservoir when oil is added. A baffle plate extends for the length of the reservoir at its center line to separate the pump inlet line from the return line of the hydraulic circuit. This baffle prevents the pump from continuously recirculating the same fluid. Returning fluid thus is held in the tank for a period of time so that any sediment can settle out and trapped air can escape before the oil returns to the pump inlet.

The tank also has a breather to allow air to enter and escape as the oil level changes. The breather contains a filter.

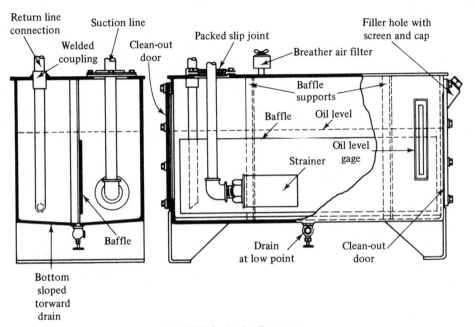

FIGURE 7-2 *Hydraulic pressure.*

The pump inlet line and all circuit return lines extend to a few inches from the bottom of the tank. This arrangement reduces foaming and aeration. The ends of the return pipes are cut at an angle of 45 degrees and this angle is positioned to direct the return flow of oil toward the tank wall and away from the pump inlet line.

7-5 STRAINERS AND FILTERS

The hydraulic oil must be kept clean if maintenance problems in the hydraulic system are to be avoided. Many of the details of reservoir construction just discussed have for their purpose the removal of water, air, and solid contaminants from the oil. In addition magnetic plugs, strainers, and filters are employed to remove solid particles. Even very small particles can be abrasive to valves and other hardware.

Contaminating particles can originate from a variety of sources. They may be introduced during fabrication of the system. The cutting of tube and pipe produces burrs and the welding of tube and pipe produces slag particles; any of these types of particles may enter the system even when the workmanship is conscientious. Lint may be introduced from cleaning rags. During operation particles may enter the system from air breathers or the surfaces of cylinder rods. Even seals and packings will contribute bits of leather, asbestos, and rubber as they are nibbled away with time.

Magnetic plugs located in the reservoir remove steel particles. Filters and strainers remove other types of particles. Both are devices for the removal of solid matter from the fluid, but in the case of the strainer the resistance to motion of such solids is a straight line, while in the case of the filter the resistance to motion of the solid matter is in a tortuous path.

Strainers are made of fine-mesh screens, and while they do not capture the smallest particles, they offer less resistance to fluid flow. Either strainers or low-pressure filters are used on pump inlet lines because the high flow resistance of a filter might starve the pump of oil.

Filter screening elements are made of such materials as paper, sintered metal, wood cellulose, or plastic. These remove particles which are very fine, even as small as 2 microns. Since filters and strainers gradually become loaded with foreign material the filtering elements must be cleaned or replaced at intervals.

The smaller the clearances between mating parts of pumps and valves the finer the filtering must be. In the case of simpler hydraulic circuits powered by gear pumps, a more relaxed standard of filtration is usually acceptable. Normally the manufacturer of the components will recommend adequate filtering requirements.

The size of small particles is measured in *microns*. A micron is a thousandth of a millimeter or a 25,000th of an inch. The smallest particle that the unaided human eye can discern is 40 microns; a grain of salt measures about 100 microns. But 40 microns is a reasonably large particle in a hydraulic system and of a size to score the critical surfaces of pumps and valves. Such particles are normally removed by filters; strainers are not designed in general to remove particles smaller than 150 microns (100 mesh screen).

For pneumatic systems a combination unit incorporating a filter, a pressure regulator, and a lubricator is frequently employed to condition compressed air (Fig. 7-3). The air line filter removes particles in the range of 25 to 50 microns. Air entering the filter is directed downward with a swirling motion to throw out solid particles and water toward the wall of the filter bowl. Such particles fall to the bottom of the bowl where a drain cock is located for their removal. In filter sizes up to 2-inch pipe size, the filter bowl is removable for cleaning or for replacing the filter (after air pressure is removed).

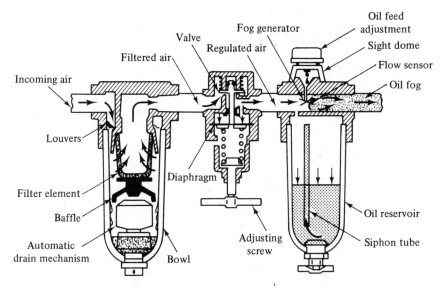

FIGURE 7-3 *Filter-regulator-lubricator unit for a pneumatic system.*

An air compressor operates with two pressure switches, a cut-in and a cut-out switch. If these switches are set at, say, 80 psi for cut-in and 100 psi for cut-out, then the air compressor will be switched on when pressure drops to 80 psi and stop when pressure reaches 100 psi, the cut-out pressure. To eliminate such pressure fluctuations from the pneumatic system, or to use lower pressures than the compressor output, the regulator is needed.

Lubrication for pneumatic equipment such as air cylinders is provided by the lubricator, which injects a controlled amount of oil into the air.

Air becomes dirtier and wetter with pressure, and the higher the pressure the dirtier and wetter it becomes. The reason is that any such contamination is concentrated into a smaller volume of air when the air is compressed.

The compressed and conditioned air is stored in a receiver tank. From this receiver air is withdrawn to the pneumatic system.

7-6 HYDRAULIC PLUMBING

Pipe and tube are both classified by nominal size and wall thickness, but different dimensions are used for pipe and tube. Except for very small sizes, the nominal size of a pipe corresponds reasonably closely with the actual inside diameter of standard wall pipe. A 1-inch tube is exactly 1.00 inches in outside diameter; a 1-inch pipe is 1.315 inches in O.D. and 1.049 inches I.D. in standard wall thickness. Pipe is dimensioned for threading with standard pipe threading dies; tubing is not usually threaded. While pipe is not usually used for bends in hydraulic systems, hydraulic tubing is often formed into bends; a minimum bend radius of 3 tube diameters is recommended. Pipe dimensions for small pipe are given in the table.

Table of pipe sizes.

Nominal Pipe Size	O.D.	I.D. for Schedule 40 or Standard Pipe	I.D. for Schedule 80 or Extra Heavy	Threads per Inch
⅛	0.405	0.269	0.215	18
¼	0.540	0.364	0.302	18
⅜	0.675	0.493	0.423	18
½	0.840	0.622	0.546	14
¾	1.050	0.824	0.742	14
1	1.315	1.049	0.957	11½
1¼	1.660	1.380	1.278	11½
1½	1.900	1.610	1.500	11½
2	2.375	2.067	1.939	11½
2½	2.875	2.469	2.323	8
3	3.500	3.068	2.900	8

Flexible hose (Fig. 7-5) allows relative motion between the components it joins, and is selected instead of tubing for the following circumstances:

1.   Vibration.

2.   Complex routing of conduit through confined space or complex contours.

3.   Frequent connection and disconnection of lines.

The typical flexible hose has an inner tube with a reinforcement of wire braid, metal wire, or fiber, and a protective cover tube.

Flexible hose is usually classified in nominal sizes which are equivalent tubing sizes. For example, a ⁵⁹⁄₆₄ O.D. by ½ in. I.D. hose is given a nominal size of ⅝ in, indicating that it is the equivalent of ⅝ in. tubing. Such flexible hose is also referred to by number, the number giving the number of sixteenths of an inch in the nominal size. The above example would be a No. 10 flexible hose, since ⅝ is 10 sixteenths. Besides a range of sizes, hose is made in several pressure ratings.

The most suitable materials for hydraulic plumbing are steel and plastic, though plastics are used only at low pressures. Copper is not used in high-temperature circuits because it promotes the oxidation of petroleum fluids. Copper also tends to crack under vibration conditions. Galvanized pipe is hazardous to hydraulic systems because the zinc coating can flake off.

The correct pipe size for hydraulic conduit can be found from Fig. 7-4.

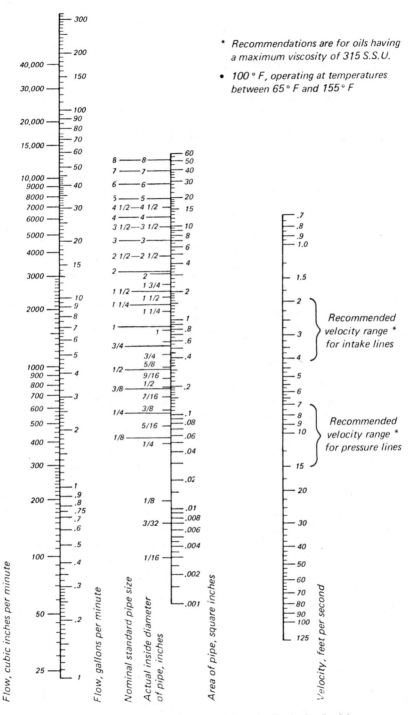

* Recommendations are for oils having
  a maximum viscosity of 315 S.S.U.

• 100° F, operating at temperatures
  between 65° F and 155° F

Recommended
velocity range *
for intake lines

Recommended
velocity range *
for pressure lines

Flow, cubic inches per minute

Flow, gallons per minute

Nominal standard pipe size

Actual inside diameter
of pipe, inches

Area of pipe, square inches

Velocity, feet per second

FIGURE 7-4 *Nomograph for selecting hydraulic piping.*

197

FIGURE 7-5 *A neat and skillful layout of hydraulic plumbing. Every bend in the tubing is exactly where it should be. Note the two unions below the electric solenoid valve (upper right) to allow this valve to be removed for maintenance, and the four shut-off valves to isolate lines for maintenance. The pump delivers 356 pm and is mounted on the reservoir. Flexible hose provides ease of disconnection and maintenance and isolates vibration.*

It will be noted that slower fluid velocities and larger diameters for the same flow are required on pump inlet lines. The use of this nomograph is illustrated by the following examples.

What size conduit would be selected for the inlet line to a pump delivering 35 gpm to a hydraulic system?

At the right-hand side of the nomograph a flow velocity range of 2 to 4 fps is recommended for intake lines. Suppose we use 3 fps. Connect 3 fps with a straight line to 35 gpm flow. The line intersects a pipe size of nearly 2½ in. I.D. Use 2½ or 2 in. I.D.

For the discharge from the same pump what conduit size would be selected?

If a velocity of 15 fps is chosen, then a pipe size of 1 in. I.D. is indicated.

Except for very high pressures, say more than 3000 psi, the wall thickness of pipe and tubing is calculated from the formula

$$\text{Wall thickness} = \frac{\text{max psi} \times \text{tube O.D.}}{2 \times \text{tensile strength of tube}} \times \text{safety factor.}$$

EXAMPLE 7-1: A steel tube must carry 20 gpm at 15 fps and a pressure of 2500 psi. The steel is an annealed hydraulic tubing with a tensile strength of 55000 psi. A factor of safety of 4 will be used. Select tube I.D., O.D., and wall thickness.

SOLUTION: The inside diameter must be obtained from Fig. 7-4; the outside diameter depends on the wall thickness.

From Fig. 7-4 the I.D. for 15 fps and 20 gpm must be ¾ in. Assume an O.D. of 1.0 in. Then wall thickness equals

$$\frac{2500 \times 1}{2 \times 55000} \times 4 = 0.09 \text{ in.}$$

But I.D. + 2 × wall = 0.75 + 0.18 = 0.93 in. This is slightly less than an O.D. of 1.00 in. but is conservative. Tubing other than 1.00 in. O.D. by 0.75 in. I.D. may not be available, and this selection is a standard size. If the calculation is made for ⅞ in. O.D., 0.75 in. I.D., this smaller tube will be found to have too thin a wall.

7-7 CONNECTIONS

Threading of hydraulic conduit is not recommended. Leaky connections and weakened pipe wall are possibilities, besides which threading produces slivers of metal which may enter the hydraulic system to cause scoring of cylinder rods, valve spools, seals, and pumps. Flaring, brazing, or welding are preferred joining methods.

Pipe threads are of two general types: taper pipe thread and straight pipe thread. The thread size corresponds to nominal pipe size. The tapered pipe thread has two designs. The National Standard Taper Pipe Thread (NPT) seals by contact along the flanks of the threads. There is leakage along the helical clearance in the thread roots. This clearance is sealed with the use of a sealing compound applied to the threads. See Fig. 7-6. In the Dryseal American or National Taper Pipe Thread (NPTF) the roots and crests of the thread engage before the thread flanks make contact (Fig. 7-6). Sealing compound is not necessary, though a lubricating thread compound should be used to prevent galling (welding) of the threads when they are tightened. The NPT and NPTF threads are interchangeable. The NPTF type is used on most fluid power fittings.

Welded joints are preferred for permanent joints in high-pressure systems. To prevent weld spatter or welding slag from contaminating the system, socket joints (Fig. 7-7) are used. Such a joint also provides alignment for the welding operation and also is vibration-resistant.

The flared joints of Fig. 7-8 are preferred for thin-wall tubing. The end of the tube is flared with a flaring tool and is held against the body of the hydraulic fitting, which has either a 37° or 45° flare. The 45-degree flare is suited to softer nonferrous tubing materials, while the 37-degree flare is used for harder carbon steel and stainless steel tubing, which may split if flared to 45 degrees. The flared fitting may be a two-piece or a three-piece connection. The figure shows two types of three-piece connections. The flareless connection must be used with thick-walled tubing; it uses a bite-type ferrule to grip the tube. The bite-type fitting should not be used on thin tube or plastics, since it may collapse the tube.

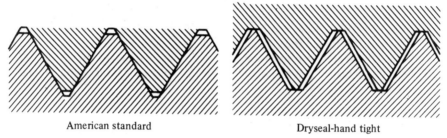

American standard   Dryseal-hand tight

FIGURE 7-6 *Standard and dryseal pipe threads.*

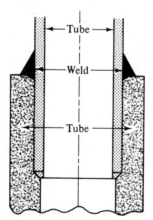

FIGURE 7-7 *Socket welded tube joint.*

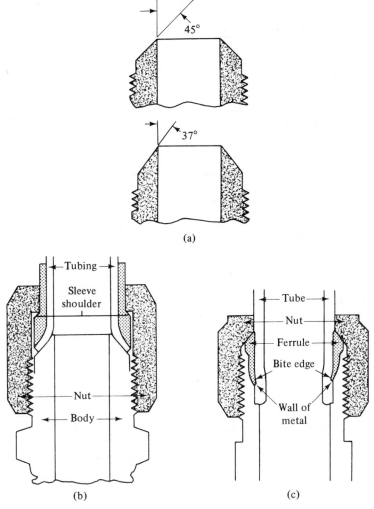

FIGURE 7-8 *Tube joints: (a) 45° and 37° flares; (b) three-piece flared tubing connector; (c) three-piece flareless connector.*

Self-flaring fittings do not require the tubing to be first flared. These fittings may be used on thin-wall tube, because there is no large torque on the tube as is used when flaring. When the nut of the fitting is tightened, a welding sleeve presses against the end of the tube and the mating female part of the fitting to produce a flare.

Most fittings for steel tubing can be used for plastic tubing if a sleeve is inserted into the plastic tube to give it resistance to crushing. A fitting specially designed for plastics is the Poly-Flo fitting of Fig. 7-9.

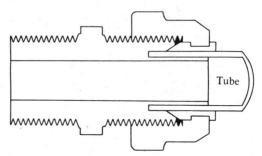

FIGURE 7-9 *Poly-flo connector for plastic tubing.*

7-8 QUICK-CONNECT COUPLINGS

Quick-connect couplings, also called quick-disconnect couplings and QC couplings, are used to attach and disconnect pneumatic and hydraulic hoses. They are a necessity for air-operated tools such as impact wrenches, nut-runners and air drills, or for connecting and disconnecting a tractor and its hydraulically operated farm equipment. Connection and disconnection require no tools and virtually no time.

QC's have two components. The female part is called the *coupler,* socket, or body. The male part of the coupling is referred to as a *plug,* tip, or nipple.

Three types of QC are available. The *straight-through* type is the simplest, since it has no valve in either the plug or the coupler. Before disconnecting this type, pressure must be shut off with a valve in the line. *Single-shutoff* QC couplings are chiefly used with air lines. There is only one shut-off valve, usually in the coupler. This must be installed in the pressure side of the coupling. *Double-shutoff couplings* (Fig. 7-10) are valved both in the coupler and the plug. The valve is spring-loaded and seats when the parts of the couplings are disconnected.

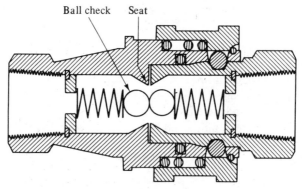

FIGURE 7-10 *A double-shutoff quick-connect coupling. When the connection is made, the ball checks are pushed off their seats.*

All QC couplings have a locking mechanism which holds the plug securely in the coupler while connected. The locking member is usually a number of balls, though wire rings, collets, pins, or other devices are also in use.

7-9 VALVES FOR HYDRAULIC AND PNEUMATIC SYSTEMS

The common globe and gate valves familiar in domestic water supply lines (Fig. 7-11) are also used as shutoff valves in fluid power circuits. In addition a number of valves for special functions are required. A relief valve is

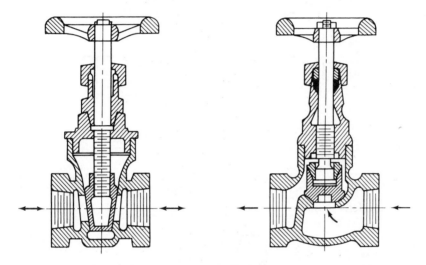

FIGURE 7-11 *Gate valve and globe valve. The straight-line flow pattern of the gate valve offers less resistance to fluid flow and less pressure drop.*

necessary in the circuit immediately downstream of the pump to prevent the generation of excessive pressures that could burst a hose or crack a fitting. Reversing valves are required so that cylinders and fluid motors can reverse their direction of movement. Flow control valves meter the fluid so that a controlled rate of speed can be applied to the movement of a cylinder rod. Check valves prevent reverse flow. These are the more usual valve requirements; others will be noted.

Fluid power valves may have the following flow path arrangements:

1. Two-way or straight-way valves. These valves have two ports, and may be normally open normally closed. Fig. 7-13 shows the graphcal symbol for a two-way valve, in one case normally closed and opened manually, in the second case normally open and closed man-

ually. The check valve of Fig. 7-12 is closed for flow in one direction but open for flow in the opposite direction. The piloted check valve is normally closed to flow in one direction, but on receipt of a pressure signal from a small pilot line will open to flow.

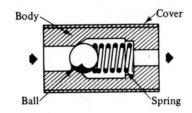

FIGURE 7-12 *Simple check valve.*

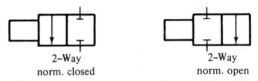

FIGURE 7-13 *Standard symbols for manually-operated two-way valves.*

2. Three-way valves have three ports, usually one inlet port and two outlet ports (Fig. 7-14). The valve may be shifted to supply either outlet.

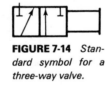

FIGURE 7-14 *Standard symbol for a three-way valve.*

3. Four-way valves have an oil supply port, two ports which connect to the two ends of a cylinder, one open and one closed, and an exhaust port. This type of valve is further discussed presently.

Valves may be operated either manually with a hand lever, electrically by means of a solenoid, or by pilot. In pilot operation a small pilot line supplies pressure to one end of the valve spool to shift it.

A simple case of pilot operation is shown in Fig. 7-15. This valve is a pilot-operated check valve. The purpose of a check valve is to allow flow in only one direction; in this valve the flow is from the inlet port on the right-hand side to the outlet port on the left-hand side. Such flow will occur when pressure at the inlet is sufficient to overcome the spring force holding the poppet against its seat. Pressure at the outlet port cannot open the poppet to allow flow in the opposite direction. If such a valve as this is used in the circuit for a load-lifting device, flow through the check valve allows the load

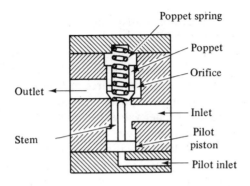

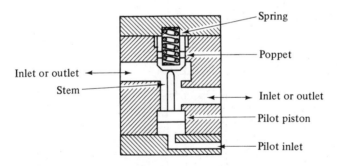

FIGURE 7-15 *Pilot-operated check valve: (a) valve in closed position; (b) valve opened by pilot operation.*

to be lifted and the poppet spring will hold the valve closed to prevent the load from accidentally descending and perhaps causing an accident. However, there must be some method of reversing flow to allow the load to be lowered. The pilot piston and its stem make reverse flow possible. For reverse flow from outlet to inlet, pressure is applied underneath the pilot piston from a small pilot line. If pilot pressure is sufficiently high, the pilot stem will lift and force the poppet off its seat to allow reverse flow. Pilot pressure must overcome the pressure on the top side of the pilot piston as well as the spring force.

Pilot-operated check valves are used in the circuit of Fig. 7-31.

7-10 RELIEF VALVES

The relief valve is a pressure control valve, designed primarily to provide overload protection for the fluid power circuit, but also used to limit the force exerted by a cylinder or the torque exerted by a fluid motor. If used for overload protection, the relief valve is installed immediately downstream of the hydraulic pump, which is the source of flow and pressure. No other valving must be installed between pump and relief valve. Pneumatic circuits do not normally require a relief valve, because the air compressor delivers air at a controlled maximum pressure.

The simplest type of relief valve is shown in Fig. 7-16. One port is connected to the pressure line and the other discharges to the reservoir. The ball check is held against its seat by spring pressure. The pressure setting is adjusted by turning the adjusting screw. When spring force is exceeded by

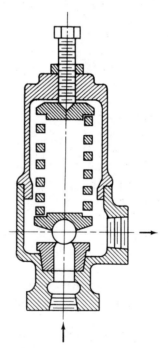

FIGURE 7-16 *Relief valve.*

the hydraulic force against the ball, the ball lifts and oil is discharged to the reservoir.

Pressure reducing valves are used to reduce the pressure in a branch circuit to a level below the operating pressure of the main circuit. These valves also have an adjustable spring setting so that the required maximum branch pressure can be obtained.

7-11 SEQUENCE VALVE

A hydraulic circuit may have two cylinders, one of which may have to operate before the other. For example, consider a circuit which includes a clamp cylinder to clamp a workpiece and a drill cylinder which holds a rotating drill. The drill must not advance until the workpiece is clamped. At the end of the drill cycle the drill cylinder must be fully retracted before the clamp cylinder releases the workpiece. In both the clamp and the unclamp parts of the whole cycle there must be a proper sequence of operation of the two cylinders.

A sequence valve controls this sequence of operation. In Fig. 7-17 oil enters the sequence valve at port C and flows out to the line feeding the first cylinder in the sequence at D. Using this case of a clamp and drill sequence, the clamp cylinder receives oil and closes on the workpiece. When the clamp is closed on the workpiece, the clamp cylinder can receive no more oil and pressure in the circuit rises suddenly. This increased pressure overcomes the force of the spring in the sequence valve and the piston rises to open port E which connects to the second cylinder in the circuit. Port D is still open, but since this line is already full of oil, pressure is maintained on this line while oil flows to E.

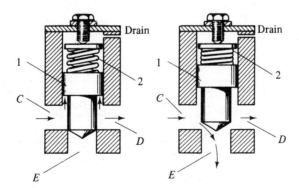

FIGURE 7-17 *Successive positions of the piston in a sequence valve.*

It is not usual to employ sequence valve in penumatic circuits. Pressure variations in pneumatic circuits may produce irregular operation of a sequence valve.

7-12 FOUR-WAY VALVES

If a cylinder is to advance and then to retract, oil must be supplied first to one end of the cylinder for advance, and then to the other end for retraction, unless the cylinder is single-acting with spring return. But for a double-acting cylinder, with oil flow to both ends, there must be four oil flows, two flows in and two out. This sequence of flows requires a four-way valve to supply oil to either end of the cylinder and to drain oil from either end. Schematically, the operation of the four-way valve is shown in Fig. 7-18. To supply the head end of the cylinder, the ports of the four-way valve are connected as in Fig. 7-18(a). To supply the rod end, the ports are connected as in Fig. 7-18(b). The spool of the valve must be shifted into either of two positions to give these two connection arrangements. The shifting may be done manually with a lever-operated valve, or with a solenoid, or with a pilot.

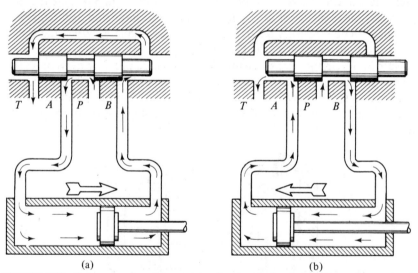

(a)   (b)

FIGURE 7-18 *Four-way valve: (a) supplying head end of cylinder; (b) supplying rod end.*

7-13 SYMBOLS AND CIRCUITS

The standard symbols for hydraulic and pneumatic components are reproduced in Fig. 7-19.

A basic circuit for a single cylinder is diagrammed in Fig. 7-20. The cylinder can be reversed manually and the relief valve gives circuit protection.

Cylinders

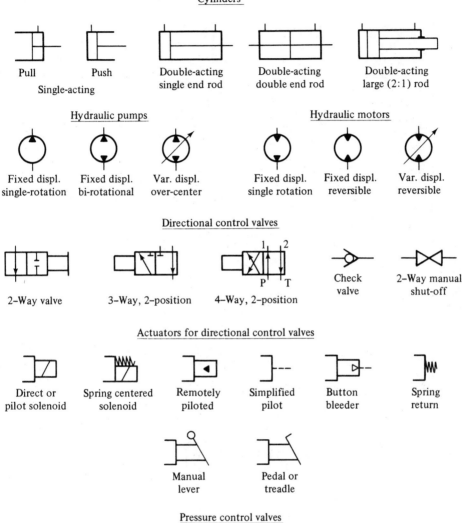

Pull   Push   Double-acting   Double-acting   Double-acting

Single-acting   single end rod   double end rod   large (2:1) rod

Hydraulic pumps   Hydraulic motors

Fixed displ.   Fixed displ.   Var. displ.   Fixed displ.   Fixed displ.   Var. displ.
single-rotation   bi-rotational   over-center   single rotation   reversible   reversible

Directional control valves

2–Way valve   3–Way, 2–position   4–Way, 2–position   Check   2–Way manual
valve   shut-off

Actuators for directional control valves

Direct or   Spring centered   Remotely   Simplified   Button   Spring
pilot solenoid   solenoid   piloted   pilot   bleeder   return

Manual   Pedal or
lever   treadle

Pressure control valves

Pressure   Sequence or   By-pass valve   Pressure
relief valve   by-pass valve   external pilot   reducing valve

FIGURE 7-19   *Standard symbols for hydraulic and pneumatic circuits.*

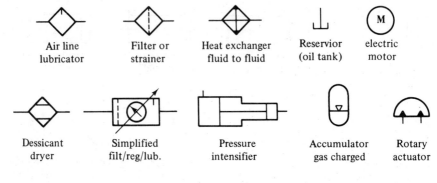

Air line lubricator | Filter or strainer | Heat exchanger fluid to fluid | Reservior (oil tank) | electric motor

Dessicant dryer | Simplified filt/reg/lub. | Pressure intensifier | Accumulator gas charged | Rotary actuator

Flow control valves

Restriction fixed | Var. restriction (needle valve) | Flow control

Figure 7-19 *(Continued)*

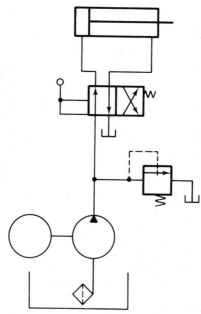

FIGURE 7-20 *Simple one-way cylinder circuit.*

A clamp and drill circuit is shown in Fig. 7-21, using a sequence valve to operate the drill cylinder only after the clamp cylinder has operated. However, the circuit as given does not sequence the return of the drill and clamp, for which a second sequence valve is required. The complete circuit is given in Fig. 7-22, for clamping before drilling and retracting the drill before the retracting clamp.

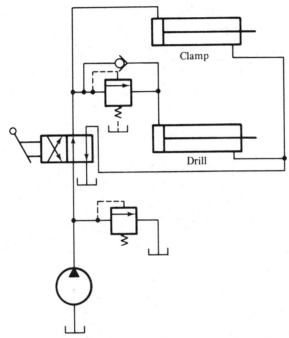

FIGURE 7-21 *Clamp and drill circuit. Clamp must close before drill advances. There is only one reservoir, though the reservoir symbol appears four times.*

7-14   VARIATIONS OF THE BASIC FOUR-WAY VALVE

The four-way valves previously described had two positions: forward and reverse. Many four-way valves have three positions: forward, neutral, and reverse. Figure 7-23 shows a three-position four-way valve. The neutral position shown is called a *tandem center*.

Consider a tractor fitted with a backhoe at one end and a front-end loader at the other end. The two tractor attachments are never operated together. The circuit most suited to this pair of attachments is that of Fig. 7-24, using tandem center four-way valves. Either attachment can be operated alone, while the idling position shown allows the pump to unload oil

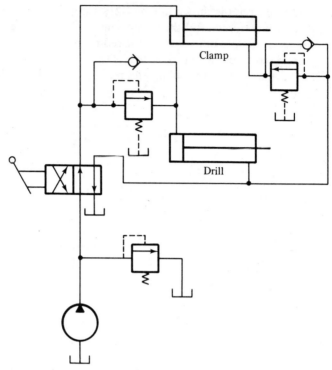

FIGURE 7-22 *Clamp and drill circuit with retraction of cylinders also sequenced.*

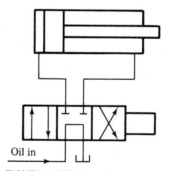

FIGURE 7-23 *Tandem center three-position four-way valve.*

at low pressure back to the reservoir. In the idling position the two ports of each four-way valve are blocked, preventing either the loader or the backhoe from moving.

Other neutral configurations are shown in Fig. 7-25. In the *closed center* neutral position all ports are blocked and some means other than the relief valve must be provided for unloading the pump discharge. The *float center*

212

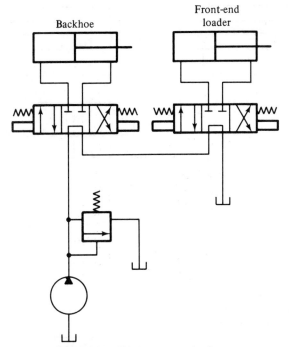

FIGURE 7-24 *Tandem center circuit.*

spool connects both cylinder ports together and to the reservoir. This prevents what is called "fluid lock" on both sides of a piston. On some machines the cylinder rod is attached to a moving machine member. The cylinder provides power for most of the machine cycle then floats with the machine movement. In such an application the float center spool is used.

The *regenerative* spool connects both cylinder ports to the pressure port. The name "regenerative" comes from the regenerative circuit of Fig. 7-25(c), for which this type of four-way spool is suited. The oil exhausted from one end of the cylinder is injected into the supply end. The *open center* spool connects all ports together. This type is more often used with hydraulic motors than with cylinders.

In pneumatic circuits air is not returned to the air receiver but is simply exhausted to atmosphere. If the air is to be released to atmosphere from the four-way valve, then the five-way connection of Fig. 7-26 is used.

Large solenoid-operated four-way valves may have such a heavy spool that a solenoid big enough to shift the spool would draw excessive current. Such a valve will be piloted. The solenoid will shift a small four-way valve mounted on top of the four-way valve itself. This small valve is called a *pilot valve.* The pilot valve directs oil under pressure to the ends of the main spool to shift it (Fig. 7-27).

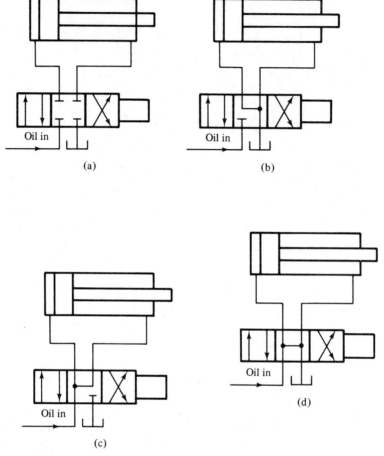

FIGURE 7-25 *Various center connections available in three-position four-way valves: (a) closed center; (b) open center; (c) regenerative center; (d) open center.*

7-15 BANK VALVES AND STACK VALVES

A *bank valve* is an assembly of two or more valve spools, often housed in a single casting, for operation of several branch circuits from a single pump. *Stack valves* are individual valves designed to be stacked together to make a bank valve. These banks usually include the relief valve for the pump.

Bank valves are of the three-position type, manually operated. The spool connections are shown in Fig. 7-28. These connections suggest that this type of valve is a six-way valve, but these are four-way valves with six ports.

Bank valves are connected either in series or in parallel. Fig. 7-29 shows the series connection, with all valve spools in neutral. If the first branch

214

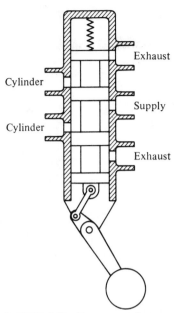

FIGURE 7-26 *Four-way valve construction for pneumatic circuits.*

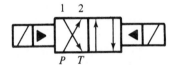

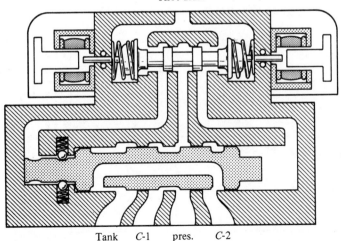

FIGURE 7-27 *A double solenoid polit-operated two-position four-way valve with its symbol.*

215

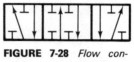

FIGURE 7-28 *Flow connections in a stack valve.*

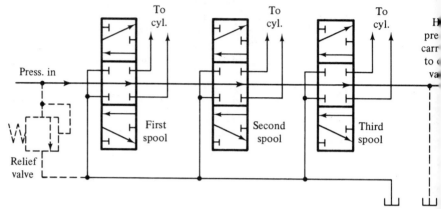

FIGURE 7-29 *Bank valves in a series circuit.*

circuit is operated by shifting the left-hand valve to the top position shown, oil from the pump goes to the cylinder and returns through the valve spool to the horizontal tank line at the bottom of the diagram. If any one valve is thrown fully to an operating position, no oil is available for any valve downstream (though a skilled operator can throttle two valves and supply oil through both).

A parallel group of bank valves is shown in Fig. 7-30. In this grouping it is possible to supply oil through more than one valve.

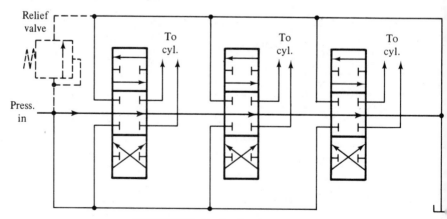

FIGURE 7-30 *Bank valves in a parallel circuit.*

A bank valve system for a more complex type of lift truck is shown in Fig. 7-31. In the diagram the three valves are shown separated instead of

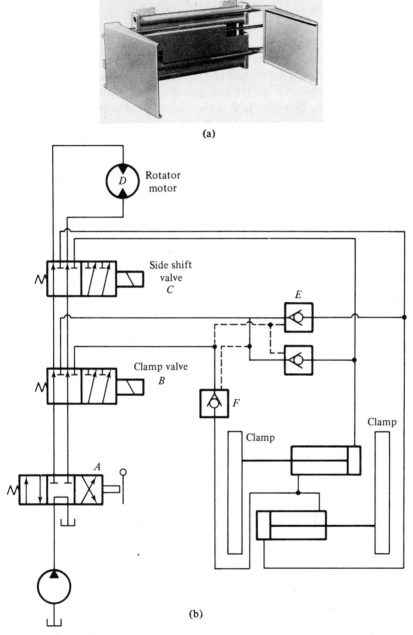

FIGURE 7-31 *Lift truck clamp attachment and the hydraulic circuit for rotating, clamping, or sideshifting the clamped load.*

banked for ease of reading the diagram. This type of lift truck does not have a pair of forks but instead large flat clamps which can squeeze and hold a pile of cartons between them. Clamps replace forks for handling such loads as large paper rolls and what is referred to in the warehouse industry as the "three K's": Kleenex, Kotex, and Korn Flakes.

In addition to the clamp circuit there is a sideshift circuit for moving the unit load in the clamps to the right or to the left for exact placement, and a rotator which can turn the clamps and the load upside down.

The sideshift circuit is shown in Fig. 7-32. Sideshifting occurs when the connections of the sideshift four-way valve are those shown on the right-hand side of the valve symbol. The choice of right or left shift is made with the manually operated four-way three-position valve that is immediately downstream of the pump (the relief valve is not shown). Oil flows to the head end of one of the clamp cylinders, while exhausted oil from the same cylinder goes to the rod end of the second cylinder. Oil exhausted from the head end of the second cylinder returns through the sideshift valve.

When the four-way sideshift valve has the connections shown at the left-hand side of the valve symbol, oil flows to the rotator motor.

The clamps are opened or closed by means of the circuit shown in Fig. 7-33. To open the clamps, oil passes from the clamp valve through check valve *F* to the head ends of both cylinders. Oil exhausts from both cylinders through check valves *E*, which are opened by pilot pressure (shown by

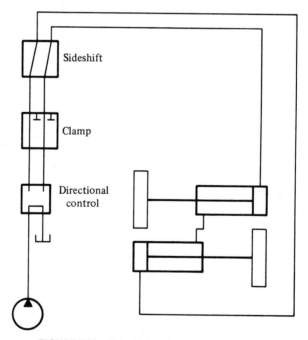

FIGURE 7-32 *Sideshifting circuit for lift truck clamps.*

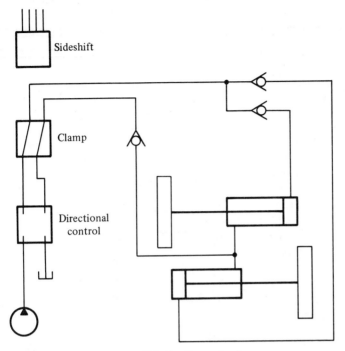

FIGURE 7-33 *Clamp circuit.*

dotted pilot lines) from the pressure in the lines through check valve *F*. To close the clamps the oil flow is the reverse of that for opening the clamps.

7-16 SPEED CONTROL

The speed of cylinders and fluid motors is controlled by the rate at which air or oil is supplied to them. Speed control is provided by flow control valves. The needle valve of Fig. 7-41 is one type of flow control valve, though other types are also in use.

There are three arrangements for flow control:

1. Meter-in, with the flow control valve in the cylinder supply.

2. Meter-out, with the flow control in the cylinder exhaust.

3. Bypass flow control.

These arrangements are given in Fig. 7-34.

Usually a meter-out circuit is to be preferred since it provides a back pressure that prevents the load from running away.

219

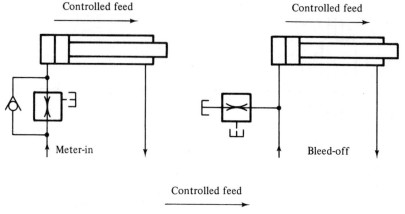

Meter-in

Controlled feed

Controlled feed

Bleed-off

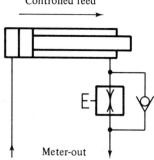

Controlled feed

Meter-out

FIGURE 7-34 *Three methods of speed control.*

7-17 ACCUMULATORS

An accumulator stores oil under pressure. The hydraulic pump supplies oil to the accumulator, which then supplies the circuit. Among the uses of accumulators is the maintaining of pressure on a circuit over an extended period of time, compensating for leakage, a function that a hydraulic pump cannot perform. Accumulators also can be used to reduce the size of the hydraulic pump, as will be shown in the example which follows.

The pressure on an accumulator may be obtained by weights, by springs, or by gas pressure (pneumatic accumulator). The pump supplies oil to the accumulator to a maximum pressure as set on the circuit relief valve or on a pressure switch. The pressure supplied by the accumulator falls as it supplies oil. Only the weight-loaded accumulator provides a constant pressure as the accumulator discharges; unfortunately this type of accumulator is large and heavy even in small capacities.

Standard accumulator sizes are 1.5 cu. in., 10 cu. in., 1 pint, 1 quart, and 1, 2½, 5, 7½, 10 and 20 gallons. The usual maximum pressure rating is 3000 psi.

Accumulator operation is exemplified in the bladder type of pneumatic accumulator shown in Fig. 7-35. A nitrogen gas precharge is used to fill the

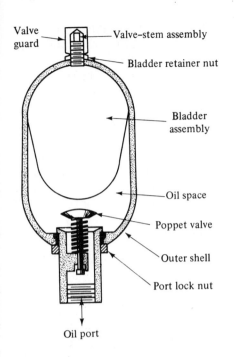

Valve guard — Valve–stem assembly

Bladder retainer nut

Bladder assembly

Oil space

Poppet valve

Outer shell

Port lock nut

Oil port

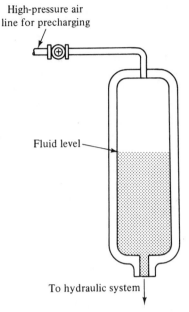

High-pressure air line for precharging

Fluid level

To hydraulic system

Hydropneumatic (gas-pressurized)

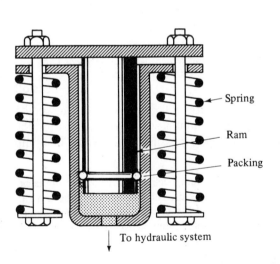

Spring

Ram

Packing

To hydraulic system

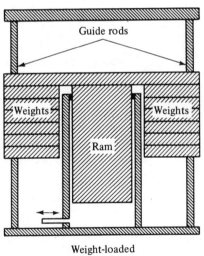

Guide rods

Weights   Weights

Ram

Weight-loaded

FIGURE 7-35 *Accumulators: (a) bladder type of pneumatic accumulator; (b) hydro-pneumatic (gas-pressurized accumulator; (c) spring-loaded and (d) weight-loaded accumulator.*

bladder to a pressure of 60 to 75% of hydraulic system pressure. The poppet valve at the bottom of the accumulator is held open by a spring, but as the bladder fills to precharge pressure it expands to close the poppet on its seat. As long as the hydraulic system pressure is below the gas precharge pressure there is no action by the accumulator, since the poppet valve remains seated. As the hydraulic pressure reaches the gas precharge pressure the poppet begins to open and oil enters the accumulator. Increasing hydraulic pressure compresses the gas bladder with the admission of more oil. Oil continues to enter the accumulator so long as oil pressure exceeds gas pressure. If the hydraulic pump is shut off, then oil will flow from the accumulator to the hydraulic circuit so long as gas pressure exceeds hydraulic pressure.

It is of course extremely hazardous to make adjustments or repairs to a hydraulic system while it is pressurized by an accumulator.

A basic accumulator circuit is given in Fig. 7-36.

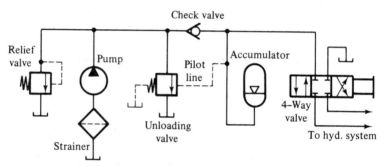

FIGURE 7-36 *Accumulator circuit. When a predetermined pressure is reached, the pump discharges to tank through the unloading valve and the system is supplied by the accumulator.*

Sometimes a fluid power circuit requires a large flow of oil for only a short time. In these circumstances an accumulator is advantageous. In the following example an accumulator makes possible a reduction in pump capacity by about two-thirds.

EXAMPLE 7-2: A fixed-displacement pump delivers oil to an accumulator. The system requires 10 gpm for 30 seconds, then 40 gpm for the next 15 seconds, then a dwell (zero demand) for 15 seconds, after which the preceding cycle immediately repeats. Find the required pump delivery.

SOLUTION: The required pump delivery must equal the average flow required by the system over a full cycle. The amount of oil delivered during the cycle

$$= 10 \text{ gpm} \times \frac{30 \text{ s}}{60 \text{ s}} + 40 \text{ gpm} \times \frac{15 \text{ s}}{60 \text{ s}} + 0 \text{ gpm} \times \frac{15 \text{ s}}{60 \text{ s}}$$

$$= 5 + 10 + 0 = 15 \text{ gal.}$$

Each minute 15 gallons must be delivered. Therefore the pump must have a capacity of 15 gpm. Without the accumulator the capacity of the pump would have to equal the maximum delivery, 40 gpm.

7-18 CYLINDERS

For rotary motion fluid motors are employed, and for linear motion cylinders. Fluid-power cylinders may be single-acting or double-acting. The single-acting cylinder receives oil on one side of the piston only and is retracted by a spring on the other side. Some large vertical cylinders can be retracted by gravity. The double-acting cylinder receives oil on both sides of the piston.

The basic construction of a cylinder for air or oil is shown in Fig. 7-37. The cylinder itself has a smooth inside surface and is sealed into *end caps* at either end. The end caps contain the intake and discharge ports. The piston is a somewhat loose fit. O-rings, cup packings, or other types of seal close the small clearance between cylinder and piston. The cylinder rod has a polished surface and may be chrome-plated. It passes out of the end cap through packings that include a seal and also a wiper that keeps out dirt.

The significant characteristics of a cylinder are its maximum pressure rating, its bore (inside diameter) and its stroke. The bore size is determined by the cylinder pressure to be used and the total force that must be exerted.

EXAMPLE 7-3: A cylinder must be selected for a small press to be rated at 20 tons. Cylinder pressure is to be 1500 psi. Determine the piston diameter.

SOLUTION:

$$20 \text{ tons } = 40,000 \text{ lb}$$

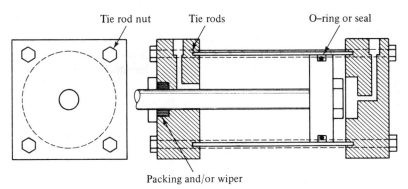

FIGURE 7-37 *Basic cylinder construction.*

But each square inch of piston receives 1500 psi.

Required piston area $= {}^{40,000}\!/_{1500} = 26.7$ sq. in.

A piston 6 in. in diameter has an area of 28.27 sq. in., and is suitable.

EXAMPLE 7-4: A ram with a five-inch bore uses a pressure of 5000 psi. What is the force exerted by the ram?

SOLUTION:

$$\text{Area of a 5-in. circle} = 19.6 \text{ sq. in.}$$

$$\text{Force of the ram} = 19.6 \times 5000 = 98,000 \text{ lb}$$

The usual port sizes (NPTF) for cylinders are given in the table below. If faster cylinder speeds are required, larger ports must be supplied and the size of the valves supplying oil must be correspondingly larger.

Cylinder port sizes and piston speeds.

Cylinder Bore	Port Size NPTF	gpm Flow at 15 fps	Piston Speed (fpm)
1½	½	14.2	155
2	½	14.2	87
2½	½	14.2	56
3¼	¾	25.0	58
4	¾	25.0	38
5	¾	25.0	24
6	1	40.3	27
7	1¼	70.0	35
8	1½	95.2	36
10	2	159.2	39
12	2½	224.2	38

Mounting arrangements for cylinders are illustrated in Fig. 7-38. Mounting and alignment must be done with care, otherwise friction and binding of the rod will damage the rod and packings. The various types of fixed center-line mounts support the cylinder in the plane of the rod. Fixed noncenter-line mounts support the cylinder at both ends and are desirable to resist heavy thrust forces. The pivoted mounts must be used if the load travels in a curved path.

Cylinder rods may either pull or push loads. The compressive force of a push load introduces complications because a long rod may buckle under a high compression load. Such buckling may put excessive pressure on the piston seals or the seals in the head of the cylinder. To prevent buckling the rod may be given a diameter larger than would be used for a tension pull,

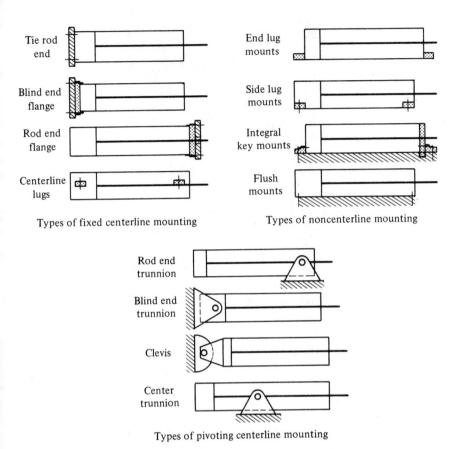

Types of fixed centerline mounting

Types of noncenterline mounting

Types of pivoting centerline mounting

FIGURE 7-38 *Methods of mounting cylinders.*

for increased stiffness. Alternatively, for additional support the minimum distance between the piston and the rod seals may be limited by a stop tube, which is simply a tube of the proper length slipped over the rod. The stop tube will of course reduce the maximum cylinder stroke, and the cylinder length will then have to be the sum of the required stroke plus the length of the stop tube.

The best mounting condition to prevent buckling is that where the front end of the cylinder and the end of the rod are both rigidly supported. Hinge-mounted cylinder if mounted horizontally or at any angle other than vertical produce a bending stress in the rod due to the weight of the cylinder.

Cushioning

Shock loads are produced when loads are stopped suddenly at the end of the piston stroke. Such shocks are prevented by cushioning. The cushion-

FIGURE 7-39 *Door-opening cylinders on a furnace. Despite the long cylinder stroke, small-diameter rods are used because there is only a tension force in the rod.*

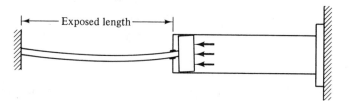

Exposed length

FIGURE 7-40 *A long slender rod may buckle under a compressive force.*

ing system operates on the principle that as the piston approaches the end of the stroke, the exhausted oil is diverted through an adjustable needle valve, thus introducing a backpressure that allows the piston to decelerate. See Fig. 7-41. When oil is supplied to the cushioned end of the cylinder it enters through the check valve shown in the figure so that pressure can apply over the whole area of the piston.

A warning should be given that conditions, both as to flow and pressure, may be different on the two sides of the piston, if on one side there is a rod and not on the other side. Consider the following two cases.

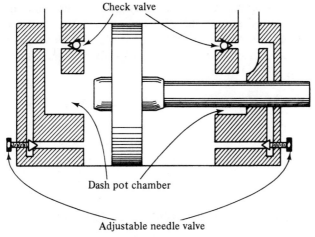

Check valve

Dash pot chamber

Adjustable needle valve

FIGURE 7-41 *A cushioned cylinder.*

1. Figure 7-42 shows a double-acting cylinder supplied with oil at the
    head end and with the exhaust blocked by a closed valve. The cyl-
    inder bore is 6 in. and rod diameter is 2½ in. If the oil supply is at a
    relief valve setting of 1500 psi, what is the pressure in the rod end of
    the cylinder?

$$\text{Cylinder area} = 28.3 \text{ in.}^2$$

$$\text{Rod area} = 4.9 \text{ in.}^2$$

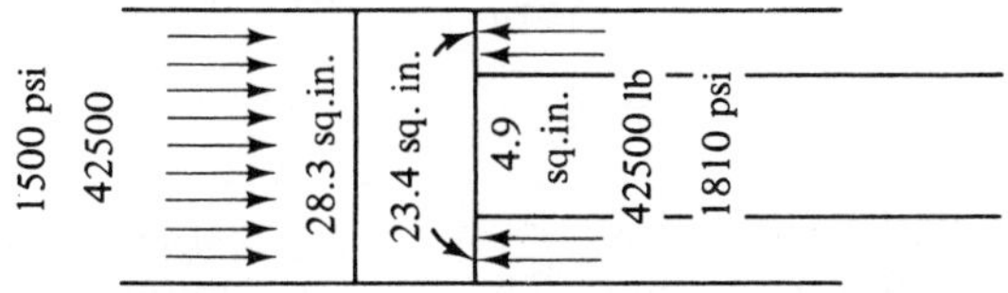

FIGURE 7-42 *Pressure on the rod side of the piston is
higher than system pressure if the oil on the rod side is
blocked.*

The force on both sides of the piston must be the same. The force
on the head end of the piston = 1500 psi × 28.3 = 42,500 lb. The
same force is exerted on the opposite side, but the next area on this
side due to the presence of the piston = 28.3 − 4.9 = 23.4 in.²
The pressure on the rod side = $^{42,500}/_{23.4}$ = 1810 psi.

2. Suppose that the pump can supply oil at a rate that moves the piston

in the above example at a velocity of 80 in. per minute when oil is supplied to the head end. When the four-way valve is reversed and oil is supplied to the rod end, what is the cylinder speed on return?

There is a smaller volume to fill at the rod end, therefore the return speed will be faster.

$$\text{Area at head end} = 28.3$$

$$\text{Area at rod end} = 23.4$$

Then if oil is supplied to the rod end, the rate of travel will be $^{28.3}\!/_{23.4}$ times faster, or 97 ipm.

7-19   HEAT GENERATION IN HYDRAULIC SYSTEMS

The energy put into the oil by the hydraulic pump will appear either as useful work or as heat. As an example of the heating effect of circuitry upon the oil, consider the following case. When the circuit is idle, the pump discharges oil through the relief valve.

This is a poor circuit. A relief valve should be used as protection, not as in this case, as a part of the oil flow circuit. Ideally a relief valve, like a fire extinguisher, should never be used.

The pump delivers 7½ gpm through the relief valve when the cylinder is idle. Relief valve setting is 1500 psi.

$$\text{Horsepower when idling} = \frac{7\frac{1}{2} \times 1500}{1714} \quad \text{(see Sec. 9.1 for this formula)}$$

$$= 6.55$$

Since no useful work is done, this horsepower must appear as heat in the oil. But 1 HP = 42.4 Btu per minute. Therefore in 1 minute of idling 6.55 × 42.4 Btu of heat are developed, which is 278 Btu/min, enough heat to raise oil temperature about 5 degrees per min. In a very long idling period the oil would be seriously overheated and would have to be replaced. Alternatively a large heat exchanger could be used to extract the heat from the oil, but this is an expensive method of correcting a bad circuit.

Suggest a better neutral connection for the four-way valve.

EXAMPLE 7-5: In a circuit in which a hydraulic pump drives a hydraulic motor, the pump is driven by a gasoline engine. The pump receives 16 HP from the engine, and the hydraulic motor delivers 10 HP to the load. What is the total heat generated in the circuit in 1 hour?

SOLUTION: Since 16 HP is put into the hydraulic circuit and only 10 HP is taken out as useful work, the missing 6 HP must be converted into waste heat.

$$\text{Energy loss in Btu/hour} = 2544 \times 6\,\text{HP} = 15,260\,\text{Btuh}.$$

This is a large quantity of heat, and a heat exchanger will be required to remove it.

7-20 COOLING CAPACITY OF RESERVOIRS

As much as a third of the waste heat generated in oil circuits may be radiated from cylinders, pumps, and plumbing, provided the circuit is well designed and the heat generation not excessive. In order to be conservative, it could be assumed that the system radiates no heat, except for the reservoir.

The amount of heat which can be removed by the reservoir depends on its total surface area and the temperature difference between the oil and the air surrounding the reservoir. The following formula is reasonably accurate.

Heat radiated from the reservoir in horsepower
= 0.001 × reservoir surface area × temperature difference

This formula assumes that the bottom of the reservoir is at least 6 in. above the floor so that the bottom also radiates heat. The following table gives the surface area of reservoirs in square feet.

Reservoir Capacity (gallons)	Surface Area (square ft)
10	10.8
15	12.8
20	14.0
30	16.1
40	24.3
50	29.2
60	31.6
80	40.2
100	47.4
120	52.9
150	55.4
200	69.8

EXAMPLE 7-6: How much heat, expressed in horsepower, can be radiated from a 40-gallon reservoir if the surrounding air is at a temperature of 70 degrees and the oil temperature must not exceed 130°?

SOLUTION: The temperature difference is 60 degrees.

Surface area of the tank = 25 sq. ft closely

Heat lost by tank = $0.001 \times 60 \times 25$ = 1.5 HP

If the heat generation exceeds this amount, then a heat exchanger is needed.

QUESTIONS

7-1. Define demulsibility.

7-2. How does an antiwear additive perform its function of reducing wear?

7-3. What are the several functions served by an oil reservoir?

7-4. How large is a micron in English and S.I. units?

7-5. How is filtering performed in an air filter?

7-6. Why is air always dirtier after compression?

7-7. Why is galvanized pipe unsuitable for fluid power plumbing?

7-8. Size the hydraulic lines designated by letter in the accompanying figure.

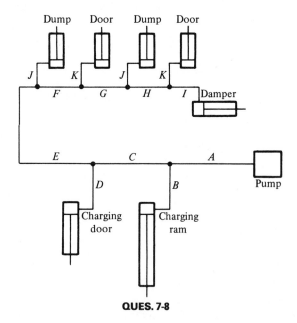

QUES. 7-8

The hydraulic circuit operates a small city incinerator. The charging door cylinder requires 10 gpm and the charging ram that pushes refuse into the incinerator furnace has a 4-in. bore, a stroke of 8 ft, and must extend in 5 seconds. The charging door first opens, then the charging ram operates, then the door closes after the ram is retracted. The sequence of door opening and charging is a reasonably constant operation. The two dump cylinders each require 5 gpm to operate and the two door cylinders each require 8 gpm. The damper cylinder requires 4 gpm to operate. Only one of these five cylinders is operated at a time.

7-9. Why is threaded pipe not recommended for hydraulic systems?

7-10. Explain the difference between a standard and a Dryseal pipe thread.

7-11. What is the function of the following valves:

  (a) relief valve

  (b) sequence valve

7-12. Sketch the following center positions for four-way valves:

  (a) tandem center

  (b) closed center

  (c) float center

  (d) regenerative center

  (e) open center

7-13. How is a cylinder cushioned?

7-14. If a hydraulic circuit that delivers 16 HP is 88% efficient, how much heat is generated in the circuit each minute?

7-15. Estimate the amount of heat in horsepower that is radiated from a 200-gallon reservoir, if the temperature of the oil returning from the circuit is 140° and air temperature is 70°F.

7-16. The figure shows a regenerative circuit, in which the cylinder rod advances with full pressure on both sides of the piston. Explain how this circuit gives a rapid advance and a slow retraction of the piston.

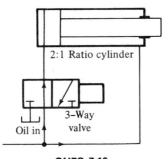

QUES. 7-16

7-17. The circuit shown uses only two-way valves. Indicate which valves must be open and which closed for the following cases:

(a) advance at full force

(b) retract

(c) regenerative extension (as in Question 16)

(d) floating piston

(e) stop in midtravel.

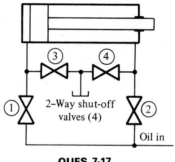

QUES. 7-17

8

SEALS

Fluid power did not become an important method of power transmission until the era of World War II. Its acceptance as a useful technology was impeded by the lack of suitable seals, and the development of adequate seals was delayed by the lack of suitable sealing materials. The rubber O-ring was ineffective until a suitable rubber was developed that was resistant to oils. Before World War II almost all rubber was natural rubber, which is swelled and attacked by mineral oils. Nitrile, urethane, and other synthetic rubbers are the only suitable rubbers for oil seals.

The seals and sealing methods discussed in this chapter are not confined to fluid power equipment, but are used widely in other types of equipment and machinery.

8-1 TERMINOLOGY OF SEALS

Every technical area has its special language. The following terms must be understood if sealing techniques and requirements are to be understood.

Compression set: Failure of a material to return to its original shape after removal of a compressive load.

Durometer hardness: Sealing materials are soft and special methods are used to measure their hardness. For rubbers the Shore durometer, a small hand-held instrument, is used to measure hardness. Sealing rubbers usually have a durometer hardness of A70, which is exactly the hardness of an automobile tire. A hardness of A80 indicates a greater hardness, while

A60 would be softer. Harder rubbers produce less friction but require more force to compress.

Elastomer: An organic material with the ealstic properties of a rubber. The term includes the familiar rubbers, both natural and synthetic.

Gasket: A flat thin sheet of sealing material clamped between mating metal parts.

Gland: The cavity in which a seal is installed. An O-ring for example must be installed in a groove, the groove being called the gland.

Packing: Soft material which is packed under slight compression to seal pressurized fluids.

Swell: The volume increase in a seal caused by absorption of the fluid being sealed.

8-2 STATIC SEALS

Static seals prevent leakage between two components fastened together. At least four methods are in use to produce a static seal, shown in Fig. 8-1.

1. Flat gasket.

2. O-ring.

3. Gask-O-Seal (Parker Seal Co.).

4. Liquid elastomers cured to solid condition either by heat or catalyst.

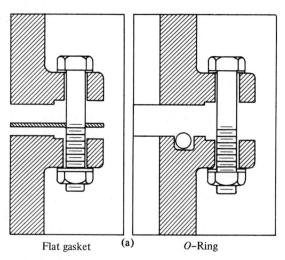

Flat gasket (a) O–Ring

FIGURE 8-1 *Static seals: (a) flat gasket and O-ring.*

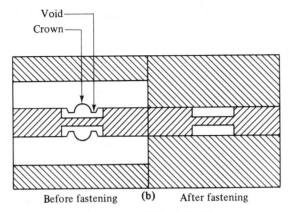

Void ——
Crown ——

Before fastening **(b)** After fastening

FIGURE 8-1 *(b) Gask-O-seal.*

The flat gasket is the simplest to install. Such gaskets are made of paper, asbestos, cork, or rubber. The gasket is sealed by heavy pressure from bolts or studs. Failure occurs in time either due to compression set or sudden rupture.

The O-ring static seal is discussed below under dynamic seals. The gland is a groove in which the O-ring sits. The groove being shallower than the O-ring, it is compressed when the mating parts are bolted together.

The Gask-O-Seal uses an elastomer in a metal retainer. The elastomer is deformed when the parts are assembled. See Fig. 8-1.

The silicone rubbers are used for formed-in-place seals. Several methods are used to harden these rubbers: heat-vulcanizing, two-component, room-temperature curing (RTV type), and one-component RTV. Heat-curing is an inconvenience, and the RTV types are preferred. Two-part RTV silicone rubbers have a curing catalyst as one component, while a one-component formulation uses moisture from the air for the curing action.

Silicone rubbers are excellent for high-temperature and low-temperature applications, but are generally inferior in physical properties to other synthetic rubbers in the more standard applications. The tensile strength, elongation, and tear resistance of silicone rubbers are all relatively low an compression set is high. Durometer hardness of these rubbers is also low, in the range of 50 to 60.

8-3 DESIGN OF O-RING GLANDS

Details for a suitable O-ring gland are shown in Fig. 8-2. To prevent cutting and abrading of the O-ring, the corners of the gland must have a radius and the surfaces of the gland must be reasonably smooth but not polished.

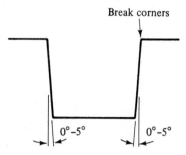

FIGURE 8-2 *O-ring groove.*

A polished surface will not attract the oil film needed to lubricate the O-ring.

For pressures up to 1500 psi in dynamic applications (that is, where one of the two components being sealed must move) a maximum clearance of 0.006 in. should be used for O-rings with section diameters of 0.1 in. or less and 0.008 in. for section diameters up to 0.2 in. "Clearance" in this case is defined as the difference in diameter of mating parts, not difference in radius. For higher pressures either the clearance can be reduced, the hardness of the O-ring increased, or backup or anti-extrusion rings used (Fig. 8-3).

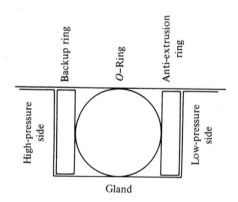

FIGURE 8-3 *O-ring with backup and antiextrusion rings.*

No harm is done the O-ring if it must be slightly stretched or compressed to put it in place. But sharp-edged tools must not be used for inserting or removing O-rings.

The O-ring gland may be cut into either the male or the female member of the seal. For either static or dynamic sealing, the following procedure is used to design an O-ring groove.

For illustration, assume that an O-ring is to be seated in the gland of a piston in a hydraulic cylinder, a dynamic sealing application. The inside diameter of the cylinder must be known, also the clearance between piston and cylinder. The cross-sectional diameter of the O-ring is decided. Two rules are followed:

1. The depth of the gland should be such as to squeeze the O-ring between 20 and 30% of its section diameter.

2. The width of the O-ring gland should be the diameter of the O-ring plus twice the above squeeze.

Suppose the I.D. of the cylinder is 4.000 in., the clearance between piston and cylinder is 0.008 in. on diameter (0.004 in. on radius) and the O-ring is 0.25 in. in diameter. The ring O.D. of the O-ring will of course be 4 in. Suppose we select a squeeze of 20%. Then 20% of 0.25 in. = 0.050 in.

Now if the O-ring were not compressed (zero squeeze), the depth of the gland would have to be 0.25 in. less 0.004 in., the radial clearance, or 0.246 in. For a 20% squeeze, this depth must be reduced by 0.050, so that the gland depth will actually be 0.246–0.050 or 0.196 in. To give the machinist some latitude in which to work, a depth of 0.193–0.196 would be acceptable. If the groove should be cut 0.193 deep, the rubber will absorb some oil and increase in size to compensate.

The width of the gland must be

$$0.250 + (2 \times 0.050) = 0.350 \text{ in.}$$

If the gland were cut into the cylinder wall, the procedure would be identical.

However it may be noted that O-ring dimensions change slightly in service through two effects which oppose each other: compression set and swell. Compression set flattens the compressed O-ring over a prolonged period of time. Compression set increases with temperature but roughly can be estimated as 10% of the section diameter. The maximum allowable swell for 0-ring rubbers is 20%.

Now if we suppose that compression set is 12% and swell 15% for the above O-ring, the final squeeze would be

Initial squeeze + swell − compression set = 20% + 15% − 12% = 23%

Twenty-three percent is within the maximum allowable squeeze of 30%.

Two O-ring accessories are sometimes employed for the support of the O-ring against high pressures. Both are flat or contoured rings or rubber, leather, or felt. If the accessory ring is located in the O-ring groove on the high-pressure side of the O-ring, it is referred to as a *backup ring*. The combination of O-ring and backup ring can withstand much higher pressures than an O-ring alone, since a portion of the total pressure is sustained by the backup ring. If the same ring is located in the O-ring groove on the low-pressure side of the O-ring, the accessory ring is referred to as an anti-extrusion ring, since it will prevent the O-ring from extruding into the clearance space. Sometimes both a back-up and an anti-extrusion ring are employed with the O-ring in the gland (Fig. 8-3).

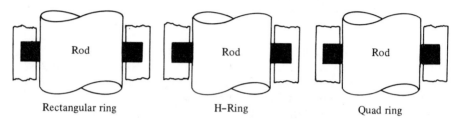

Rectangular ring   H–Ring   Quad ring

FIGURE 8-4 *Dynamic seals that serve the same function as an O-ring.*

Without the use of these accessory rings, an O-ring with a durometer hardness of 70 can easily sustain pressures at least to 1500 psi over long periods with a diametral clearance not greater than 0.008 in. If the clearance is reduced to 0.004 in. on diameter, a safe working pressure limit is about 3000 psi. With a diametral clearance of 0.004 in. it will require a static pressure of about 20,000 psi to extrude the O-ring out of its gland. The O-ring therefore is an exceedingly accommodating and reliable device. It will seal even after pieces of the O-ring are broken off. But it must never be installed or operated without lubrication.

8-4 EXCLUSION SEALS

When a cylinder rod withdraws into the cylinder, any foreign particles on the surface of the rod may be drawn into the cylinder and would then enter the hydraulic oil. Rod wipers and scrapers, which are types of exclusion seals, prevent entry of such particles. Usually wipers have the shape of a bevelled edge facing out and toward the piston rod. The material for such wipers, such as that of Fig. 8-5, is usually a suitable synthetic rubber, such as polyurethane rubber. This rubber is tough, strong, abrasion-resistant, and with an unusually low friction coefficient for a rubber. The rubber wiper however cannot seal against pressure, being too soft and deformable for this purpose.

Another type of exclusion seal is the V-ring of Fig. 8-6. The V-ring is an annular rubber with a tapered sealing lip extending concially outward. Sealing pressure of the lip against the counter-surface is kept low to reduce frictional heat and wear.

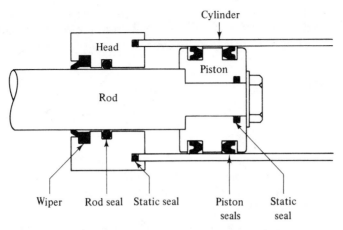

FIGURE 8-5 *Wiper and séals in a hydraulic cylinder.*

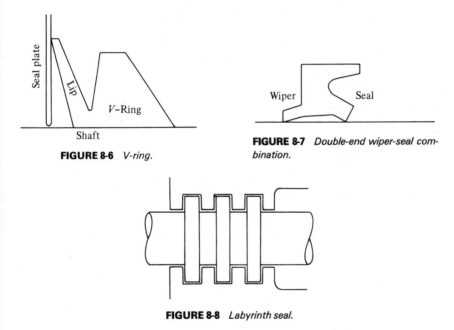

FIGURE 8-6 *V-ring.*

FIGURE 8-7 *Double-end wiper-seal combination.*

FIGURE 8-8 *Labyrinth seal.*

A sealing wiper is a double-ended seal that serves as a wiper at one end and a seal at the other. Such a component is shown in Fig. 8-7.

8-5 LABYRINTH SEALS

The labyrinth seal of Fig. 8-8 has a positive clearance and therefore a small leakage rate. This leakage is held to a small amount by the labyrinthine

239

path of small cross-section that the fluid must traverse. The number of rings required in the labyrinth can be found from the following empirical formula if the leakage rate is first decided.

$$ N = \frac{(40P - 2600)\,\dfrac{W}{A}}{540\,\dfrac{W}{A} - P} $$

where N = number of rings
             W = permissible leakage rate in pounds of fluid per second
             A = cross-section of leakage path (sq. in.)
                = $C(\pi D)$
             C = clearance (in.) (this is radial, not diametral clearance)
             D = diameter (in.)
             P = absolute pressure

    The labyrinth type of seal finds little employment in the field of fluid power. It is chiefly used to seal lubricants at the bearings of shafts.

8-6 MECHANICAL END FACE SEALS

A mechanical end face seal is a seal that prevents escape of fluid at a rotating shaft by the use of two faces in contact, one mounted on the rotating shaft and the other on the housing. Spring pressure keeps the two surfaces in contact, as in Fig. 8-9. The contacting faces must be carefully lapped to be ultraflat if any leakage is to be prevented. Such a seal causes no shaft wear, has no leakage, and can seal against pressure. In the fluid power field such seals are used on the shafts of fluid motors.

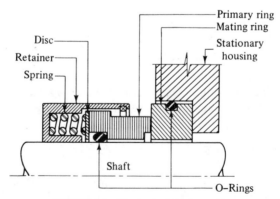

FIGURE 8-9 *Mechanical end face seal.*

8-7 PACKING AND OTHER TYPES OF SEALS

Figure 8-5 shows the dynamic seals between piston and cylinder, seals between rod and end caps, and a rod wiper for protection of the rod. In addition, a static seal is required between cylinder and end caps. A variety of seals and wipers is available for such locations and functions, though the most common types of dynamic seals are lip seals, U-seals, cup seals, V-ring packings, and O-rings. The first three types are self-energizing, meaning that pressure expands them to seal more firmly. Several of these seals are illustrated in Fig. 8-10. The self-energizing seal of course can seal in only one direction; the piston of a cylinder that is double-acting must be sealed for both directions of movement.

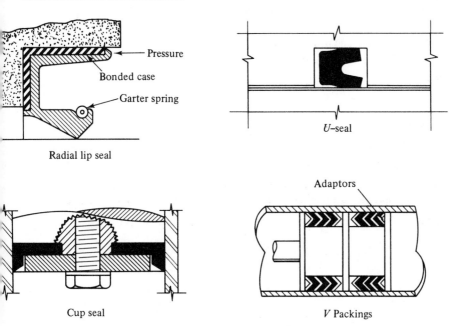

FIGURE 8-10 *Various types of seals.*

Self-energizing (pressure-energized) seals are assembled with a slight interference fit for positive sealing effect. These seals must be made of soft materials such as felt, rubber, and leather. They are easily damaged and in time will wear out. But they are inexpensive and readily replaced. The design of the gland should be such as to make replacement a simple matter.

The self-energizing effect produces higher friction forces at higher pressure. The U-seal can be used only to 1500 psi; at higher pressures the friction force is sufficient to abrade the lip.

The packing type of seal of Fig. 8-10 uses a minimum of three chevron rings, of asbestos, fiber, leather, or other soft material, packed into the

241

gland under light pressure, the opening of the vee pointing in the direction of pressure. Though this type of seal is slightly self-energizing, the friction force does not increase very much at higher pressures. Such packing or compression seals are well suited to low- or high-pressure applications. They have the disadvantage of tending to score the shaft, because foreign particles are readily embedded in this type of packing. A hard shaft therefore is necessary.

Packing seals are subject to constant wear and require periodic adjustment by tightening. They are not suited to high-speed applications.

QUESTIONS

8-1. Dimension an O-ring gland for a piston using a clearance on radius of 0.003 in. and a $\frac{3}{16}$ in. O-ring. Indicate the percent squeeze selected.

8-2. Define:

    (a) anti-extrusion ring.

    (b) backup ring.

    (c) wiper.

8-3. What is meant by the term "self-energizing" as applied to seals.

8-4. A static O-ring has a diameter of 0.275 in. with an initial squeeze of 15% on compression set reduces squeeze by 8%. What is the final squeeze as a percent?

8-5. A shaft in contact with a soft packing must be hard. Why?

9

HYDRAULIC PUMPS
AND MOTORS

Pumps of all kinds fall into either of two broad groups: positive displacement and nonpositive displacement pumps. The pumps used in fluid power applications are of the positive displacement type. Such pumps deliver a fixed volume of oil per revolution regardless of the pressure against which they work. If the outlet of such a pump were blocked, it would attempt to deliver oil, with the result that some component in the system would burst under the uncontrolled pressure thus generated. Hence the requirement of a pressure relief valve in hydraulic systems. The centrifugal pumps used in water supply systems are of the nonpositive displacement type: the delivery of the pump depends on the pressure against which the pump works. Delivery decreases as the outlet pressure on the pump increases. If the outlet of a nonpositive displacement pump is blocked, the pump simply churns the water in its casing, but no uncontrolled water pressure will develop. Such pumps are nonoverloading and do not require a pressure relief valve for protection of the fluid system.

Hydraulic pumps are available in both a fixed displacement and a variable displacement type. The variable displacement pump includes an adjustment that allows the pump output to be varied from zero to maximum displacement per revolution.

Since a positive displacement pump delivers a fixed volume of oil per revolution, increasing or decreasing its speed will increase or decrease its delivery proportionally. It is usual however to operate these pumps at a fixed speed.

Three common designs for hydraulic pumps are in use:

1. Gear pump, the least expensive and least efficient.

2. Vane pump, best suited to the movement of large volumes of oil.

3. Piston pump.

Piston pumps are produced in both radial and axial piston types, and are selected for high pressures and high-performance circuits of either low or high pressure.

These three designs of pump will be discussed presently. The symbols for pumps and motors are shown in Fig. 7-19.

9-1 PUMP EFFICIENCY AND HORSEPOWER

The piston of an automobile engine or of a hydraulic pump in its suction stroke opens a certain volume of the cylinder to be filled by the incoming gases or oil. This volume is the cylinder bore cross-sectional area multiplied by the piston stroke. Ideally this volume or displacement should measure the volume or weight of fluid drawn in on the intake stroke. But actually the volume and weight of fluid drawn into the cylinder will be reduced by a number of effects. To indicate only two of these effects, the intake volume will not be completely empty of fluid, and the effect of viscosity will delay the incoming fluid so that by the time the piston begins to return from the suction stroke the cylinder will not be completely filled. The ratio of the actual delivery to the theoretical delivery (bore area × stroke) is called the *volumetric efficiency*.

$$\text{Volumetric efficiency} = \frac{\text{actual volume}}{\text{theoretical volume}}$$

Volumetric efficiency of a piston pump will be high, above 95%, while that of a gear pump will be somewhat lower.

A different measure of efficiency and one that applies to all machines is *mechanical efficiency*. Suppose that an electric motor delivers 1 horsepower into a hydraulic pump. Then ideally all this power should be put into the oil delivered by the pump. But this does not occur. Certain mechanical inefficiencies such as friction in bearings or in moving parts of the pump will absorb some of this horsepower.

$$\text{Mechanical efficiency} = \frac{\text{useful power output}}{\text{power input}}$$

The overall efficiency of a hydraulic pump or motor is the product of these two efficiencies:

Overall efficiency = volumetric efficiency × mechanical efficiency

Overall efficiency will be in the range of 90% for a piston pump.

The useful power delivered by the pump to the oil is called the hydraulic horsepower. This is the power put into the oil, and is calculated from

$$\text{Hydraulic horsepower} = \frac{QP}{1714}$$

where Q = gallons per minute delivered by the pump
         P = pump output pressure in psi.

EXAMPLE 7-6: A hydraulic pump is to deliver 35 gpm at 1200 psi. Suggest a suitable horsepower rating for the electric motor that is to drive the pump.

SOLUTION:

$$\text{Hydraulic horsepower} = \frac{35 \times 1200}{1714} = 24\frac{1}{2}\,\text{HP}$$

The electric motor must supply this useful horsepower plus all the losses of the pump. We do not know the overall efficiency of the pump, but an 80% efficiency seems a safe assumption. Then the electric motor output should be at least

$$\frac{24\frac{1}{2}}{0.80} = 30\frac{1}{2}\,\text{HP}$$

The nearest available motor capacities are 30 and 40 HP. Then a 40-HP electric motor must be used, or else the hydraulic system redesigned such that the demand on the motor will be slightly less than 30 HP.

9-2 GEAR PUMPS

The common design of gear pumps uses spur gears (Fig. 9-1). This design comprises two mating gears enclosed in a cast iron housing that closely fits the gears—when the pump is new, the gears may actually touch the housing. Oil is introduced from the reservoir at the intake port and is carried in the spaces between adjacent pairs of gear teeth around the inner surface of the housing to the discharge port. Leakage from discharge to intake can occur between teeth and housing, in the region where the teeth of the two gears mesh, and along the side faces of the gears. Volumetric efficiency therefore is not high for this type of pump. The use of hydraulic oil to lubricate the sleeve bearings of the pump is another source of loss.

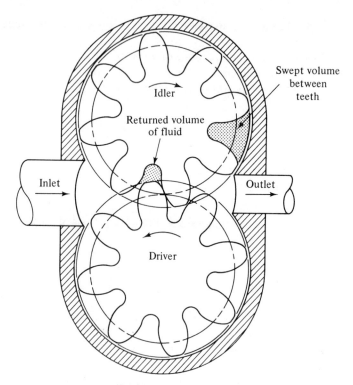

FIGURE 9-1 *Gear pump.*

The displacement per revolution of this type of pump can be determined readily by measuring the volume of the tooth space and multiplying this figure by the number of tooth spaces on both gears. If for example the gears have 13 teeth each, then in each revolution 26 tooth spaces will deliver oil.

The delivery of a gear pump varies with the diameter and width of the gears, the size of the gear teeth, and the speed in rpm.

Close fit between gears and housing is essential. Any clearance allows pressurized oil to leak back from the pump outlet to the inlet. This leakage in a gear pump is termed *slip*. Slip is greater in a gear pump than in other types of hydraulic pumps, and increases as the system pressure is increased.

Outlet pressure forces the gears toward the inlet side of the pump housing, causing the gears gradually to wear the housing in this region. As a result of this wear the clearance between gears and housing increases, resulting in increased slip and some reduction in output volume of the pump. Such wear is greatly accelerated by extended operation at high pressures, with resulting slip and reduced service life.

The useful life of the gear pump therefore depends on housing wear.

246

This life may depend on the bearings also. A bearing has limitations of pressure and velocity, expressed as its PV value as discussed in an earlier chapter. If the pump speed is increased in order to obtain a greater pump delivery, then the bearing life is proportionally reduced. Again, if the bearing load is increased due to increased pump pressure, bearing life is quite seriously reduced; doubling pump pressure reduces bearing life to one-eighth. For high-pressure conditions, roller bearings are preferable to sleeve bearings, and wear plates on the side faces of the gears are employed.

The gerotor pump of Fig. 9-2 is a different design of gear pump. It has an inner rotor with one tooth less than the outer rotor. Each tooth of the inner rotor maintains continuous sliding contact with a tooth of the outer rotor to provide a seal against leakage. The two rotors are not greatly different in diameter, and as a result the sliding speed between them is low, thus providing long life and quiet operation.

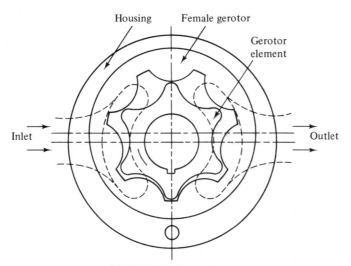

FIGURE 9-2 *Gerotor pump.*

The gerotor pump does not use the standard involute gear tooth form. The standard spur gear pump has involute teeth, but the pressure angle is usually increased to 28 degrees to provide a somewhat larger tooth space. The displacement of the gerotor pump is the volume of the extra tooth on the outer element times the number of teeth on the inner rotor.

9-3 VANE PUMPS

The basic vane pump is shown in Fig. 9-3. This pump has a series of nearly radial sliding vanes mounted in a rotor which is eccentric to the housing. The inlet is located in the region of the pump where the volume between

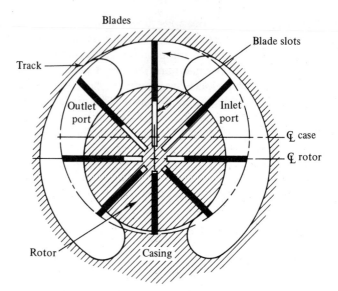

FIGURE 9-3 *Vane pump.*

vanes increases in size; the partial vacuum produced by this expansion of volume draws oil into the pump. Centrifugal force, spring pressure, or fluid pressure are used to force the vanes against the outer casing to trap the oil in the spaces between vanes. Volumetric efficiency does not suffer as a result of wear, as occurs in a gear pump, because wear of the vanes is compensated by outward movement of the vanes.

The capacity of the vane pump varies with diameter, width of vanes, speed, and eccentricity. Variable displacement without speed change is arranged by varying the eccentricity of the rotor with respect to its casing. See Fig. 9-4. Here the rotor is enclosed in a movable cylindrical casing, and

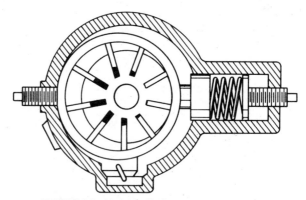

FIGURE 9-4 *Variable displacement vane pump.*

the discharge volume is varied by moving the casing with respect to the rotor. The fluid flow may also be reversed by moving the axis of the casing to the opposite side of the rotor center. At zero eccentricity there is of course no flow of oil. Eccentricity may be adjusted or the flow reversed manually by using a screw and handwheel to shift the rotor. Or the adjustment may be made automatically by sensing system hydraulic pressure. For example, suppose a variable-volume pump feeds a clamp cylinder. The pump will supply maximum displacement at maximum eccentricity to move the clamp cylinder up to the workpiece. When the clamp closes on the workpiece the system pressure will rise rapidly. This pressure can be piloted back to the pump to shift the rotor to zero eccentricity against spring pressure.

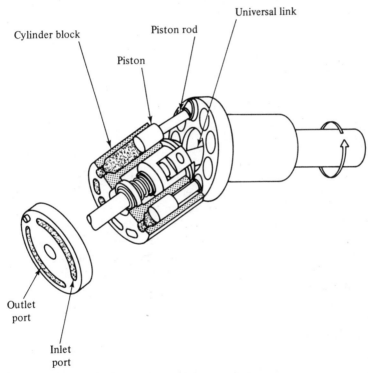

FIGURE 9-5 *Bent-axis type of axial piston pump.*

9-4 AXIAL PISTON PUMPS

The axial piston pump consists of a ring of pistons approximately parallel to the drive shaft of the pump. Pistons and cylinder block are connected to the drive shaft by universal connections. The rear of the cylinder block has a valve plate containing the inlet and outlet ports. The rate of discharge is determined by the angle between pistons and drive shaft if the pump is a variable-volume type. Figure 9-6 shows the configuration for zero flow. At zero angle there is no reciprocation of the pistons. Maximum flow occurs at maximum angle, which is about 20 degrees. Discharge varies as the diameter of the piston bore, the number of pistons (always an odd number), rpm, and stroke length or angle.

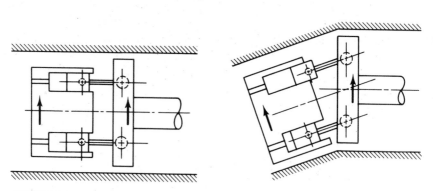

FIGURE 9-6 *Zero-flow and maximum flow positions in a variable displacement axial piston pump.*

In addition to this design of bent-axis axial piston pump, there is the in-line or swash plate type. In the latter design the cylinder block is splined to the drive shaft and therefore rotates on the same axis or is "in line" with the drive shaft. Figure 9-7 shows the swash plate that causes reciprocation of the pistons. Control of the swash plate angle makes the in-line pump a variable-displacement pump. The pump characteristic curves of Fig. 10-12 indicate that the displacement of the pump is proportional to the swash plate angle.

9-5 RADIAL PISTON PUMP

The principle of the variable-displacement radial piston pump is illustrated in Fig. 9-8. This design employs a rotating cylinder block which revolves about a central valve spindle by means of a drive shaft. Oil is supplied through holes in the valve spindle, terminating in a circumferential slot which extends over an arc of nearly 180 degrees; discharge passages include another similar circumferential slot and passages opposite the suction port. The radial pistons move outward while passing the suction slot and inward when opposite the discharge slot. The reactor ring or thrust ring can be shifted from the neutral position to maximum eccentricity in either direction.

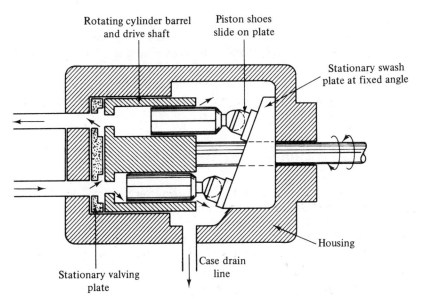

Rotating cylinder barrel
and drive shaft

Piston shoes
slide on plate

Stationary swash
plate at fixed angle

Housing

Case drain
line

Stationary valving
plate

FIGURE 9-7 *Swash plate type of axial piston pump.*

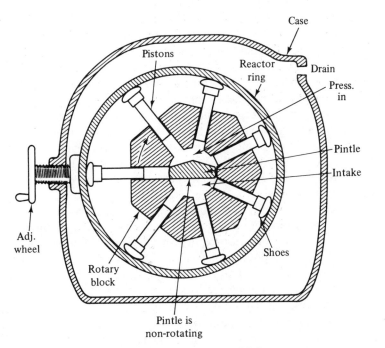

Case

Pistons

Reactor
ring

Drain

Press.
in

Pintle

Intake

Adj.
wheel

Rotary
block

Shoes

Pintle is
non-rotating

FIGURE 9-8 *Variable displacement radial piston pump.*

Piston stroke is double the eccentricity. Most radial piston pumps provide variable displacement. Displacement varies with bore diameter, eccentricity, number of pistons (always an odd number) and speed.

The clearance between piston and bore in a piston pump is only a few ten-thousandths of an inch. There must be careful attention to fine filtering of the oil to ensure that surfaces are not scored or worn; inadequate filtering greatly shortens the life of the piston pump.

9-6 ROTARY HYDRAULIC MOTORS

Hydraulic pumps are devices for converting mechanical energy into hydraulic energy. A rotary hydraulic motor does exactly the reverse. In principle at least, to use the pump as a motor, oil under pressure can be supplied to the outlet of a hydraulic pump to drive it as a hydraulic motor in the opposite direction of rotation to that as a pump.

Rotary motors are rated by displacement and torque. The *displacement* of a hydraulic motor means the volume of oil required to rotate the motor 1 revolution, that is, cubic inches per revolution. The *torque* rating is expressed in pound-inches of torque per 100 psi of oil pressure. Therefore the speed of a rotary motor is directly proportional to the volume of oil supplied to it per unit time, and the torque is proportional to oil pressure.

Hydraulic motors are made in gear, vane, and piston types, and may be of fixed or variable displacement.

Not all hydraulic pumps can effectively serve as rotary motors. Some are unable to generate torque from oil pressure, others are too inefficient, and some do not have suitable shaft seals. One very basic difference between a pump and a motor is that only one side of a pump is under high pressure; in some motor circuits both the inlet and the outlet of the motor may be pressurized. Some pumps have low-pressure shaft seals with oil supplied from the low-pressure side and such pumps could lose their seals if operated as motors. Most hydraulic motors therefore have slight differences in design from pumps.

The gear motor of Fig. 9-9 shows a deflector. This is found in some but not all gear motors. Its purpose is to prevent oil from impinging on the teeth where the gears mesh, since any torque generated in this region would oppose the useful output torque produced by the oil carried around the inside of the housing. Both gears rotate, but the output shaft of the motor is connected to one of the gears. Modifications to the shaft seals may be necessary to convert a gear pump to a motor.

However, it is possible that a used gear pump may give a better performance as a motor than a new pump. The new pump will have too close a fit between gears and housing and starting torque may be low.

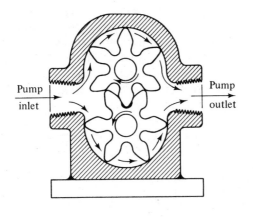

Pump inlet

Pump outlet

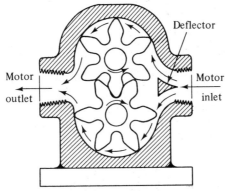

Deflector

Motor outlet

Motor inlet

FIGURE 9-9 *Gear pump and gear motor compared.*

If a vane pump is to serve as a motor then springs must be used to force the vanes out to the housing. If centrifugal force alone were used, then at startup the vanes would be retracted and the oil would pass freely from inlet to discharge without producing torque. Similarly if fluid pressure is used to extend the vanes in a vane pump, such a pump cannot function as a motor because no starting torque is developed. Few vane pumps can be reversed, and therefore vane motors must usually be operated in a rotation opposite to the rotation as a pump. If the vane assembly can be reversed, then the motor can be operated in the reverse direction, but still as a single-direction motor.

Before operating a piston pump as a motor, the manufacturer must be consulted. There may be problems with valve timing or other details.

If a hydraulic motor is operated at constant input pressure, then its torque output should be constant from zero to maximum speed. Actually torque output shows a small decrease as speed increases. the explanation for this loss of torque is a slight loss of pressure at high flow rates. When larger quantities of oil pass through conduits, ports, and passages, there is a higher fluid friction loss. This loss is called "porting loss." The pressure used in overcoming porting loss—driving oil through the passages—is not available for producing torque. This loss actually appears as heat in the oil.

Figure 10-10 shows that starting torque of a motor is less than peak running torque. Starting friction is always greater than running friction in any machine; this higher friction reduces starting torque. The lower starting torque is a disadvantage of fluid motors as compared with electric motors; electric motors give higher starting torques than running torques. However, if an excessive starting torque is required, the electric motor will tend to burn out if stalled, while the hydraulic motor can be stalled indefinitely without harm. In order to improve starting and stall torques, gear motors use ball and roller bearings; gear pumps usually have sleeve bearings.

Volumetric, mechanical, and overall efficiency for hydraulic motors are defined in exactly the same way as for pumps.

9-7 HYDRAULIC AND ELECTRIC MOTORS COMPARED

1. **Starting torque:** This has been discussed above. The unusually high starting torque of the electric motor is not a characteristic of the hydraulic motor.

2. **Stalling:** Stalling of a hydraulic motor will not overheat or damage it.

3. **Size and weight:** An electric motor averages about 30 lb per output horsepower in the smaller frames, and half this much or even somewhat less for large sizes. Hydraulic motors fall within the range of 0.5 to 5 lb weight per horsepower.

4. **Inertia:** The large size of electric motors indicates a high inertia. Such motors are difficult to stop and reverse quickly. Hydraulic motors being small have very low inertia. They can be stopped or reversed with ease in a fraction of a second.

5. **Efficiency:** Electric motors surpass in efficiency. A three-phase electric motor of several horsepower may be 90% efficient or even better. A small inexpensive gear motor may have an efficiency of only 70%, though piston motors may exceed 90% efficiency.

6. **Cost:** Electric motors are always lower in cost than all other types of hydraulic motors.

7. **Speed control:** Speed control of a hydraulic motor is easily managed with suitable valves. Speed control of a.c. electric motors is expensive. The d.c. motor is adaptable to speed control but is an expensive motor. The best speed control systems make use of variable-volume hydraulic pumps and motors.

When substituting a hydraulic motor for an electric motor the substitution cannot be made simply on the basis of equal horsepower. Both starting torque and running torque requirements of the load must be checked out, bearing in mind the lower starting torque of the hydraulic motor and its slight loss of torque at high speeds.

9-8 AIR MOTORS

Air motors, like hydraulic motors, provide a compact, lightweight and low-inertia source of power which is unharmed if stalled or overloaded. Two types are available: vane and piston air motors, both types being similar in principle to vane and piston hydraulic motors. Both obtain lubrication from a lubricated source of compressed air. The radial piston air motor is more common than the axial piston motor.

The horsepower rating of an air motor is usually expressed as the maximum horsepower available with 90 psi air. Power output however falls rapidly at lower pressures. Typical performance curves for an air motor are shown in Fig. 9-10. Notice that starting torque and stall torque are about twice the torque at maximum power.

Air consumption is 35 to 40 cfm per horsepower at maximum horsepower for air motors up to 1½ HP, and 25–30 cfm per horsepower for larger motors.

9-9 ROTARY ACTUATORS

The single-vane and double-vane rotary actuators are illustrated in Fig. 9-11. These actuators deliver a very high torque at slow motion over less than 1 revolution. Maximum rotation angle for a single-vane actuator is about 280 degrees. Clearly they must be reversed, so are controlled with a four-way valve.

Actuators are used to open and close very large valves for steam, water, oil, and compressed gas, for dumping, for closing toggle clamps, and other such uses where only limited rotation is necessary.

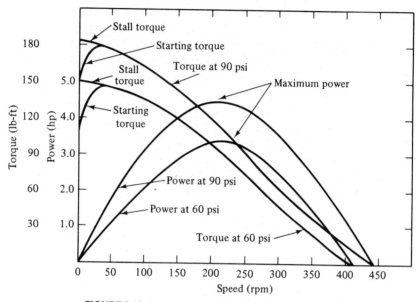

FIGURE 9-10 *Typical performance curves for an air motor.*

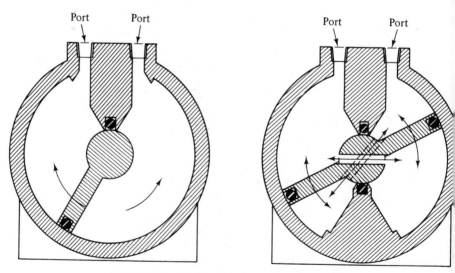

FIGURE 9-11 *Single and double vane rotary actuators.*

QUESTIONS

9-1. What is the meaning of volumetric efficiency?

9-2. Calculate the hydraulic horsepower output required of a pump supplying 15 gpm against a pressure of 2400 psi.

9-3. If 10 gpm of oil flow through a four-way valve with a pressure drop across it of 20 psi due to fluid friction, what is the heat loss in horsepower and in Btu/hour?

9-4. Estimate the volume of oil in cubic inches per minute delivered from a gear pump with gear teeth of 5 diametral pitch, 18 teeth 1¼ in. wide, and a speed of 1200 rpm. You will require a profile of the gear teeth, which can be obtained from a Boston Gear or other catalogue. Use a 20° pressure angle. Assume a volumetric efficiency of 93%.

9-5. Why are O-rings not used in the pistons of piston pumps?

9-6. In a fluid motor, how do you increase

    (a) speed

    (b) torque

9-7. Suggest some differences in construction between hydraulic pumps and motors.

9-8. Explain "porting loss" in a hydraulic motor.

9-9. Why is starting torque lower than running torque in a hydraulic motor?

9-10. Indicate the advantages and disadvantages of hydraulic motors as compared with electric motors.

9-11. **(a)** A hydraulic motor is connected to a fixed displacement pump. If a second motor identical to the first is connected in parallel with it, what is the speed of the parallel connection as compared with that of the first motor?

    (b) Is the combined torque of the two motors one-half, twice, or the same as that of one motor?

9-12. **(a)** See Question 11. If the second motor is connected in series with the first, is the speed of the two motors one-half, the same, or twice that of the first motor alone?

    (b) How does the combined torque of the two motors compare with that of one motor?

10

HYDROSTATIC TRANSMISSIONS

Hydrostatic transmission is defined as the transmission of power by a fluid using positive displacement pumps and motors. The fundamental characteristics of a hydrostatic drive then are that the hydraulic pump supplies a fixed volume of fluid in each revolution, and that the hydraulic motor provides one shaft revolution when it receives a certain fixed volume of fluid from the pump. The prime mover driving the pump will usually be either an internal combustion engine or an electric motor.

10-1 PUMP AND MOTOR SYSTEMS

There are four possible pump-motor combinations for a hydrostatic drive, shown in Fig. 10-1.

1. **Fixed-displacement pump with fixed-displacement motor:** This arrangement gives a fixed ratio drive. If the displacements of pump and motor are the same, then so are their rotational speeds. If the motor has 0.50 the displacement of the pump, then it runs at twice the pump speed. Speed, torque, and power output are constant if the pump speed is constant.

2. **Fixed-displacement pump with variable-displacement motor:** The speed ratio may be changed by adjusting motor displacement. A reduction in displacement of the motor increases motor speed but reduces motor torque. Power remains nearly constant except for

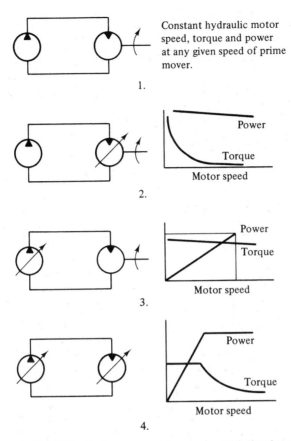

Constant hydraulic motor speed, torque and power at any given speed of prime mover.

1.

Power

Torque

Motor speed

2.

Power

Torque

Motor speed

3.

Power

Torque

Motor speed

4.

FIGURE 10-1 *Various pump and motor combinations in hydrostatic transmissions.*

leakage. This system is not as common as the other pump-motor systems.

3. **Variable-displacement pump with fixed-displacement motor:** This arrangement results in a constant torque, variable speed, variable horsepower drive. If the pump is adjusted to zero displacement, this gives an idling condition similar to a disengaged clutch. The motor is reversed by reversing the pump.

4. **Variable-displacement pump with variable-displacement motor:** This arrangement will provide either constant horsepower or constant torque. A wide speed range is possible, from full output of pump with minimum motor displacement to the opposite case.

10-2 OPEN AND CLOSED CIRCUITS

An open and a closed hydrostatic circuit are shown in Fig. 10-2; the difference between the open and the closed circuit is evident. The open circuit requires a reservoir in the motor-to-pump circuit. The closed circuit also requires a reservoir, but in an auxiliary circuit. A booster pump or makeup pump supplies fluid losses to the circuit to make up for leakage.

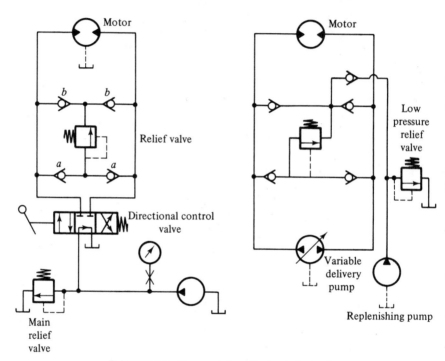

FIGURE 10-2 *Open and closed hydrostatic circuits.*

Reversal of the motor is performed either by the use of a four-way valve, as in Fig. 10-2, or by reversing a variable-displacement pump. Hydraulic motors are not designed to be reversed.

10-3 BASIC MOTOR CONTROL

The simple circuit of Fig. 10-3 gives start/stop control of a nonreversible motor. This arrangement is suited only to low-power and low-speed motors driving low-inertia loads. Inertia of the load may drive the motor after the oil supply is shut off. The motor could then run dry and would start up

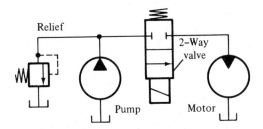

FIGURE 10-3 *Simple start-stop control for a motor driving a low-inertial load.*

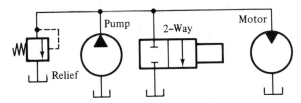

FIGURE 10-4 *Bypassing oil to tank provides a smoother stop.*

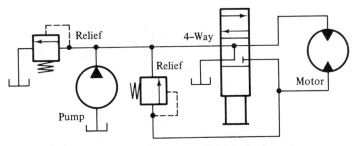

FIGURE 10-5 *Deceleration from relief valve back pressure.*

again without oil in it. There is also no provision for unloading the pump except through the relief valve.

A better arrangement is the parallel or bypass arrangement of Fig. 10-4. After shutting off the motor, it is still connected to an oil supply, and the pump unloads through the two-way valve.

These two basic circuits do not provide deceleration for the motor. Figure 10-5 shows a method that provides a cushioned stop. When the four-way valve is moved to neutral, the motor discharges through a low-pressure relief valve which provides back pressure for deceleration. The third position of the four-way valve is not used. For this circuit a reversible motor is needed, because back pressure from the cushioning valve would blow out the seal on a nonreversing motor.

Three-position four-way valves are used for reversing motors. See Fig. 10-6, which shows a circuit giving forward, reverse, and stop operation. With an open-center valve the motor can coast to a gradual stop. This circuit however will allow the motor to creep after stopping; this may not be desirable in some cases.

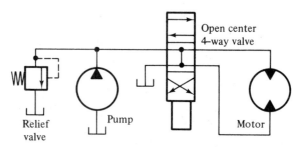

FIGURE 10-6 *Forward, reverse, and coasting to a stop by means of a three-position four-way valve with open center.*

10-4 INERTIA PROBLEMS

Any hydrostatic drive is connected to a prime mover at the input and to some load at the output, and the characteristics of the input drive and the output load influence the design and operation of the system. Consider the influence of the load on the circuit.

Suppose we use an open-center four-way valve for motor control and stop the motor by putting this valve into neutral position. The pump now discharges to the tank instead of to the motor. the load will have some inertia and this inertia will force the motor to continue rotating. Suppose the drive to be on a tractor, and the tractor to be descending a slope. The weight of the tractor on the slope will force the motor to rotate. We have two dangerous conditions here. First we have no means of stopping the tractor, unless the motor is thrown into reverse by the four-way valve or a mechanical brake is provided. Also we are not supplying oil to the motor from the pump, and if the motor is run dry it will be destroyed.

In order to supply the idling motor with oil, we can use the motor as its own pump. Oil leaving the motor can be returned to the motor input through check valves, as in Fig. 10-2. One set of check valves is used for each direction of rotation.

In order to stop the load, we can use a tandem center valve. Note that this circuit will lead to disaster. The motor will be rotated by the load, thus discharging oil, but there is not the available volume to receive this discharge. The pressure in the circuit will rise until something breaks. However, a tandem center valve in association with the check valves of Fig. 10-2 will protect against destructive pressures.

There remains the problem of stopping the load in a short period of time. Suppose a heavy flywheel or other high-inertia load is driven by the transmission. If the oil continues to circulate across the check valves, the load and motor may require many minutes to decelerate to a stop. To stop the load more quickly we introduce a relief valve as shown in Fig. 10-2. This valve, however, does not function as a relief valve, but as a deceleration valve or brake valve. If the valve is adjusted to a low pressure, oil will be forced through it with relative ease and deceleration will be slow. If the valve is adjusted to a higher pressure, deceleration of the motor and its load will be more rapid. Thus the hydraulic system can be used also as a brake. However, it must be noted that the discharge of oil across this valve generates heat; in a closed loop system with only a small quantity of oil this heating effect can quickly produce a high temperature rise, so that a heat exchanger may be required.

The flexibility of the hydrostatic transmission has made it a popular drive for construction equipment. Shovels, backhoes, front-end loaders, cranes, etc., all require a hydraulic system to operate cylinders; it is convenient therefore to make the transmission a hydraulic one also. The hydraulic motors, reservoir, and lines can be placed on the machine wherever it happens to be convenient to locate them, and both cylinders and piping may be located in any position, either horizontal, vertical, or oblique.

Hydrostatic transmissions are not used in automobiles for reasons of cost and because efficiencies are rather low, around 65 or 70%. The automobile uses a more efficient transmission, either "standard" or "automatic." If a low-efficiency hydrostatic transmission were used with the low-efficiency gasoline engine, gasoline consumption of the family car would be even worse than it is. In addition to a radiator for the engine, a second cooler would be needed for the hydrostatic transmission.

The advantages of hydrostatic transmissions may be summarized thus:

1. Stepless speed variation over a wide speed range.

2. Brakes, clutch, and reverse gear are not needed, since their functions can be performed by the hydraulic circuit.

3. Small weight, size, and inertia, compared to mechanical or electrical alternatives.

4. Instant reversal if necessary.

5. Complete freedom of location of input and output shafts. Most other types of drives require that these two shafts be either parallel (chain drive or spur gears) or at right angles (worm drive or differential on a car).

Sometimes there is no practical alternative to a hydrostatic transmission. Consider a road roller used in black-topping a highway. If this roller is stopped to put it in reverse, its weight will result in an indentation in the road surface. Such a machine must use a hydrostatic transmission with its capacity for instant reversal.

10-5 DESIGN OF A SIMPLE HYDROSTATIC TRANSMISSION

In order to understand the characteristics and performance of pumps, motors, and hydrostatic transmissions, the following example of a hydrostatic design is offered.

An inexpensive hydrostatic drive is to be designed to satisfy the following load requirements:

1. Hydraulic motor speed must be continuously adjustable from 500 rpm minimum to 1375 rpm maximum.

2. The motor is not to be reversible.

3. Load torque on the motor is to be 100 lb-in. at all speeds.

In order to put together an inexpensive circuit a gear pump and a gear motor will be selected. The motor speed must be varied. Rather than use a variable-speed device, an adjustable flow control valve will bypass oil back to the reservoir for speed control. The circuit is that of Fig. 10-7, an open circuit being less expensive than a closed circuit.

Manufacturers' catalogues are consulted for a suitable pump and motor. The characteristic curves of a suitable motor are given in Fig. 10-8. By "characteristic curve" we mean a graphical display of the performance

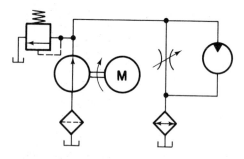

FIGURE 10-7 *Simple variable-speed constant torque hydrostatic drive.*

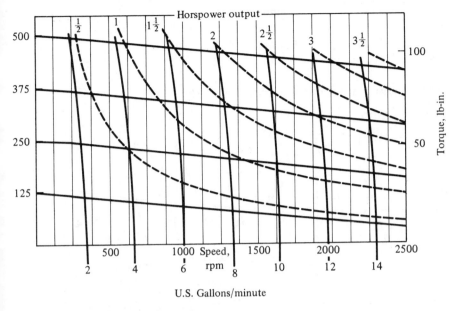

FIGURE 10-8 *Characteristic curves (performance curves) for a small gear motor.*

characteristics of the item of hardware. In reading these curves, note first the four presure lines beginning at the left-hand side, marked 125, 250, 375, and 500 psi. These four pressure lines droop from the horizontal as speed increases, due to porting and other losses. Speeds are given at the bottom of the graph in lines that run vertically upward. Lines of flow rate run upward, but incline to the left slightly. The torque scale is on the right-hand side, the torque lines being horizontal. Finally output horsepower lines at the top of the graph are given as dashed lines falling toward the right-hand side.

To find the operating point on the curves for this motor at 1375 rpm, follow the torque line for 100 lb-in. horizontally to meet the vertical speed curves at 1375 rpm. This intersection lies on the 500 psi pressure line and also the 9 gpm line. The hydraulic power output will be approximately 2.2 HP. Alternately

$$\text{Output HP} = \text{torque} \times \frac{\text{rpm}}{63,000} = 2.18\,\text{HP}$$

The power input to the motor is

$$\text{gpm} \times \frac{\text{Pressure}}{1714} = 2.62\,\text{HP}$$

265

The efficiency of this motor under these conditions is

$$\frac{\text{Output}}{\text{Input}} = \frac{2.18}{2.62} = 0.83$$

Characteristic curves of a suitable pump are given in Fig. 10-9.

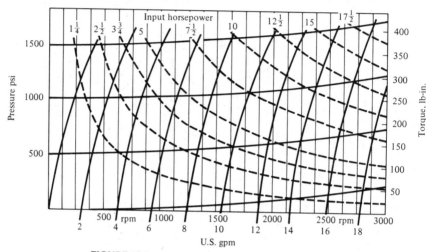

FIGURE 10-9   *Gear pump characteristic curves.*

To find the operating point, recall that the motor requires a pressure of 500 psi. The pump must supply a somewhat higher pressure than this in order to allow for pressure drop due to fluid friction in valves and plumbing. Suppose the supplier of the four-way valve advises us to assume a pressure drop of 20 psi through this valve at 9 gpm. There will be additional pressure losses through piping. In this simple circuit this may be another 20 psi perhaps. This makes a total assumed circuit loss of 40 psi, or say 50 psi. The pump output pressure must then be 550 psi. We can now find the operating point for 550 psi with a delivery of 9 gpm.

The pressure scale is the left-hand scale as for the motor curves, and the pressure curves incline slightly upward to the right. Torque scale is on the right-hand scale, and torque lines on the graph are horizontal. Speed lines are vertical, and flow rate lines are shown inclining to the right upwards. Enter the graph at 550 psi, slightly above the 500 psi line to meet 9 gpm. The operating point lies on the 3¾ input horsepower line approximately, and the speed of the pump is 1500 rpm closely.

The output power of the pump is

$$9 \times \frac{550}{1714} = 2.9 \text{ HP}$$

The efficiency of the pump is

$$\frac{2.9}{3.75} = 0.77$$

The power lost in the circuit through fluid friction and assuming 50 psi pressure drop (probably a little too high) is

$$9 \times \frac{50}{1714} = 0.26 \text{ HP}$$

This 0.26 HP must be the difference between output HP of the pump and the input HP of the motor. Both these have been calculated:

$$\text{Output HP of pump} = 2.9$$
$$\text{Input HP of motor} = \underline{2.62}$$
$$= 0.28 \text{ HP circuit loss.}$$

This wasted horsepower appears as heat in the oil. Since it is only a small quantity of heat, it will be dissipated in the reservoir.

At this point we should size the inlet filter to the pump and the reservoir capacity. The pump must deliver 9 gpm. Reservoir capacity must be about three times pump gpm, or say 30 gallons.

Assuming a volumetric efficiency of 90% for the pump (this might be an optimistic figure), then the filter must be sized for 10 gpm flow.

So far we have checked out the pump, motor, and circuit at maximum motor speed. We should also examine the performance at the minimum speed of 500 rpm.

At 1375 rpm the motor requires 9 gpm. At 500 rpm the motor requires $^{500}/_{1375} \times 9$ gpm or 3.64 gpm. Then the flow control valve must be capable of passing $9 - 3.64$ or 5.36 gpm maximum.

At a speed of 500 rpm the curves for the motor indicate that an inlet pressure of about 460 psi is required. Motor output horsepower is about 0.8 HP. Note the disadvantage of bypassing oil, as in this transmission. This method of speed control means a loss of power with a loss of speed, and this may not be acceptable for some loads, though it is acceptable in this case. The requirement here is for constant torque, not constant horsepower.

Bypassing oil will produce a heating effect. With the flow control valve closed:

$$\text{pump output} = 2.9 \text{ HP}$$
$$\text{Motor output} = \underline{2.13 \text{ HP}}$$
$$= 0.7 \text{ HP of heat}$$

With the flow control valve open for a minimum motor speed of 500 rpm:

$$\text{Pump output} = 2.9 \text{ HP}$$

$$\text{Motor output} = \underline{0.8 \text{ HP}}$$

$$= 2.1 \text{ HP of heat}$$

But 1 HP is the equivalent of 2544 Btu every hour. The use of a bypass flow control valve results in excessive heat. A heat exchanger must be installed. This heat exchanger is shown in the bypass line in the circuit diagram.

Finally, in order to obtain an idea of overall efficiency of hydrostatic transmissions, we can determine how efficient this one is.

$$\text{Input HP to pump} = 3.75$$

$$\text{Output HP of motor at 1375 rpm} = 2.18$$

Overall system efficiency $= {}^{2.18}\!/_{3.75} = 58\%$. At a lower motor speed the efficiency of this circuit will be lower. At a motor speed of 500 rpm

$$\text{Input HP to pump} = 3.0 \text{ approximately}$$

$$\text{Output HP of motor} = 0.8$$

and overall system efficiency $= {}^{0.8}\!/_{3.0}$ or about 27%.

In selecting an electric motor to operate this hydrostatic transmission, recall that the pump input horsepower was 3.75 and pump rpm 1500. The nearest suitable horsepower rating in electric motors is 5 HP, and motor speed will be 1725 rpm. If a chain drive is used between electric motor and hydraulic pump, the diameter ratio for the sprockets must be 1500 to 1725, which is 60 to 69, or closely 6 to 7.

10-6 HYDROSTATIC TRANSMISSION FOR A BULK CONVEYOR

The transmission is to be a closed loop system driving the drive pulley of a small bulk conveyor. The conveyor drive pulley is 24 inches in diameter and must be rotated at 30 rpm at maximum conveyor speed; lower speeds are occasionally used. The conveyor is laid on an upward slope climbing 1 foot in 10 feet. Friction force in the conveyor is estimated at 600 lb, and inertia force to accelerate the conveyor up to speed is estimated at 800 lb. Maximum conveyor load is about 12,000 lb.

Since variable speed is required, a variable-displacement pump and fixed-displacement motor will be selected.

The hydraulic motor must overcome the following forces at the surface of the conveyor drive pulley at startup (zero speed):

1. Friction   600 lb

2. Inertia   800

3. Elevation of load up incline $^{1200}\!/_{10}$ = 1200
   Total force at startup   2600 lb

This total force has a lever arm equal to the radius of the drive pulley, or 1 foot. Therefore total starting torque is 2600 lb-ft.

The hydraulic motor selected has the characteristic curves shown in Fig. 10-10. To obtain a starting torque of 2600 lb-ft at zero speed, a pressure of about 2850 psi is required. The pressure drop in the system between pump and motor cannot possibly exceed 50 psi, so that a pump output pressure of 2900 psi is adequate for starting.

The running torque at operating speed includes only friction and elevation torques, but not inertia, for a total torque of 1800 lb-in. The hydraulic motor is a slow-speed type, since its best efficiency, 94%, occurs at about 70 rpm. Suppose we select a maximum speed of 60 rpm, with a power chain drive to reduce the speed to 30 rpm at the drive pulley. Because of the difference in speed, the torque of the motor will be 900 lb-in. The hydraulic pressure will be less than 1000 psi, and motor efficiency better than 90%. Motor input horsepower will be about 12.

A suitable pump must next be selected, with a maximum pressure rating of 3000 psi, and reversible.

10-7 HYDROSTATIC TRANSMISSION FOR A CONSTANT TORQUE DRIVE

In this example the maximum torque requirement is 160 lb-ft over a speed range of 200 to 2000 rpm. Since torque is constant and speed variable, the motor will have a fixed delivery and the pump must have a variable displacement.

The motor selected has the characteristics shown in Fig. 10-11. At 2000 rpm and a torque of 160 lb-ft, pressure must be 2700 psi at the motor and output horsepower 60. The flow rate to the motor at 2000 rpm is 2400 gph; at 200 rpm 240 gph.

The pump selected has characteristics as shown in Fig. 10-12. In estimating the pump flow rates recall that the volumetric efficiency of the motor is less than 1.00. The actual volumetric efficiency can be obtained from the

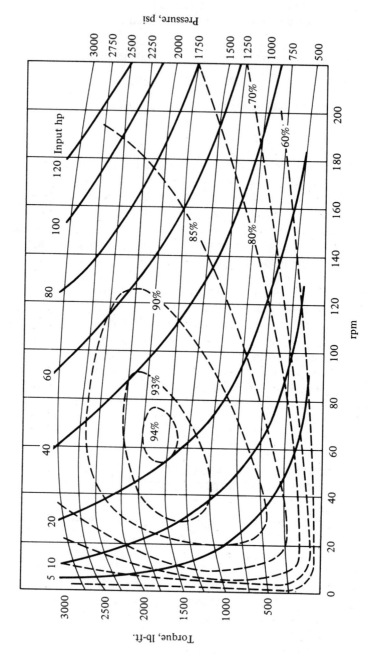

FIGURE 10-10 *Piston motor characteristics.*

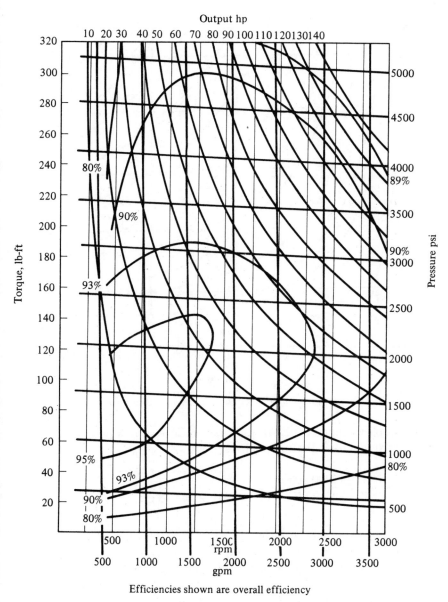

Output hp

10 20 30 40 50 60 70 80 90 100 110 120 130 140

Torque, lb-ft

Pressure psi

80%

90%

93%

95%

93%

90%

80%

89%

90%

80%

500

1000

1500

2000

2500

3000

3500

4000

4500

5000

500 1000 1500 2000 2500 3000
rpm

500 1000 1500 2000 2500 3000 3500
gpm

Efficiencies shown are overall efficiency

FIGURE 10-11 *Performance curves of a high-pressure fluid motor.*

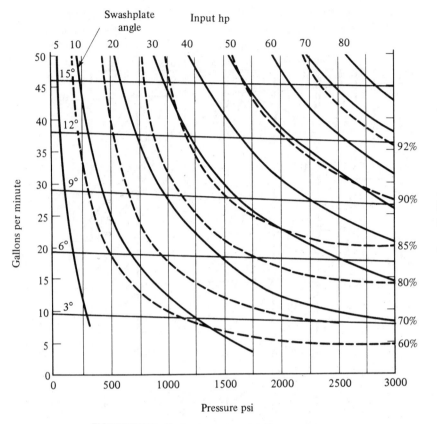

FIGURE 10-12 *Performance curves of a swash plate pump.*

motor supplier. Suppose it is 90%. If the motor requires a flow rate of 2400 gph at 2000 rpm, then the pump must supply:

$$\frac{2400 \text{ gph}}{\text{Vol. eff.}} \quad \text{or} \quad 2670 \text{ gph (44.75 gpm)}$$

Assuming a negligible pressure drop in the circuit, which sould be almost true for a closed ciruit, then the pump must supply 44.75 gpm at 2700 psi. At this point on the graph the pump input power is 76 HP. The swash plate will be set at 15 degrees.

The overall hydraulic efficiency at 2000 rpm is

$$\frac{\text{Motor output HP}}{\text{Pump input HP}} = \frac{60}{76} = 79\%$$

Fig. 10-13 shows the closed loop transmission with a reversible pump. Since the motor can revolve in either direction, there is a high-pressure relief valve across the circuit for each direction of rotation. Either line to the pump may be an input line, so that the replenishing pump must be able to supply oil to either side of the reversible pump, using check valves to protect the replenishing circuit from the pump output pressure.

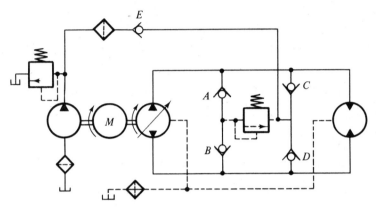

FIGURE 10-13 *Closed loop transmission with a reversible pump.*

QUESTIONS

10-1. Which type of hydrostatic transmission of the four types shown in Fig. 10-1 would be best suited to the operation of an automobile?

10-2. Sketch an open-circuit hydrostatic transmission with two identical motors in series, both rated at 50 gpm and 1000 psi. State the approximate delivery and the pressure required at the fixed-displacement pump.

10-3. Sketch an open-circuit hydrostatic transmission with two identical motors in parallel, both rated at 50 gpm and 1000 psi. State the approximate delivery and pressure required at the fixed-displacement pump.

10-4. Repeat the procedure and analysis of Sec. 10.5 using the same circuit, pump, and motor. the motor must supply a torque of 100 lb-in. at a constant speed of 1750 rpm. Assume a pressure drop in the circuit between pump and motor of 50 psi.

10-5. What is a hydrostatic transmission?

10-6. Why are hydrostatic transmissions not used in automobiles?

10-7. What is the basic difference between an open and a closed loop system?

10-8. Why is the inertia of the load a basic consideration in the design of a hydrostatic transmission?

10-9. How is a hydraulic motor braked hydraulically?

10-10. For what reasons are hydrostatic transmissions used on tractors and construction equipment?

10-11. Why do hydrostatic transmissions require radiators?

10-12. Why is it better to adjust the speed of a hydraulic motor by varying displacement than by using a flow control valve?

10-13. Which type of flow control would generate less heat: series or bypass?

10-14. Using Fig. 10-9, what torque is produced by a pressure of 500 psi.

10-15. Using Fig. 10-9, at 100 rpm and 1100 psi, what is the flow rate?

10-16. In Fig. 10-12, approximately how many gallons per minute are given per degree of swash plate angle?

10-17. When operating the pump of Fig. 10-12 at a swash plate angle of 6° and a pressure of 2500 psi. what is the output HP?

INDEX